Common Statistical Methods for Clinical Research

with SAS® Examples

Glenn A. Walker

Comments or Questions?

The author assumes complete responsibility for the technical accuracy of the content of this book. If you have any questions about the material in this book, please write to the author at this address:

SAS Institute Inc.
Books by Users
Attn: Glenn A. Walker
SAS Campus Drive
Cary, NC 27513

If you prefer, you can send e-mail to sasbbu@sas.com with "comments for Glenn A. Walker" as the subject line, or you can fax the Books by Users program at (919) 677-4444.

PREFACE

This book was written for those involved in clinical research and who may, from time to time, need a guide to help demystify some of the most commonly used statistical methods encountered in our profession.

All too often, I have heard medical directors of clinical research departments express frustration at seemingly cryptic statistical methods sections of protocols which they are responsible for approving. Other nonstatisticians, including medical monitors, investigators, clinical project managers, medical writers and regulatory personnel, often voice similar sentiment when it comes to statistics, despite the profound reliance upon statistical methods in the success of the clinical program. For these people, I offer this book (sans technical details) as a reference guide to better understand statistical methods as applied to clinical investigation and the conditions and assumptions under which they are applied.

For the clinical data analyst and statistician new to clinical applications, the examples from a clinical trials setting may help in making the transition from other statistical fields to that of clinical trials. The discussions of 'Least-Squares' means, distinguishing features of the various SAS® types of sums-of-squares, and relationships among various tests (such as the *Chi-Square Test*, the *Cochran-Mantel-Haenszel Test* and the *Log-Rank Test*) may help crystalize the analyst's understanding of these methods. Analysts with no prior SAS experience should benefit by the simplifed SAS programming statements provided with each example as an introduction to SAS analyses.

This book may also aid the SAS programmer with limited statistical knowledge in better grasping an overall picture of the clinical trials process. Many times knowledge of the hypotheses being tested and appropriate interpretation of the SAS output relative to those hypotheses will help the programmer become more efficient in responding to the requests of other clinical project team members.

Finally, the medical student will find the focused presentation on the specific methods presented to be of value while proceeding through a first course in biostatistics.

For all readers, my goal was to provide a unique approach to the description of commonly used statistical methods by integrating both manual and computerized solutions to a wide variety of examples taken from clinical research. Those who learn best by example should find this approach rewarding. I have found no other book which demonstrates that the SAS output actually *does* have the same results as the manual solution of a problem using the calculating formulas. So ever reassuring this is for the student of clinical data analysis!

Each statistical test is presented in a separate chapter, and includes a brief, non-technical introduction, a synopsis of the test, one or two examples worked manually followed by an appropriate solution using the SAS statistical package, and finally, a discussion with details and relevant notes.

Chapters 1 and 2 are introductory in nature, and should be carefully read by all with no prior formal exposure to statistics. Chapter 1 provides an introduction to statistics and some of the basic concepts involved in inference-making. Chapter 2 goes into more detail with regard to the main aspects of hypothesis testing, including significance levels, power and sample size determination. For those who use analysis-of-variance, Appendix C provides a non-technical introduction to ANOVA methods. The remainder of the book may be used as a text or reference. As a reference, the reader should keep in mind that many of the tests discussed in later chapters rely on concepts presented earlier in the book, strongly suggesting prerequisite review.

This book focuses on statistical hypothesis testing as opposed to other inferential techniques. For each statistical method, the test summary is clearly provided, including the null hypothesis tested, the test statistic and the decision rule. Each statistical test is presented in one of its most elementary forms to provide the reader with a basic framework. Many of the tests discussed have extensions or variations which can be used with more complex data sets. The 18 statistical methods presented here (Chapters 3-20) represent a composite of those which, in my experience, are most commonly used in the analysis of clinical research data. I can't think of a single study I've analyzed in nearly 20 years which did not use at least one of these tests. Furthermore, many of the studies I've encountered have used exclusively the methods presented here, or variations or extensions thereof. Thus, the word 'common' in the title.

Understanding of many parts of this book requires some degree of statistical knowledge. The clinician without such a background may skip over many of the technical details and still come away with an overview of the test's applications, assumptions and limitations. Basic algebra is the only prerequisite, as derivations of test procedures are omitted, and matrix algebra is mentioned only in an appendix. My hope is that the statistical and SAS analysis aspects of the examples would provide a springboard for the motivated reader, both to go back to more elementary texts for additional background and to go forward to more advanced texts for further reading.

Many of the examples are based on actual clinical trials which I have analyzed. In all cases, the data are contrived, and in many cases fictitious names are used for different treatments or research facilities. Any resemblence of the data or the tests' results to actual cases is purely coincidental.

Glenn A. Walker
May 1996

CONTENTS

APPENDICES

EXAMPLES

FIGURES

CHAPTER 1
INTRODUCTION & BASICS

WHAT IS STATISTICS?

In some ways, we are all born statisticians. Inferring general patterns from limited knowledge is nearly as automatic to the human consiousness as breathing. Yet, when the process of inference is formalized through mathematics to a field called **Statistics**, it often becomes clouded by preconceptions of abstruse theory. Let's see if we can provide some formalization by appealing to the natural process of rational inference without getting caught up in theoretical developments.

The purpose of **Statistics** is to characterize a *population* based on the information contained in a *sample* taken from the population. The concepts of 'populations', 'samples' and what we mean be 'characterizing' are discussed through this chapter.

The sample information is conveyed by functions of the observed data called *statistics*. The field of **Statistics** is a discipline which endeavors to determine which functions are the most relevant in the characterization of various populations.

The arithmetic mean, for example, may be the most appropriate statistic to help characterize certain populations, while the median may be more appropriate for others. Statisticians use statistical and probability theory to develop new methodology and apply the methods best suited for different types of data sets.

Applied **Statistics** can be viewed as a set of methodologies used to help carry out scientific experiments. The scientific method consists of developing an hypothesis, determining the best experiment to test the hypothesis, conducting the experiment, observing the results and making conclusions. The statistician's responsiblities include study design, data collection, statistical analysis and drawing appropriate inferences from the data. In doing so, the applied statistician carries out the scientific method, attempting to limit bias, maximize objectivity and obtain results which are scientifically valid.

▸ *Populations*

By *population*, we mean a universe of entities which we would like to characterize but is too vast to study in its entirety. The population to be studied in a clinical trial is defined by its limiting conditions, usually specified by way of study inclusion and exclusion requirements.

Examples of populations include:

1) patients with mild to moderate hypertension
2) obese teenagers
3) adult insulin-dependent diabetic patients.

In the first example, there is only one limiting factor defining the population, that being mild to moderate hypertension. This might be defined more precisely as patients with diastolic blood pressure within a specific range as an inclusion criterion for the clinical protocol. Additional criteria would further limit the population.

Example 2 uses both age and weight as limiting conditions, while Example 3 uses age, diagnosis and treatment as criteria in defining the population.

It is important to identify the population of interest in a clinical study at the time of protocol development because it is the 'universe' to which statistical inferences might apply. Severely restricting the population with the use of many specific admission criteria may ultimately limit the clinical indication to a restricted subset of the intended market.

▸ *Samples*

Intuitively, we can describe a population by describing some representative entities from it. Measurements obtained from the sample entities would tend to characterize the entire population through inference. **Statistics** provides a method of formalizing such intuition, as discussed later in this chapter.

The degree of representation of the entities in a sample taken from the population of interest depends on the sampling plan used. Conceptually, the simplest type of sampling plan is called a 'simple random sample'. This type of plan describes any method of selecting a sample of population entities such that each entity has the same chance of being selected as any other entity in the population. It is intuitively easy to see how random samples should represent the population, and the larger the sample, the greater the representation.

The method of obtaining a simple random sample from the population of interest is not always clearcut. Simple random samples are rarely, if ever, used in clinical trials. One can envision the patients comprising the populations in the three examples cited being scattered all over the world, making the collection of a simple random sample an overwhelming task.

Although inferences can be biased if the sample is not random, adjustments can sometimes be used to control bias introduced by non-random sampling. An entire branch of **Statistics** known as '*Sampling Theory*' has been developed to handle alternative approaches to simple random sampling which minimize bias. The techniques can become quite complex and are beyond the scope of this overview.

For logistical reasons, clinical studies are conducted at a convenient study center with the assumption that the patients enrolled at that center would be typical of those that might be enrolled elsewhere. Multi-center studies are often used to blunt the effect of patient characteristics or procedural anomalies which might be unique to any single center.

Stratified sampling is another technique which is often used to better target representative patients. This method uses random samples from each of several subgroups of the population, called 'strata'. Study enrollment is sometimes stratified by disease severity, age group or some other patient characteristic.

Because inferences from non-random samples may not be as reliable as those made from random samples, the clinical statistician must specifically address the issue of selection bias in the analysis. Statistical methods can be applied to determine whether the treatment group assignment 'appears' random for certain response variables. For example, baseline values might be lower for Group A than Group B in a comparative clinical study. If Group A is found to show a larger response, part of that response may be a 'regression-toward-the-mean' effect, that is, a tendency to return to normal from an artificially low base-line level. Such effects should be investigated thoroughly to avoid making faulty conclusions due to selection bias.

Additional confirmatory studies in separate, independent samples from the same population can also be important in allaying concerns regarding possible sampling biases.

▸ *Characterization*

So how is the population characterized from a sample? Two types of statistical procedures used to characterize populations include *descriptive* and *inferential* procedures.

Descriptive statistics are used to describe the distribution of population measurements by providing estimates of central tendency and measures of variability, or by using graphical techniques such as histograms. Inferential methods use probability to express the level of certainty about estimates and to test specific hypotheses.

Exploratory analyses represent a third type of statistical procedure used to characterize populations. Although exploratory methods use both descriptive and inferential techniques, conclusions cannot be drawn with the same level of certainty since hypotheses are not pre-planned. Given a large data set, it is very likely that at least one statistically significant result can be found using exploratory analyses. Such results are 'hypothesis-generating' and often lead to new studies prospectively designed to test these new hypotheses.

Two main inferential techniques, confidence interval estimation and hypothesis testing, are discussed in more detail later in this chapter.

PROBABILITY DISTRIBUTIONS

An understanding of basic probability concepts is essential to grasp the fundamentals of statistical inference. Most introductory statistics texts discuss these basics, which are not repeated here. We do, however, review some elements of probability distributions.

Each outcome of a statistical experiment can be mapped to a numeric-valued function called a 'random variable'. Some values of the random variable may be more likely to occur than others. The probability distribution associated with a random variable, X, describes the likelihood of obtaining certain values or ranges of values of the random variable.

As an example, consider 2 cancer patients, each with a 50-50 chance of surviving at least 3 months. Three months later, there are 4 possible outcomes, shown in the table below.

Outcome	Patient 1	Patient 2	X	Pr{X}
1	Died	Died	0	0.25
2	Died	Survived	1	0.25
3	Survived	Died	1	0.25
4	Survived	Survived	2	0.25

Each outcome can be mapped to a random variable, X, defined as the number of patients surviving at least 3 months. X can take values 0, 1 or 2 with probabilities 0.25, 0.50 and 0.25, respectively, since each outcome is equally likely.

The probability distribution for X is given by P_X as follows:

X	P_X
0	0.25
1	0.50
2	0.25

▶ *Discrete Distributions*

The above example is a *discrete* probability distribution, since the random variable, X, can only take discrete values, in this case integers from 0 to 2.

The *Binomial* distribution is, perhaps, the most commonly used discrete distribution in clinical biostatistics. This distribution is used to model experiments involving n independent trials, each with 2 possible outcomes, say '*event*' or 'non-*event*', and the probabilty of '*event*', p, is the same for all n trials. The example just discussed involving two cancer patients is an example of a binomial distribution with n = 2 (patients), p = 0.5 and '*event*' is 'survival of at least 3 months'.

Other common discrete distributions include the *Poisson* and the *Hypergeometric* distributions.

▶ *Continuous Distributions*

If a random variable can take any value within an interval or continuum, it is called a *continuous* random variable. Height, weight, blood pressure and serum bilirubin are usually considered continuous random variables since they can take any value within certain intervals, even though the observed measurement is limited by the accuracy of the measuring device.

The probability distribution for a continuous random variable cannot be specified in a simple form as in the discrete example above. To do so would entail an infinite list of probabilities, one for each possible value within the interval. One way to specify the distribution for continuous random variables is to list the probabilities for ranges of X-values. However, such a specification can also be very cumbersome.

Continuous distributions are most conveniently approximated by functions of the random variable, X, say P_X. Such functions may have a form such as

$$P_X = 2x \qquad for \quad 0 < x < 1$$

or,

$$P_X = ae^{-aX} \qquad for \quad 0 < x < \infty .$$

The *Normal* distribution is the most commonly used continuous distribution in clinical research statistics. Many naturally occurring phenomena follow the normal distribution, which can be explained by a powerful result from probability theory known as the '*Central Limit Theorem*', discussed below.

The normal probability distribution is given by the function:

$$P_x = \frac{1}{\sqrt{2\pi}\,\sigma}\, e^{-\frac{(x-\mu)^2}{2\sigma^2}} \qquad for \quad -\infty < x < +\infty$$

where μ and σ are called 'parameters' of the distribution. For any values of μ and σ (>0), a plot of P_x versus x has a mound or 'bell' shape (illustrated in Appendix B).

Other common continuous distributions include the exponential distribution, the chi-square distribution, the F-distribution and the Student t-distribution. Appendix B lists some analytic properties of common continuous distributions used in statistical inference mentioned throughout this book. The *Normal*, *Chi-Square*, *F-* and the *t*-distributions are all inter-related, and some of these relationships are shown in Appendix B.

Whether discrete or continuous, every probability distribution has the property that the sum of the probabilities over all X-values equals 1.

▸ *The Central Limit Theorem*
Briefly, the *Central Limit Theorem* states that, regardless of the distribution of measurements, sums and averages of a large number of measurements tend to follow the normal distribution. Since many measurements related to growth, healing, or disease progression might be represented by a

sum or accumulation of incremental measurements over time, the normal distribution is often applicable to clinical data for large samples.

To illustrate the *Central Limit Theorem*, we consider the following experiment. A placebo (inactive pill) is given to n patients, followed by an evaluation one hour later. Suppose that each patient's evaluation can result in 'improvement', coded as $+1$, 'no change' (0), or 'deterioration' (-1), each equally likely. Let X_1, X_2, ... X_n represent the measurements for the n patients, and define Z to be a random variable representing the sum of these evaluation scores for all n patients, $Z = X_1 + X_2 + ... + X_n$.

For $n = 1$, the probability distribution of Z is the same as X, which is constant for all possible values of X. This is called a 'uniform' distribution, shown as follows:

Z	P_Z
-1	1/3
0	1/3
+1	1/3

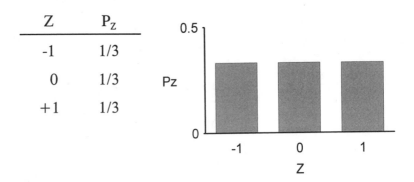

For $n = 2$, Z has the probability distribution shown as follows:

Z	P_Z
-2	1/9
-1	2/9
0	3/9
+1	2/9
+2	1/9

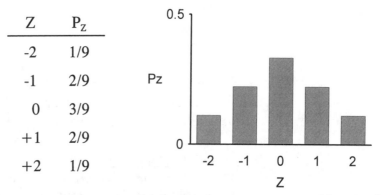

since, there are 9 equally likely outcomes resulting in 5 possible values for Z:

Patient 1	Patient 2	Z	Prob.
-1	-1	-2	1/9
-1	0	-1	1/9
0	-1	-1	1/9
-1	+1	0	1/9
0	0	0	1/9
+1	-1	0	1/9
0	+1	+1	1/9
+1	0	+1	1/9
+1	+1	+2	1/9

For n = 3, Z can take values from -3 to +3 with the distribution:

Z	P_Z
-3	1/18
-2	3/18
-1	6/18
0	7/18
+1	6/18
+2	3/18
+3	1/18

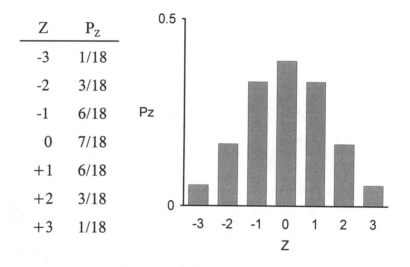

We can see from the histograms that, as n becomes larger, the distribution of Z takes on the bell-shaped characteristic of the normal distribution. The distribution of Z for 8 patients (n = 8) is shown on the next page.

While the probability distribution of the measurements (X) is 'uniform', the sum of these measurements (Z) is a random variable which tends toward a normal distribution as n increases. The *Central Limit Theorem* states that this will be the case regardless of the distribution of the X measurements. Since the sample mean, $\bar{x}$, is the sum of measurements (times a constant, 1/n), the *Central Limit Theorem* implies that $\bar{x}$ has an approximate normal distribution for large n regardless of the probability distribution of the measurements comprising $\bar{x}$.

Z	P_Z
-8	0.000
-7	0.001
-6	0.005
-5	0.017
-4	0.041
-3	0.077
-2	0.119
-1	0.155
0	0.169
+1	0.155
+2	0.119
+3	0.077
+4	0.041
+5	0.017
+6	0.005
+7	0.001
+8	0.000

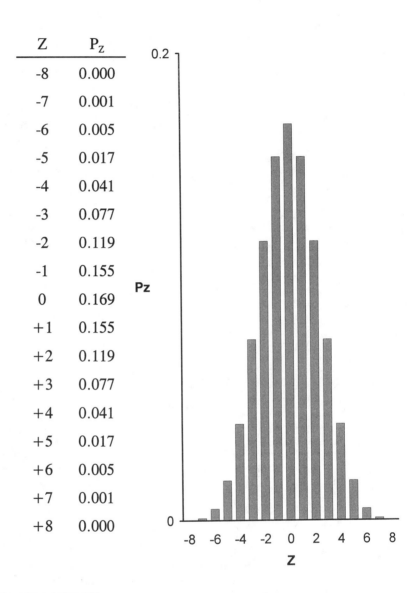

STUDY DESIGN FEATURES

Sound statistical results can be valid only if the study plan is well thought out and accompanied by appropriate data collection techniques. Even the most sophisticated statistical tests may not lead to valid inferences or appropriate characterizations of the population if the study itself is flawed. It is imperative, therefore, that statistical design considerations be addressed in clinical studies during protocol development.

There are a number of statistical design considerations that go into the planning stage of a new study. The probability distribution of the primary response variables will help predict how the measurements will vary. Since greater variability of the measurements requires a larger sample size, distributional assumptions enable the computation of sample size requirements to distinguish a real trend from statistical variation. Sample size determination is discussed further in Chapter 2.

Features which help reduce the response variability can also be incorporated into the study design. Features of controlled clinical trials such as *randomization* and *blinding*, as well as statistical 'noise-reducing' techniques such as the use of covariates, stratification or blocking factors and use of within-patient controls are ways to help control extraneous variability and focus on the primary response measurements.

▸ *Controlled Studies*

A controlled trial is one in which a known treatment, called a 'control', is used in the same study as the test treatments. Controls may be inactive, such as a placebo or sham, or another active treatment, perhaps a currently marketed product. A study which uses a separate, independent group of patients in a control group is called a *parallel-group* study. Studies which give both the test treatments and control to the same patients are called *within-patient control* studies.

▸ *Randomization*

Randomization is a means of objectively assigning experimental units or patients to treatment groups. In clinical trials, this is done by means of a randomization schedule generated prior to commencement of patient enrollment. The randomization scheme should have the property that any randomly selected patient has the same chance as any other patient of being included in any treatment group.

Randomization is used in controlled clinical trials to eliminate systematic treatment group assignment which may lead to bias. In a non-randomized setting, patients with the most severe condition may be assigned to a group based on the treatment's perceived benefit, whether intentional or not. This creates bias since the treatment groups would represent samples from different populations, some more severe than others. Randomization filters out such selection bias and helps establish baseline comparability among the treatment groups.

▸ *Blinding*

Blinded randomization is one of the most important features of a controlled study. Single-blind, double-blind and even triple-blind studies are common among clinical trials.

A single-blind study is one in which the patients are not aware of which treatment they receive. Many patients actually show a clinical response with medical care, even if they are not treated. Others may also respond when treated with a placebo, but are unaware that their medication is inactive. These are examples of the well-known 'placebo effect', which may have a psychological component dependent on the patient's belief that he is receiving appropriate care. A 20% placebo response is not uncommon in many clinical indications.

Suppose that a response, Y, can be represented by a true therapeutic response component, TR, and a placebo effect, PE. Letting subscripts A and P denote 'active' and 'placebo' treatments, respectively, the estimated therapeutic benefit of the active compound might be measured by the difference:

$$Y_A - Y_P = (TR_A + PE_A) - (TR_P + PE_P).$$

Since placebo has no therapeutic benefit, $TR_P = 0$, and with $PE_\Delta = PE_A - PE_P$, we obtain,

$$Y_A - Y_P = TR_A + PE_\Delta.$$

When patients are unaware of their treatment, the placebo effect (PE) should be the same for both groups, making $PE_\Delta = 0$. Thus, the difference in response values estimates the true therapeutic benefit of the active compound.

If, however, patients know which treatment they have been assigned, the 'placebo effect' of the active group may differ from that of the control group, perhaps due to better compliance or expectation of benefit. In this case, the estimate of therapeutic benefit is contaminated by a non-zero PE_Δ.

Bias may affect the investigator's evaluations as well. Evaluation of study measurements such as global assessments and decisions regarding dosing changes, visit timing, use of concomitant medications and degree of followup on adverse events or abnormal labs, may be affected by the investigator's knowledge of the patient's treatment, whether conscious or not.   Blinding the investigator <u>and</u> the patient will help eliminate these biases. Such studies are known as *double-blind* studies.

Double-blinding is a common and important feature of a controlled clinical trial, especially when evaluations are open to some degree of subjectivity. However, double-blinding is not always possible or practical. For example, test and control treatments may not be available in the same formulation. In such cases, treatment can sometimes be administered by one investigator and the evaluations performed by a co-investigator at the same center in an attempt to maintain some sort of investigator blind.

Studies can also be *triple-blind*, wherein the patient, investigator and clinical project team (including the statistician), are all masked as to the treatment administered until the statistical analysis is complete. This reduces a third level of potential bias -- that of the interpretation of the results.

DESCRIPTIVE STATISTICS

Descriptive statistics are used to describe the probability distribution of the population. This is done by using histograms to depict the shape of the distribution, by estimating distributional parameters and by computing various measures of central tendency and dispersion.

A histogram is a plot of the measured values of a random variable by their frequency. Height measurements for 16-

year olds, for example, can be described by a sample histogram as follows, based on 25 students:

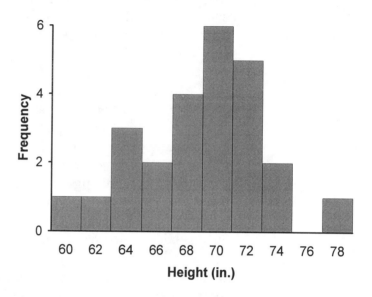

If more and more measurements are taken, the histogram may begin looking like a 'bell-shaped' curve, which is characteristic of the normal distribution, as follows.

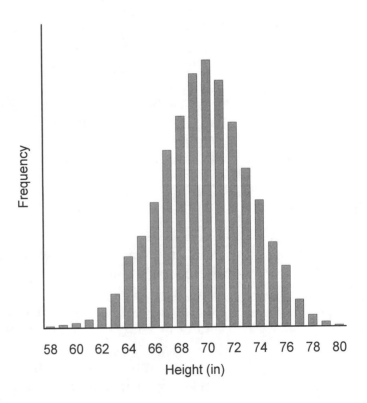

If we assume the population distribution can be modelled with a known distribution, such as the normal, we need only estimate the parameters associated with that distribution in order to fully describe it. The binomial distribution has only one parameter, p, which can be directly estimated from the observed data. The normal distribution has two parameters, μ and σ^2, representing the mean and variance, respectively.

Suppose a sample of n measurements, denoted by x_1, x_2, ..., x_n is obtained. A number of descriptive statistics can be computed from these measurements to help describe the population. These include measures of *central tendency* which describe the center of the distribution, and measures of *dispersion* which describe the variation of the data. Common examples of each are shown in Table 2-1 on the following page.

In addition to distributional parameters, we sometimes want to estimate parameters associated with a statistical 'model'. If an unknown response can be modelled as a function of known or controlled variables, we can often obtain valuable information regarding the response by estimating the weights or coefficients of each of these known variables. These coefficients are called model parameters, and are estimated in a manner which results in the greatest consistency between the model and the observed data.

Descriptive statistical methods are often the only approach that can be used for analyzing the results of pilot studies or Phase I clinical trials. Due to small sample sizes, the lack of blinding or omission of other features of a controlled trial, statistical inference may not be possible in such studies. However, trends or patterns observed in the data using descriptive or exploratory methods will often help in building hypotheses to be tested in a more controlled manner in subsequent studies. Inferential statistical methods are used in such situations.

TABLE 2-1: **Common Descriptive Statistics**

Measures of 'Central Tendency'	
Arithmetic Mean	$\bar{x} = (\Sigma\ x_i)/n$ $= (x_1 + x_2 + \ldots + x_n)\ /\ n$
Median	the middle value, if n is odd; the average of the 2 middle values if n is even
Mode	the most frequently occurring value
Geometric Mean	$(\Pi x_i)^{1/n} = (x_1 \cdot x_2 \cdot \ldots \cdot x_n)^{1/n}$
Harmonic Mean	$n/\Sigma(x_i)^{-1} =$ $n\{(1/x_1) + (1/x_2) + \ldots + (1/x_n)\}^{-1}$
Weighted Mean	$\bar{x}_w = (\Sigma w_i x_i)/W$, where $W = \Sigma w_i$
Trimmed Mean	Arithmetic mean omitting the largest and smallest observations
Winsorized Mean	Arithmetic mean after replacing outliers with the closest non-outlier values

Measures of 'Dispersion'	
Variance	$s^2 = \Sigma(x_i - \bar{x})^2\ /\ (n-1)$
Standard Deviation	$s = $ square-root of the variance
Standard Error (of the mean)	$(s^2/n)^{1/2} = $ Standard deviation of $\bar{x}$
Range	Largest value - Smallest value
Mean Absolute Deviation	$(\Sigma\ \lvert x_i - \bar{x}\rvert)\ /\ n$
Inter-Quartile Range	75th percentile - 25th percentile
Coefficient of Variation	$s/\bar{x}$

INFERENTIAL STATISTICS

The two primary statistical methods for making inferences are confidence interval estimation and hypothesis testing.

▸ *Confidence Intervals*

Population parameters, such as the mean, μ, or standard deviation, σ, can be estimated using a point estimate, such as the sample mean, $\bar{x}$, or sample standard deviation, s. A confidence interval is an interval around the point estimate which contains the parameter with a certain high probability or 'confidence' level. A 95% confidence interval for the mean, μ, can be constructed from the sample data with the following interpretation: if the same experiment were conducted a large number of times, and confidence intervals were constructed for each, 95% of those intervals would contain the population mean, μ.

The general form of a confidence interval is $[\theta_L - \theta_U]$, where θ_L represents the lower limit and θ_U is the upper limit of the interval. If the probability distribution of the point estimate is symmetric (such as the normal distribution), the interval can be found by:

$$\hat{\theta} \pm C \cdot \sigma_{\hat{\theta}}$$

where,

$\hat{\theta}$ *is the point estimate of the population parameter,* θ,

$\sigma_{\hat{\theta}}$ *is the standard error of the estimate , and*

C represents a value determined by the probability distribution of the estimate and the desired significance level.

As an example, for α between 0 and 1, a $100(1-\alpha)\%$ confidence interval for a normal population mean, μ, is

$$\bar{x} \pm Z_{\alpha/2} \cdot \frac{\sigma}{\sqrt{n}}$$

where,

$\bar{x}$ *is the point estimate of* μ,

$\dfrac{\sigma}{\sqrt{n}}$ *is the standard error of* $\bar{x}$, *and*

$Z_{\alpha/2}$ is found from the normal probability tables (e.g., Appendix A.1). Some commonly used values of α and the corresponding critical Z-values are shown below:

α	$Z_{\alpha/2}$
0.10	1.645
0.05	1.96
0.02	2.33
0.01	2.575

▸ *Hypothesis Testing*
Hypothesis testing is a means of formalizing the inferential process for decision making purposes. It is a statistical approach for testing hypothesized statements about population parameters based on logical argument. To understand the concept behind the hypothesis test, we first review the form of a certain deductive argument from logic.

Consider the following argument: "If you have an apple, then you do not have an orange. You have an orange. Therefore, you do not have an apple."

The first two statements of the argument are premises and the third is the conclusion. The conclusion is logically deduced from the two premises, and its truth depends only on the truth of the premises.

If we let **P** represent the statement 'you have an apple', and **Q** represent the statement 'you have an orange', the argument may be formulated as:

if **P** then not **Q**   (conditional premise)
Q   (premise)
_____

therefore, not **P**   (conclusion)

This is a deductively valid argument of logic which applies to any two statements, **P** and **Q**, whether true or false. Note that if you have both an apple and an orange, the conditional premise would be false making the conclusion false since the argument is still valid.

Statistical arguments take the same form as this logical argument, but must account for random variations in statements that may not be known to be completely true. A statistical argument might be paraphrased from the logical argument above as:

if **P** then *probably* not **Q**   (conditional premise)
Q   (premise)
_____

therefore, *probably* not **P**   (conclusion)

The following examples illustrate such 'statistical arguments':

Example 1

Statements:
  P = 'the coin is fair'
  Q = 'we observe 10 tails in a row'

Argument:
  If the coin is fair, we would probably not observe 10 tails in a row. We observe 10 tails in a row. Therefore, the coin is probably not fair.

Example 2

Statements:
  P = 'Drug A has no effect on arthritis'
  Q = '23 of a sample of 25 patients showed improvement in their arthritis after taking Drug A'

Argument:
  If Drug A has no effect on arthritis, we would probably not see improvement in 23 or more of our sample of 25 arthritic patients with Drug A. We observe improvement in 23 of our sample of 25 arthritic patients on Drug A. Therefore, Drug A is probably effective for arthritis.

In the first example, we might initially suspect the coin of being biased in favor of tails. To test this hypothesis, we assume the null case, that is, that the coin is fair. We then design an experiment consisting of tossing the coin ten times and recording the outcomes of each toss. We decide to reject the hypothesis concluding that the coin is biased in favor of tails if the experiment results in 10 consecutive tails.

Formally, the study is set out by identifying the hypothesis, developing a test criterion and formulating a decision rule. For this example, we have:

Null hypothesis: the coin is fair

Alternative: the coin is biased in favor of tails

Test criterion: the number of tails in 10 consecutive tosses of the coin

Decision rule: reject the null hypothesis if all 10 tosses result in 'tails'

We establish the hypothesis, **P**. The hypothesis is tested by observing the results of a study whose outcome is **Q**. If we can determine that the probability of observing **Q** is very small when **P** is true, and we do observe **Q**, we can conclude that **P** is probably not true. The degree of certainty of the conclusion is related to the probability associated with **Q**, assuming **P** is true.

Hypothesis testing can be set forth in an algorithm with 5 parts:

> a. the null hypothesis, abbreviated H_0
> b. the alternative hypothesis, abbreviated H_A
> c. the test criterion
> d. the decision rule
>
> and, e. the conclusion.

The null hypothesis is the statement **P** translated into terms involving the population parameters. In the first example, 'the coin is fair' is equivalent to 'the probability of tails on any toss is 1/2'. Parametrically, this is stated in terms of the binomial parameter, p, representing the probability of tails:

$$H_0: \ p \leq 0.5.$$

The alternative hypothesis is 'not **P**', or

$$H_A: p > 0.5.$$

We generally take 'not **P**' as the hypothesis to be demonstrated based on an acceptable risk for defining 'probably' as used in the examples.

The test criterion or 'test statistic' is some function of the observed data. This is statement **Q** of our statistical argument, and may be the number of tails in 10 tosses of a coin or the number of improved arthritic patients, as in the examples, or we may use a more complex function of the data. Often the test statistic is a function of the sample mean and variance or some other summary statistics.

The decision rule results in the rejection of the null hypothesis if unlikely values of the test statistic are observed when assuming it is true. To determine a decision rule, the degree of such 'unlikeliness' needs to be specified. This is referred to as the *significance level* of the test, denoted α, and in clinical trials, is often (but not always) set to 0.05. By knowing the probability distribution of the test statistic when the null hypothesis is true, we can identify the most extreme $100\alpha\%$ of the values as a 'rejection region'. The decision rule is simply, "reject H_0 when the test statistic falls in the rejection region".

Significance levels are discussed further in Chapter 2.

SUMMARY

This introduction discusses some of the basic concepts of statistics, provides an overview of statistics as a scientific discipline, and shows that the results of a statistical analysis can be no better than the data collected. We have seen that the researcher must be vigilante of biases which can enter into a data set from a multitude of sources. With this in mind, it is important to emphasize the proper application of statistical techniques in study design and data collection as well as at the analysis stage.

Methods of characterizing populations from sample data include descriptive and inferential procedures, most notably parameter estimates by confidence intervals and hypothesis testing. These techniques are the focus of the methods presented in this book, Chapters 3-20.

CHAPTER 2
TOPICS in HYPOTHESIS TESTING

SIGNIFICANCE LEVELS

When conducting hypothesis testing, an erroneous conclusion is made if the null hypothesis is rejected when it is really true. This error is called a 'Type I error', and its probability is denoted by α, known as the 'significance level' of the test.

When setting up the hypothesis test, the rejection region is selected based on a predetermined value for α, usually a small value such as 0.05. This means that there is only a 5% chance of rejecting a true null hypothesis.

As an example, suppose that administration of a drug was suspected to cause increased alkaline phosphatase levels in adult males, a population known to have an alkaline phosphatase mean of 60 U/l in a certain laboratory. To test this, we set up the null and alternative hypotheses as:

$$H_0: \ \mu = 60$$

vs.

$$H_A: \ \mu > 60$$

where μ represents the population mean alkaline phosphatase in all men who might qualify to receive the drug and be tested at this testing laboratory.

A sample of n men treated with the drug is observed and their alkaline phosphatase levels are measured. We choose as our test statistic the 'Z-test', based on the standard normal distribution which is computed from the sample mean, $\bar{x}$. According to the *Central Limit Theorem* (Chapter 1), $\bar{x}$ has a normal distribution with mean μ and standard error $\sigma/\sqrt{n}$ for large n, so that

$$Z = \frac{\bar{x} - \mu}{\sigma/\sqrt{n}}$$

has a 'standard normal' distribution (see also Appendix B).

The null hypothesis would be contradicted if the sample mean, $\bar{x}$, is much greater than the known mean, 60. Therefore, we decide to reject H_0 in favor of H_A when the test statistic is too large, computed under the assumption that H_0 is true,

$$Z_0 = \frac{\bar{x} - 60}{\sigma/\sqrt{n}} \quad .$$

The rejection region is $Z_0 > c$, where c is selected according to the desired signficance level, α. That is,

$$\alpha = Pr\{\text{reject } H_0 \text{ when } H_0 \text{ is true}\} = Pr\{Z_0 > c\} \quad .$$

We denote c by Z_α, which is found from widely available tables of the probabilities for the standard normal distribution, including Appendix A.1 of this book. For the commonly used value of $\alpha = 0.05$, $Z_\alpha = 1.645$.

Suppose that previous laboratory testing at the study lab established a mean alkaline phosphatase level of 60 U/l with a standard deviation of $\sigma = 15$. A current sample of 100 treated men resulted in a sample mean of 62 U/l. The 'Z-test' summary is:

null hypothesis: H_0: $\mu = 60$
alt. hypothesis: H_A: $\mu > 60$

test statistic: $Z_0 = \dfrac{\bar{x} - 60}{\sigma/\sqrt{n}} = \dfrac{62 - 60}{15/\sqrt{100}} = 1.33$

rejection region: reject H_0 if $Z_0 > 1.645$ at a significance level of $\alpha = 0.05$

conclusion: since 1.33 < 1.645, we do not reject H_0. Insufficient evidence exists to indicate an increase in mean alkaline phosphatase levels.

POWER

Accepting the null hypothesis when it is not true is a second type of error which could occur when testing an hypothesis. This is known as the 'Type II error', and has probability, β.

For a given test, β is partly determined by the choice for α. Ideally, we would like both α and β to be small. However, in general there is an inverse relationship between α and β. Decreasing α, the probability of a Type I error, increases β, the probability of a Type II error, and, if carried too far, tends to render the test *powerless* in its ability to detect real deviations from the null hypothesis.

A test's *power* is defined by $1 - \beta$, the probability of rejecting the null hypothesis when it is not true. For a fixed significance level, α, the sample size will determine β and therefore, the power of the test.

In the example just discussed, if we accept H_0 concluding that there is no increase in mean alkaline phosphatase levels with treatment, we would be guilty of a Type II error if a true increase goes undetected by the statistical test. Until the test's power can be investigated, we must conclude simply that there is 'insufficient evidence to indicate a change', rather than 'there is no change'.

Note that β is not only a function of the significance level and the sample size, but also of the value of the alternative hypothesis. The Type II error probability for this alkaline phosphatase example is given by:

$$\beta = \Pr\{\text{accept } H_0 \text{ when } H_A \text{ is true}\}$$
$$= \Pr\{Z_0 \leq 1.645 \text{ when } \mu > 60\}$$

which will differ for each alternative value of μ (> 60).

For example , the probability of a Type II error when $\mu = 64$ is:

$$\beta = Pr\left[Z_0 \leq 1.645 \; when \; \mu = 64\right] \qquad =$$

$$Pr\left[\frac{\bar{x} - 60}{\sigma/\sqrt{n}} \leq 1.645 \; when \; \mu = 64\right] \quad =$$

$$Pr\left[\frac{\bar{x} - 64}{\sigma/\sqrt{n}} \leq 1.645 - \frac{4}{\sigma/\sqrt{n}}\right] \qquad =$$

$$Pr\left[Z \leq -1.022\right] \quad ,$$

since $\sigma = 15$ and n = 100. From the normal probability tables (Appendix A.1), we obtain $\beta = 0.153$, and a power of $1-\beta = 0.847$. Similar calculations when $\mu = 62$ result in $\beta = 0.623$ which gives a power of 0.377.

The power function of the test can be described by a plot of alternative values of μ vs. the power, computed as demonstrated above. The power curve for the Z-test in the example is shown below.

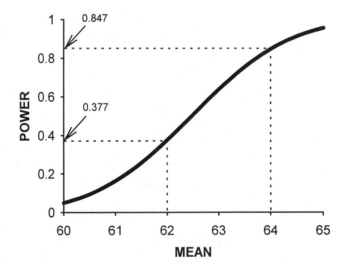

Power curves are important for determining the best test statistic to use. When more than one statistical test is a logical candidate for testing the same hypothesis, the statistician uses the test's power function to determine the more powerful test for a range of likely alternative values. Power curves are also important in sample size determination during study design. Sample size calculations are discussed later in this chapter.

ONE-TAILED and TWO-TAILED TESTS

The form of the alternative hypothesis determines whether the test is a *one-* or *two-tailed* test. The alkaline phosphatase example is a one-tailed test because the alternative hypothesis, $H_A: \mu > 60$, is only concerned with alternative mean values in one direction, namely greater than 60. The two-tailed alternative for this example would be specified as, $H_A: \mu \neq 60$, indicating an interest in alternative values of the mean either greater or less than 60.

The rejection region for the two-tailed Z-test would include both very large and very small values of the test statistic. For a signficance level of α, we reject H_0 in favor of the two-tailed alternative if $Z_0 > Z_{\alpha/2}$ or $Z_0 < -Z_{\alpha/2}$. For $\alpha = 0.05$, we have $\alpha/2 = 0.025$ in each 'tail' of the normal distribution, obtaining $Z_{0.025} = 1.96$ as the critical value for rejection from the normal probability tables (Appendix A.1). The rejection region, for the two-tailed Z-test when $\alpha = 0.05$ is

$$|Z_0| > 1.96.$$

When the distribution of the test statistic is not symmetric (like the normal distribution), the relationship between one- and two-tailed tests is more complex and beyond the scope of this book.

p-VALUES

Formally, the conclusion of a statistical hypothesis test is to 'reject' or to 'not reject' the null hypothesis at a preset significance level. Another way to convey a test's level of significance is with *p-values*, which have come into popular usage with increasing use of computer programs. The p-value is the actual probability of obtaining the calculated test statistic, or one in a more extreme part of the rejection region, when H_0 is true.

In the alkaline phosphatase example of Section 2.1, we obtained the test statistic of $Z_0 = 1.33$. The p-value is computed as

$$p = Pr\{Z_0 \geq 1.33, \text{ assuming } H_0 \text{ is true}\} = 0.0918$$

based on the normal probability tables. Calculated p-values less than the nominal significance level, say 0.05, would be considered 'statistically significant'.

If the probability distribution of the test statistic is symmetric, the p-value corresponding to a 2-tailed test can be halved to obtain the 1-tailed p-value. This is the case for the Z-test (Section 2.1) which has the standard normal distribution (Chapter 1) and for the t-test (Chapters 3-4) which has the Student t-distribution, both of which are symmetrically distributed about zero.

The results of a statistical test are often described as 'highly significant' when very small p-values (such as $p < 0.01$, $p < 0.001$, etc.) are obtained.

SAMPLE SIZE DETERMINATION

Sample size requirements are determined from the desired power of the test, the significance level, the measurement variability and the stated alternative to the null hypothesis. In designing comparative clinical studies, we often use $\alpha = 0.05$ and desire a power of at least 80%. Variability is estimated from previous studies or known data sets, and the alternative value of the hypothesis is determined by that which is clinically important.

Many excellent sources are available showing methods for computing sample sizes, including Lachin [1981], and these are not repeated here. We do consider three examples used quite frequently in determining sample sizes for clinical studies. These are approximate formulas based on the commonly used significance level of 0.05.

▸ *One-Sample Test of a Mean*
For the one sample test about a population mean using the *Z-test* presented earlier in this chapter or the *One Sample t-Test* (Chapter 3), the sample size needed is given by

$$n = \frac{C}{(\Delta / \sigma)^2}$$

where σ is the standard deviation, Δ represents the difference between the hypothesized value and the alternative value, and C is obtained from Table 2.1 depending on the power and type of test.

In the alkaline phosphatase example discussed previously, the sample size required to detect an increase in mean alkaline phosphatase from 60 to 63 U/l, based on a standard deviation of 15, is

$$n = 6.2 / (3/15)^2 = 155 \text{ patients.}$$

This sample size will result in a power of 80% based on a 1-tailed significance level of 0.05.

▸ *Two-Sample Comparison of Means*
The comparison of two means using a *Two-Sample Z-test* or the *Two-Sample t-Test* (Chapter 4) typically tests whether the difference in means between two independent groups is zero. The alternative is that the difference is a non-zero value, say Δ. If patients will be equally divided between two groups, based on a standard deviation in each group of σ, the sample size for each group is found by

$$n = \frac{2 \cdot C}{(\Delta / \sigma)^2}$$

where C is found from Table 2.1.

For example, based on a 2-tailed test at 90% power and a standard deviation of 10, a difference in means of at least 5 can be detected with a sample size of

$$n = 2(10.5) / (5/10)^2 = 84 \text{ patients per group.}$$

▸ *Two-Sample Comparison of Proportions*
The comparison of two independent binomial proportions using a normal approximation (Z-test) or *Chi-Square Test* (Chapter 14) tests for a zero difference in proportions,

$$H_0: \ p_1 - p_2 = 0.$$

The alternative is that the difference is a non-zero value, say Δ. The sample size (per group) required to detect a difference when the true difference is Δ is given by

$$n = \frac{2 \cdot C \cdot \bar{p} \cdot (1 - \bar{p})}{\Delta^2}$$

where $\bar{p} = (p_1 + p_2)/2$, and C is found from Table 2.1. As in the 2-sample means comparison, this formula can be used when the study calls for two groups with the same number of patients in each.

As an example, the sample size needed to detect a difference in true response rates of 25% vs. 35% with at least 80% power, is found as:

n = 2(7.85)(0.3)(0.7) / (.1^2) = 330 patients per group.

This is based on a 2-tailed test at a significance level of 0.05.

TABLE 2.1. C Values for $\alpha = 0.05$

POWER	β	Type	C
80%	0.20	1-Tailed	6.2
80%	0.20	2-Tailed	7.85
85%	0.15	1-Tailed	7.2
85%	0.15	2-Tailed	9.0
90%	0.10	1-Tailed	8.6
90%	0.10	2-Tailed	10.5

MULTIPLE HYPOTHESIS TESTS

Consider the alkaline phosphatase example discussed at the beginning of this chapter, and suppose that two such studies are conducted, one in each of two independent centers. The significance level, α, is the probability of an erroneously significant finding, i.e., the probability of a significant result in Center 1 or in Center 2 when H_0 is true. Using a law of probability which states that, for any event A,

$$Pr\{A\} = 1 - Pr\{not\ A\},$$

we have, $\alpha = 1 - Pr\{$a non-significant result in both Centers 1 and 2, when H_0 is true$\}$. If α_1 and α_2 represent the signficance levels of the tests for Centers 1 and 2, respectively, we have

$$Pr\{\text{a non-significant result in Center i when } H_0 \text{ is true}\}$$
$$= 1 - \alpha_i \qquad (\text{for i} = 1, 2).$$

Applying another law of probabilty which states that, for any two independent events A and B,

$$Pr\{A \text{ and } B\} = Pr\{A\} \cdot Pr\{B\},$$

we obtain $\alpha = 1 - (1-\alpha_1)(1-\alpha_2)$. If $\alpha_1 = \alpha_2 = 0.05$, we have

$$\alpha = 1 - (1 - 0.05)^2 = 0.0975.$$

In general, if there are k centers, or k independent tests, each conducted at a significance level of 0.05, the overall signficance level, α, is

$$\alpha = 1 - (1 - 0.05)^k,$$

which is seen to increase markedly even for small values of k:

k	α
1	0.050
2	0.098
3	0.143
4	0.185
5	0.226

This illustrates a problem encountered with simultaneously conducting many hypothesis tests. Although the tests usually will not be independent, the fact is that the overall significance level will differ from that at which the individual tests are performed.

Multiple hypothesis testing arises in a number of ways in the analysis of clinical trials data, and the researcher must be aware of any effects on the overall conclusions resulting from these situations.

One manner in which multiple testing arises is in conducting a large number of tests on many response variables. For example, testing for significant pre- to poststudy changes in laboratory values by conducting individual Z- or t-tests on a large number of laboratory parameters may result in chance significance. With 20 independent t-tests each at a significance level of 0.05, we would expect one to be significant due to chance variation when there is no real deviation from the null hypothesis. If 30 or 50 or 100 tests are conducted on the laboratory data, although not independent, one might expect a number of these to be falsely significant.

Another type of multiple testing situation arises in the comparison of a response variable among more than two randomized treatment groups. With three groups, say a low and high active dose group and a placebo group, we may want to compare the response of each active group to that of placebo, and compare the low and high dose group responses.

Three groups result in 3 pairwise comparisons, four groups, in 6, etc. as follows:

No. of Groups:	2	3	4	5	6	7
No. of Comparisons:	1	3	6	10	15	21

In a study with 5 dose groups, for example, there would be 10 possible pairwise comparisons. If each of these is conducted at a significance level of 0.05, the overall significance level is affected so that the likelihood of obtaining at least one erroneous finding increases. Analysis-of-variance techniques and various multiple comparison adjustments, described in Chapters 5-7, are used to overcome the problem associated with the multiple testing in these situations.

Interim analyses of ongoing studies presents a third situation involving multiple testing. When a decision is made to stop or continue the study, or to change the study in some other manner, based on an interim look at the data, the final significance levels will be altered. A branch of statistics called *Sequential Analysis* deals with such problems, and in some cases can offer adjustments in order to maintain an overall significance level at a predetermined value. Methods described by O'Brien and Fleming [1979] and Pocock [1982] are widely used for such adjustments which are easy to apply when there is only one interim evaluation. Other adjustments can sometimes be made under more complex situations. Careful planning at the design stage is very important in studies with anticipated interim analyses. When interim analyses occur without pre-planning, careful documentation must be kept to avoid compromising the study integrity.

SUMMARY

This chapter presents a brief discussion of some of the most fundamental elements of hypothesis testing, including significance levels, power, p-values, illustration of the difference between one- and two-tailed tests, the idea behind sample size computations and the effect of multiple testing on significance levels. Many of the statistical terms used in this chapter to discuss these ideas are frequently used by clinical researchers from protocol development through regulatory submission, statisticians and nonstatisticians alike. These concepts form a basis for a general overview of hypothesis testing, the primary inferential tool used in presenting the statistical methods in Chapters 3-20.

CHAPTER 3
The ONE-SAMPLE t-TEST

INTRODUCTION

The *One-Sample t-Test* is used to infer whether an unknown population mean differs from a hypothesized value. The test is based on a single sample of 'n' measurements from the population.

A special case of the *One-Sample t-Test* is often used to determine if a mean response changes under different experimental conditions using paired observations, such as 'pre-' and 'post-' study measurements. Since the analyst uses the changes or 'differences' in the paired measurements, this test is often referred to as the 'paired-difference' t-test. A hypothesized mean difference of zero may be interpreted as 'no clinical response'.

The *One-Sample t-Test*, along with its two-sample counterpart presented in the next chapter, must surely be the most frequently cited inferential tests used in statistics.

SYNOPSIS

A sample of n data points, y_1, y_2, ..., y_n, is randomly selected from a normally distributed population with unknown mean, μ. This mean is estimated by the sample mean, $\bar{y}$. We hypothesize the mean to be some value, μ_0. The greater the deviation between $\bar{y}$ and μ_0, the greater the evidence that the hypothesis is untrue.

The test statistic, t, is a function of this deviation, standardized by the standard error of $\bar{y}$, namely $s/\sqrt{n}$. Large values of t will lead to rejection of the null hypothesis. When H_0 is true, t has the 'Student-t' distribution with n-1 degrees-of-freedom.

The *One-Sample t-Test* is summarized as follows:

null hypothesis:	H_0: $\mu = \mu_0$
alt. hypothesis:	H_A: $\mu \neq \mu_0$
test statistic:	$t = \dfrac{\bar{y} - \mu_0}{s / \sqrt{n}}$
decision rule:	*reject H_0 if $\mid t \mid > t_{\alpha/2,\,n-1}$*

The value $t_{\alpha/2,n-1}$ represents the 'critical t-value' of the Student t-distribution at a 2-tailed significance level, α, and n-1 degrees-of-freedom. This value can be obtained from Appendix A.2, or from SAS as described later (DETAILS & NOTES).

The *One-Sample t-Test* is often used in matched-pairs situations, such as testing for pre- to poststudy changes. The goal is to determine whether a difference exists between two time points or between two treatments based on data values from the same patients for both measures. The 'paired-difference' t-test is conducted using the procedures outlined for the *One-Sample t-Test* with $\mu =$ 'the mean difference' (sometimes denoted μ_d), $\mu_0 = 0$, and the y_i's = the paired-differences. Examples 3.1 and 3.2 demonstrate application of the *One-Sample t-Test* in non-matched and matched situations, respectively.

EXAMPLE 3.1 -- "Body-Mass Index"

In a number of previous Phase I and II studies of male, non-insulin-dependent diabetic (NIIDM) patients conducted by Mylitech Biosystems, Inc., the mean body mass index (BMI) was found to be 28.4. An investigator has 17 male NIIDM patients enrolled in a new study and wants to know if the BMI from this sample is consistent with previous findings. BMI is computed as the ratio of weight in kilograms to the square of the height in meters. What conclusion can the investigator make based on the following height and weight data from his 17 patients?

Pat. No.	Height (cm)	Weight (kg)	Pat. No.	Height (cm)	Weight (Kg)
1	178	101.7	10	183	97.8
2	170	97.1	11	n/a	78.7
3	191	114.2	12	172	77.5
4	179	101.9	13	183	102.8
5	182	93.1	14	169	81.1
6	177	108.1	15	177	102.1
7	184	85.0	16	180	112.1
8	182	89.1	17	184	89.7
9	179	95.8			

SOLUTION

We first calculate BMI as follows: convert height in centimeters to meters by dividing by 100, square this quantity, then divide it into the weight. BMI data (y_i) are shown below, along with the squares and summations. Since no height measurement is available for Patient No. 11, BMI cannot be computed and is considered a missing value.

Pat. No.	BMI (y)	BMI^2 (y^2)	Pat. No.	BMI (y)	BMI^2 (y^2)
1	32.1	1030.30	10	29.2	852.85
2	33.6	1128.87	11	.	.
3	31.3	979.94	12	26.2	686.26
4	31.8	1011.43	13	30.7	942.28
5	28.1	789.98	14	28.4	806.30
6	34.5	1190.58	15	32.6	1062.08
7	25.1	630.33	16	34.6	1197.07
8	26.9	723.55	17	26.5	701.96
9	29.9	893.96			
			TOTAL	481.5	14627.74

The sample mean BMI, $\bar{y}$, and standard deviation, s, are computed from the $n=16$ patients with non-missing data as follows. The formula shown for s is equivalent to that given in Chapter 1, but is in a more convenient format for manual computations.

$$\bar{y} = \frac{\sum y_i}{n} = \frac{481.5}{16} = 30.093 \quad , \quad and$$

$$s = \sqrt{\frac{\sum y_i^2 - n(\bar{y})^2}{(n-1)}} = \sqrt{\frac{14627.74 - 16(30.093)^2}{15}} = 3.03 \quad .$$

With a 0.05 significance level, the test summary becomes:

null hypothesis:	H_0:	$\mu = 28.4$
alt. hypothesis:	H_A:	$\mu \neq 28.4$

test statistic: $\quad t = \dfrac{\bar{y} - \mu_0}{s/\sqrt{n}} = \dfrac{30.09 - 28.4}{3.03/\sqrt{16}} = 2.23$

decision rule: $\quad$ *reject H_0 if $|t| > t_{0.025,15} = 2.131$*

conclusion: $\quad$ Since 2.23 > 2.131, we reject H_0 and conclude that the BMI of the new patients differs from that of the patients studied previously.

SAS Analysis of Example 3.1

The SAS code and output for analyzing this data set are shown on the next page. The program first computes the BMI from the height and weight, then prints a listing of the data using PROC PRINT (1). The t-test is conducted using PROC MEANS, although PROC UNIVARIATE could also be used. The hypothesized value, 28.4, is subtracted from each data point (variable=BMI0) prior to computing the t-value (2), in effect testing whether the mean deviation from 28.4 differs from zero.

BMI is also included in the VAR statement to obtain the mean (3) and standard deviation (4) of the BMI data. The test is significant if the p-value (5) is less than the significance level of the test. In this case, we reject the null hypothesis at a two-tailed signficance level of 0.05, since the p-value of 0.041 is less than 0.05.

```
* SAS Code for Example 3.1 ;

DATA DIAB;
INPUT PATNO WT_KG HT_CM @@;
  BMI  = WT_KG / ((HT_CM/100)**2);
  BMI0 = BMI - 28.4;
LABEL BMI0 = 'BMI-28.4';
CARDS;
 1 101.7 178    2  97.1 170    3 114.2 191
 4 101.9 179    5  93.1 182    6 108.1 177
 7  85.0 184    8  89.1 182    9  95.8 179
10  97.8 183   11  78.7  .    12  77.5 172
13 102.8 183   14  81.1 169   15 102.1 177
16 112.1 180   17  89.7 184
; RUN;

PROC PRINT LABEL DATA = DIAB;
VAR PATNO HT_CM WT_KG BMI BMI0;
FORMAT BMI BMI0 5.1;
TITLE1 'One-Sample t-Test';
TITLE2 'EXAMPLE 3.1: Body-Mass Index Data';
RUN;

PROC MEANS MEAN STD N T PRT DATA = DIAB;
VAR BMI BMI0;
RUN;
```

```
* SAS Output for Example 3.1

                    One-Sample t-Test
              EXAMPLE 3.1: Body-Mass Index Data

    OBS    PATNO    HT_CM    WT_KG     BMI    BMI-28.4

     1       1       178     101.7    32.1      3.7
     2       2       170      97.1    33.6      5.2
     3       3       191     114.2    31.3      2.9
     4       4       179     101.9    31.8      3.4
     5       5       182      93.1    28.1     -0.3
     6       6       177     108.1    34.5      6.1
     7       7       184      85.0    25.1     -3.3
     8       8       182      89.1    26.9     -1.5     (1)
     9       9       179      95.8    29.9      1.5
    10      10       183      97.8    29.2      0.8
    11      11        .       78.7     .         .
    12      12       172      77.5    26.2     -2.2
    13      13       183     102.8    30.7      2.3
    14      14       169      81.1    28.4     -0.0
    15      15       177     102.1    32.6      4.2
    16      16       180     112.1    34.6      6.2
    17      17       184      89.7    26.5     -1.9


Variable  Label      Mean       Std Dev    N      T       Prob>|T|
--------------------------(3)--------(4)----------------------------
BMI                 30.0934189  3.0322739  16  39.6974939  0.0001
BMI0     BMI-28.4    1.6934189  3.0322739  16   2.2338600  0.0411
-----------------------------------------------(2)-----------(5)
```

EXAMPLE 3.2 -- "Paired-Difference in Weight Loss"
Mylitech is developing a new appetite suppressing compound for use in weight reduction. A preliminary study of 35 obese patients provided the following data on patients' body weights (in pounds) before and after 10 weeks of treatment with the new compound. Does the new treatment look at all promising?

Subj No.	Pre-	Post-	Subj. No.	Pre-	Post-
1	165	160	19	177	171
2	202	200	20	181	170
3	256	259	21	148	154
4	155	156	22	167	170
5	135	134	23	190	180
6	175	162	24	165	154
7	180	187	25	155	150
8	174	172	26	153	145
9	136	138	27	205	206
10	168	162	28	186	184
11	207	197	29	178	166
12	155	155	30	129	132
13	220	205	31	125	127
14	163	153	32	165	169
15	159	150	33	156	158
16	253	255	34	170	161
17	138	128	35	145	152
18	287	280			

SOLUTION

We first calculate the weight loss for each patient (y_i) by subtracting the 'post-' weight from the 'pre-' weight (see SAS printout). The mean and standard deviation of these differences are: $\bar{y}_d = 3.457$, and $s = 6.340$, based on $n = 35$ patients. A test for significant mean weight loss is equivalent to testing whether the mean loss, μ_d, is greater than zero. We use a one-tailed test since the interest is in weight loss (not weight 'change'). The hypothesis test is summarized as follows:

null hypothesis: $\quad$ H_0: $\mu_d = 0$

alt. hypothesis: $\quad$ H_A: $\mu_d > 0$

test statistic: $\qquad t = \dfrac{\overline{y}_d}{s_d / \sqrt{n}} = \dfrac{3.457}{6.340 / \sqrt{35}} = 3.226$

decision rule: $\qquad$ reject H_0 if t > $t_{0.05,34}$ = 1.691

conclusion: $\qquad$ Since 3.226 > 1.691, reject H_0 at a significance level of 0.05, concluding that a significant mean weight loss occurs following treatment.

SAS Analysis of Example 3.2

The SAS code and output for analyzing this data set are shown on the next page. The program first computes the paired differences (variable=WTLOSS), then prints a listing of the data using PROC PRINT. A portion of this printout is shown (1).

PROC MEANS with the 'T' and 'PRT' options is used to conduct the *One-Sample t-Test* on these differences. The output shows a t-statistic of 3.22594 (2), which corroborates the manual computations. Since SAS prints the 2-tailed p-value (3), this must be halved to obtain the one-tailed result, p= 0.0028/2 = 0.0014. We reject the null hypothesis concluding that a significant weight loss occurs, since this p-value is less than the nominal significance level of $\alpha = 0.05$.

The pre- and posttreatment body weights (variables WTPRE and WTPST) are included in the VAR statement with PROC MEANS to obtain the summary statistics (4) for these measures. The T values for these 2 variables are not meaningful and should be ignored.

```
*   SAS Code for Example 3.2  ;

DATA OBESE;
INPUT SUBJ WTPRE WTPST @@;
  WTLOSS = WTPRE - WTPST;
CARDS;
 1 165 160    2 202 200    3 256 259    4 155 156
 5 135 134    6 175 162    7 180 187    8 174 172
 9 136 138   10 168 162   11 207 197   12 155 155
13 220 205   14 163 153   15 159 150   16 253 255
17 138 128   18 287 280   19 177 171   20 181 170
21 148 154   22 167 170   23 190 180   24 165 154
25 155 150   26 153 145   27 205 206   28 186 184
29 178 166   30 129 132   31 125 127   32 165 169
33 156 158   34 170 161   35 145 152
; RUN;

PROC PRINT DATA = OBESE;
VAR SUBJ WTPRE WTPST WTLOSS;
TITLE1 'One-Sample t-Test';
TITLE2 'EXAMPLE 3.2: Paired-Difference in Weight
         Loss';
RUN;

PROC MEANS MEAN STD N T PRT DATA = OBESE;
VAR WTPRE WTPST WTLOSS;
RUN;
```

*   SAS Output for Example 3.2

One-Sample t-Test
EXAMPLE 3.2: Paired-Difference in Weight Loss

OBS	SUBJ	WTPRE	WTPST	WTLOSS	
1	1	165	160	5	
2	2	202	200	2	
3	3	256	259	-3	
4	4	155	156	-1	
5	5	135	134	1	
6	6	175	162	13	
7	7	180	187	-7	(1)
8	8	174	172	2	
9	9	136	138	-2	
10	10	168	162	6	
.	.	.	.	.	
.	.	.	.	.	
.	.	.	.	.	
33	33	156	158	-2	
34	34	170	161	9	
35	35	145	152	-7	

Variable		Mean	Std Dev	N	T	Prob>|T|
WTPRE	(4)	174.9428571	35.9353528	35	28.8010502	0.0001
WTPST	(4)	171.4857143	35.4495262	35	28.6188075	0.0001
WTLOSS		3.4571429	6.3400819	35	3.2259414	0.0028

---(2)---------(3)---

DETAILS & NOTES

▸ The main difference between the Z-test (Chapter 2) and the t-test is that the Z-statistic is based on a known standard deviation, σ, while the t-statistic uses the sample standard deviation, s, as an estimate of σ. With the assumption of normally distributed data, the variance σ^2 is more closely estimated by the sample variance s^2 as n gets large. It can be shown that the t-test is equivalent to the Z-test for infinite degrees-of-freedom. In practice, a 'large' sample is usually considered $n \geq 30$. The distributional relationship between the Z- and t-statistics is shown in Appendix B.

If the assumption of normally distributed data cannot be made, the mean may not represent the best measure of central tendency. In such cases, a non-parametric rank test such as the *Wilcoxon Signed-Rank Test* (Chapter 10) may be more appropriate. The SAS UNIVARIATE procedure can be used to test for normality.

▸ Because Example 3.1 tests for any difference from a hypothesized value, a two-tailed test is used. A one-tailed test would be used when it is desired to test whether the population mean is strictly <u>greater than</u> *or* strictly <u>less than</u> the hypothesized threshhold level (μ_0), such as in Example 3.2. We use the rejection region according to the alternative hypothesis as follows:

Type of Test	Alternative Hypothesis	Corresponding Rejection Region
2-tailed	H_A: $\mu \neq \mu_0$	reject H_0 if t $>$ $t_{\alpha/2,n-1}$ or t $<$ -$t_{\alpha/2,n-1}$
1-tailed (right)	H_A: $\mu > \mu_0$	reject H_0 if t $>$ $t_{\alpha,n-1}$
1-tailed (left)	H_A: $\mu < \mu_0$	reject H_0 if t $<$ -$t_{\alpha,n-1}$

▸ Most statistics text books have tables of the t-distribution in an appendix. These generally give the critical t-values for levels of α = 0.10, 0.05 0.025, 0.01 and 0.005, as in Appendix A.2. Critical t-values can also be found from most statistical programs, including SAS using the function TINV(1-a,n-1), where a=α for a one-tailed test and a=$\alpha/2$ for a two-tailed test. For Example 3.1, the critical t-value of 2.131 with 15 degrees-of-freedom can be found with the SAS function TINV(0.975,15).

▸ A non-significant result does not necessarily imply that the null hypothesis is true, only that insufficient evidence exists to contradict it. Larger sample sizes are often needed and an investigation of the power curve (see Chapter 2) is necessary for 'equivalency studies'.

▸ Significance does not imply causality. For example, concluding that the treatment *caused* the significant weight loss in Example 3.2 would be presumptuous. Causality can better be investigated using a concurrent untreated or 'control' group in the study, and strictly controlling other experimental conditions. In controlled studies, comparison of responses between two (or more) groups is carried out with tests such as the *Two-Sample t-Test* (Chapter 4) or analysis-of-variance methods (Chapters 5-7).

▸ Known values of n measurements uniquely determine the sample mean, $\bar{y}$. But given $\bar{y}$, the n measurements cannot uniquely be determined. In fact, n-1 of the measurements can be freely selected, with the n-th determined by $\bar{y}$. Thus the term n-1 'degrees-of-freedom'.

The number of degrees-of-freedom, often denoted by the Greek letter υ ('nu'), is a parameter of the Student-t probability distribution.

CHAPTER 4
The TWO-SAMPLE t-TEST

INTRODUCTION

The *Two-Sample t-Test* is used to compare the means of two independent populations, denoted μ_1 and μ_2. This test has ubiquitous application in the analysis of controlled clinical trials. Examples might include the comparison of mean decreases in diastolic blood pressure between two groups of patients receiving different antihypertensive agents, or estimating pain relief of a new treatment relative to that of placebo based on subjective assesment of percent-improvement in two parallel groups.

We assume that the two populations are normally distributed and have the same variance (σ^2).

SYNOPSIS

Samples of n_1 and n_2 observations are randomly selected from the two populations, with the measurements from Population i denoted by y_{i1}, y_{i2}, ..., y_{ini} (for i = 1, 2). The unknown means, μ_1 and μ_2, are estimated by the sample means, $\bar{y}_1$ and $\bar{y}_2$, respectively. The greater the difference between the sample means, the greater the evidence that the hypothesis of equality of population means (H_0) is untrue.

The test statistic, t, is a function of this difference standardized by its standard error, namely $s(1/n_1 + 1/n_2)^{1/2}$. Large values of t will lead to rejection of the null hypothesis. When H_0 is true, t has the 'Student-t' distribution with N-2 degrees-of-freedom, where $N = n_1 + n_2$.

The best estimate of the common unknown population variance (σ^2), is the 'pooled' variance (s_p^2), computed as the weighted average of the sample variances using the formula:

$$s_p^2 = \frac{(n_1-1)s_1^2 + (n_2-1)s_2^2}{(N-2)} \quad .$$

The *Two-Sample t-Test* is summarized as follows:

null hypothesis:	H_0: $\mu_1 = \mu_2$
alt. hypothesis:	H_A: $\mu_1 \neq \mu_2$
test statistic:	$t = \dfrac{\overline{y_1} - \overline{y_2}}{\sqrt{s_p^2\left(\dfrac{1}{n_1}+\dfrac{1}{n_2}\right)}}$
decision rule:	*reject H_0 if $\lvert t \rvert > t_{\alpha/2,\,N-1}$*

EXAMPLE 4.1 -- "FEV$_1$ Changes"

A new compound, ABC-123, is being developed for long-term treatment of patients with chronic asthma. Asthmatic patients were enrolled in a double-blind study and randomized to receive daily oral doses of ABC-123 or placebo for 6 weeks. The primary measurement of interest is the resting FEV$_1$ (forced expiratory volume during the first second of expiration), which is measured before and at the end of the 6-week treatment period. Data (in liters) are shown in the table which follows. Does administration of ABC-123 appear to have any effect on FEV$_1$?

	ABC-123 Group			Placebo Group		
Pat. No.	Base-line	Week 6		Pat. No.	Base-line	Week 6
101	1.35	n/a		102	3.01	3.90
103	3.22	3.55		104	2.24	3.01
106	2.78	3.15		105	2.25	2.47
108	2.45	2.30		107	1.65	1.99
109	1.84	2.37		111	1.95	n/a
110	2.81	3.20		112	3.05	3.26
113	1.90	2.65		114	2.75	2.55
116	3.00	3.96		115	1.60	2.20
118	2.25	2.97		117	2.77	2.56
120	2.86	2.28		119	2.06	2.90
121	1.56	2.67		122	1.71	n/a
124	2.66	3.76		123	3.54	2.92

SOLUTION ▬▬▬▬▬▬▬▬▬

Let μ_1 and μ_2 represent the mean increases in FEV$_1$ for the ABC-123 and the placebo groups, respectively. The first step is to calculate each patient's increase in FEV$_1$ from baseline to Week-6 (shown in SAS output). Patients 101, 111 and 122 are excluded from this analysis since no Week-6 measurements are available. The FEV$_1$ increases (in liters) can be summarized by treatment group as follows:

		ABC-123	Placebo
Mean	$(\bar{y}_i)$	0.503	0.284
S.D.	(s_i)	0.520	0.508
Sample Size	(n_i)	11	10

The poooled variance is

$$s_p^2 = \frac{(11-1)\cdot 0.520^2 + (10-1)\cdot 0.508^2}{(21-2)} = 0.265 \quad .$$

Since we are looking for 'any effect', we use a 2-tailed test as follows:

null hypothesis: H_0: $\mu_1 = \mu_2$
alt. hypothesis: H_A: $\mu_1 \neq \mu_2$

test statistic:

$$t = \frac{0.503 - 0.284}{\sqrt{0.265\left(\frac{1}{11}+\frac{1}{10}\right)}} = 0.974$$

decision rule: *reject H_0 if $|t| > t_{0.025,\ 19} = 2.093$*

conclusion: Since 0.974 is not $>$ 2.093, we cannot reject H_0, concluding that our samples fail to provide significant evidence of any effect of ABC-123 on FEV$_1$. This test is based on a significance level of $\alpha = 0.05$.

SAS Analysis of Example 4.1

The SAS code for analyzing this data set is shown below, and the output is shown on the next page. The program first computes the pre- to poststudy changes in FEV_1 ('CHG'), then prints a listing of the data using PROC PRINT (1).

PROC MEANS is used in this example to obtain the summary statistics for the pre- and Week-6 response values for each group (2). The 'T' and 'PRT' statistics are requested in the PROC MEANS statement to conduct *One-Sample t-Test*s for the significance of the within-group changes (variable=CHG) (3). Note that the ABC-123 Group shows a significant increase in mean FEV_1 (p=0.0094), while the Placebo Group does not (p=0.1107).

The *Two-Sample t-Test* is carried out with PROC TTEST using the class variable 'TRTGRP'. Assuming equal variances, we use the t-value (T) and p-value (Prob > |T|) corresponding to 'Equal' under the 'Variances' column (4). The p-value of 0.3425 (>0.05) indicates no significant difference in the FEV_1 increases between groups.

```
* SAS Code for Example 4.1

DATA FEV;
INPUT PATNO TRTGRP $ FEV0 FEV6 @@;
  CHG = FEV6 - FEV0;
  IF CHG = . THEN DELETE;
CARDS;
101 A 1.35   .        103 A 3.22 3.55
106 A 2.78 3.15       108 A 2.45 2.30
109 A 1.84 2.37       110 A 2.81 3.20
     (more data lines)...
122 P 1.71   .        123 P 3.54 2.92
; RUN;

PROC FORMAT;
 VALUE $TRT 'A' = 'ABC-123'
            'P' = 'PLACEBO' ; RUN;

PROC PRINT DATA = FEV;
VAR PATNO TRTGRP FEV0 FEV6 CHG;
FORMAT TRTGRP $TRT.  FEV0 FEV6 CHG 5.2;
TITLE1 'Two-Sample t-Test';
TITLE2 'EXAMPLE 4.1: FEV1 Changes';
RUN;

PROC MEANS MEAN STD N T PRT DATA = FEV;
BY TRTGRP; VAR FEV0 FEV6 CHG;
FORMAT TRTGRP $TRT.; RUN;

PROC TTEST DATA = FEV; CLASS TRTGRP; VAR CHG;
FORMAT TRTGRP $TRT.; RUN;
```

```
* SAS Output for Example 4.1


                           Two-Sample t-Test
                 EXAMPLE 4.1: Comparison of FEV1 Changes

        OBS    PATNO    TRTGRP      FEV0     FEV6     CHG

         1      103    ABC-123     3.22     3.55     0.33
         2      106    ABC-123     2.78     3.15     0.37
         3      108    ABC-123     2.45     2.30    -0.15
         4      109    ABC-123     1.84     2.37     0.53
         5      110    ABC-123     2.81     3.20     0.39
         6      113    ABC-123     1.90     2.65     0.75
         7      116    ABC-123     3.00     3.96     0.96
         8      118    ABC-123     2.25     2.97     0.72
         9      120    ABC-123     2.86     2.28    -0.58
        10      121    ABC-123     1.56     2.67     1.11    (1)
        11      124    ABC-123     2.66     3.76     1.10
        12      102    PLACEBO     3.01     3.90     0.89
        13      104    PLACEBO     2.24     3.01     0.77
        14      105    PLACEBO     2.25     2.47     0.22
        15      107    PLACEBO     1.65     1.99     0.34
        16      112    PLACEBO     3.05     3.26     0.21
        17      114    PLACEBO     2.75     2.55    -0.20
        18      115    PLACEBO     1.60     2.20     0.60
        19      117    PLACEBO     2.77     2.56    -0.21
        20      119    PLACEBO     2.06     2.90     0.84
        21      123    PLACEBO     3.54     2.92    -0.62



------------------------ TRTGRP=ABC-123 ----------------------

Variable        Mean        Std Dev    N          T    Prob>|T|
---------------------------------------------------------------
FEV0         2.4845455    0.5328858   11   15.4635479    0.0001
FEV6         2.9872727    0.5916095   11   16.7469632    0.0001
CHG          0.5027273    0.5198286   11    3.2075142    0.0094
----------------------------------------------------(3)------
   (2)
------------------------ TRTGRP=PLACEBO ----------------------

Variable        Mean        Std Dev    N          T    Prob>|T|
---------------------------------------------------------------
FEV0         2.4920000    0.6355365   10   12.3995958    0.0001
FEV6         2.7760000    0.5507006   10   15.9405734    0.0001
CHG          0.2840000    0.5077882   10    1.7686248    0.1107
----------------------------------------------------(3)------


                        TTEST PROCEDURE
Variable: CHG

TRTGRP        N          Mean        Std Dev      Std Error
-----------------------------------------------------------
ABC-123      11      0.50272727     0.51982864    0.15673423
PLACEBO      10      0.28400000     0.50778823    0.16057674

                      Variances      T       DF   Prob>|T|
                   --------------------------------------
              (6)  Unequal        0.9748    18.9    0.3420
              (4)  Equal          0.9736    19.0    0.3425

For H0: Variances are equal, F' = 1.05    DF = (10,9)
                           Prob>F' = 0.9532
                              (5)
```

DETAILS & NOTES

▸ The assumption of equal variances can be tested using the 'F-test'. An F-test generally arises as a ratio of variances. When the hypothesis of equal variances is true, the ratio of sample variances should be about 1. The probability distribution of this ratio is known as the F-distribution (which is widely used in the *analysis-of-variance*).

The test for comparing two variances can be made as follows:

null hypothesis:	H_0: $\sigma_1^2 = \sigma_2^2$
alt. hypothesis:	H_A: $\sigma_1^2 \neq \sigma_2^2$
test statistic:	$F = s_U^2 / s_L^2$
decision rule:	*reject H_0 if $F > F_{n_L-1}^{n_U-1}(\alpha)$*

The subscripts U and L denote 'upper' and 'lower'. The sample with the larger sample variance (s_U^2) is considered the 'upper' sample, and that with the smaller sample variance (s_L^2) is the 'lower'. Under H_0, F has the 'F-distribution' with n_U-1 upper degrees-of-freedom and n_L-1 lower degrees-of-freedom. The critical F value can be obtained from the F-tables in most elementary statistics books or many computer packages. In SAS, the critical-F value for n_U upper and n_L lower degrees-of-freedom can be found from the function FINV($1-\alpha,n_U,n_L$).

In Example 4.1, we compute $F = 0.520^2 / 0.508^2 = 1.05$, which leads to non-rejection of the null hypothesis of equal variances. As noted in the SAS output, the p-value associated with this preliminary test is 0.9532 (5), based on 10 upper and 9 lower degrees-of-freedom. We proceed with the t-test assuming equal variances since the evidence fails to contradict that assumption.

If the hypothesis of equal variances is rejected, the t-test may give erroneous results. In such cases, a modified version of the t-test proposed by Satterthwaite is often used. The 'Satterthwaite adjustment' consists of using the statistic similar to the t-test but with an approximate degrees-of-freedom, carried out as follows.

Satterthwaite's modified t-test

test statistic:
$$t' = \frac{\overline{y}_1 - \overline{y}_2}{\sqrt{\dfrac{s_1^2}{n_1} + \dfrac{s_2^2}{n_2}}}$$

decision rule:
$$\text{reject } H_0 \text{ if } |t'| > t_{\alpha/2, q}$$

where q represents the approximate degrees-of-freedom computed as follows (with $w_i = s_i^2 / n_i$):

$$q = \frac{(w_1 + w_2)^2}{\dfrac{w_1^2}{(n_1-1)} + \dfrac{w_2^2}{(n_2-1)}} \quad .$$

For Example 4.1, we compute

$$w_1 = 0.520^2/11 = 0.0246$$

and,

$$w_2 = 0.508^2/10 = 0.0258$$

so that

$$q = \frac{(0.0246 + 0.0258)^2}{\dfrac{0.0246^2}{10} + \dfrac{0.0258^2}{9}} = 18.9$$

and,

$$t' = \frac{0.503 - 0.284}{\sqrt{\dfrac{0.520^2}{11} + \dfrac{0.508^2}{10}}} = 0.975 \quad .$$

SAS computes these quantities automatically in the output of the PROC TTEST. Satterthwaite's t-value and approximate degrees-of-freedom are given for 'Unequal' under 'Variances' in the SAS output [see (6) in output for Example 4.1]. These results should be used when the F-test for equal variances is significant, or when it is known that the population variances differ.

▸ The significance level of a statistical test will be altered if it is conditioned on the results of a preliminary test. Therefore, if a t-test depends on the results of a preliminary F-test for variance homogeneity, the actual significance level may be slightly different than what is reported. This difference gets smaller as the significance level of the preliminary test increases.   With this in mind, we sometimes conduct the preliminary F-test for variance homogeneity at a significance level greater than 0.05, usually 0.10, 0.15 or even 0.20. For example, if 0.15 were used, Satterthwaite's adjustment would be used if the F-test were significant at $p < 0.15$.

▸ The assumption of normality can be tested using the *Shapiro-Wilk Test* or the *Kolmogorov-Smirnov Test* executed with the UNIVARIATE procedure in SAS. Rejection of the assumption of normality in the small sample case precludes the use of the t-test. As n_1 and n_2 become 'large' (generally $\geq$ 30), we need not rely so heavily on the assumption that the data have an underlying normal distribution. However, with non-normal data, the mean may not represent the most appropriate measure of 'central tendency'.   With a skewed distribution, for example, the median may be more representative of the distributional center than the mean. In such cases, a rank test such as the *Wilcoxon Rank-Sum Test* (Chapter 11) or the *Log-Rank Test* (Chapter 19) should be considered.

▸ Note that if within-group tests are used for the analysis instead of the *Two-Sample t-Test*, the researcher might reach a different, erroneous conclusion. In Example 4.1, one might hastily conclude that a significant treatment-related increase in mean FEV_1 exists just by looking at the within-group results. The *Two-Sample t-Test*, however, is the more appropriate test for the comparison of between-group changes since the control group response must be factored out of the response of the active group.

In interpreting the changes, one might argue that the mean change in FEV_1 for the active group is comprised of two additive effects, namely the placebo effect plus a therapeutic benefit. If it can be established that randomization to the treatment groups provides effectively homogeneous groups, we might conclude that the FEV_1 mean change for the active group of Example 4.1 can be broken down as:

$$0.503 \quad = \quad 0.284 \quad + \quad 0.219$$
(Total Effect)   (Placebo effect)   (Therapeutic effect)

To validate such interpretations of the data, one would first establish baseline comparability of the two groups. The *Two-Sample t-Test* can also be applied for this purpose by analyzing the baseline values in the same way the changes were analyzed in Example 4.1.

▸ While larger p-values (> 0.10) give greater credence to the null hypothesis of equality, such a conclusion should not be made without considering the test's power function, especially with small sample sizes. Statistical power is the probability of rejecting the null hypothesis when it is *not* true. This probability depends on the value of the parameter assumed as the alternative, and with many alternatives, a power function can be constructed. This concept is discussed briefly in Chapter 2.

▸ In checking for differences between means in either direction, Example 4.1 uses a two-tailed test. If interest is restricted to differences in only one direction, a one-tailed test can be applied in the same manner as described for the *One-Sample t-Test* (Chapter 3). The probability given in the SAS output, "Prob > |T|", can be halved to obtain the corresponding one-tailed p-value.

CHAPTER 5

ONE-WAY ANOVA

INTRODUCTION

One-Way ANOVA ("analysis-of-variance") is used to simultaneously compare 2 or more group means based on independent samples from each group. The larger the variation among sample group means relative to the variation of individual measurements within the groups, the greater the evidence that the hypothesis of equal group means is untrue. This concept is exemplified in Appendix C.1 which provides some basic concepts of ANOVA.

In clinical trials, this ANOVA method may be appropriate for comparing mean responses among a number of parallel dose groups or among various strata based on patient background information, such as race, age group or disease severity.

We assume the samples are from normally distributed populations, all with the same variance, σ^2.

SYNOPSIS

In general, we have k (k$\geq$2) levels of a factor 'GROUP'. From each, we independently sample a number of observations, letting y_{ij} represent the j-th measurement from the i-th group and n_i represent the number of measurements within Group i (i=1,2,...,k). Data are collected in a manner shown below:

GROUP			
Group 1	Group 2	...	Group k
y_{11}	y_{21}	...	y_{k1}
y_{12}	y_{22}	...	y_{k2}
...	...	...	...
y_{1n_1}	y_{2n_2}	...	y_{kn_k}

The null hypothesis is that of "no Group effect" (i.e., no difference in mean responses among groups). The alternative hypothesis is that "the Group effect is important" (i.e., at least one pair of Group means differs). When H_0 is true, the variation among groups and the variation within groups are independent estimates of the same measurement variation, σ^2, and their ratio should be close to 1. This ratio is used as the test statistic, F, which has the 'F-distribution' with k-1 upper and N-k lower degrees-of-freedom ($N = n_1 + n_2 + \ldots + n_k$).

The test summary is given as follows:

null hypothesis:	H_0: $\mu_1 = \mu_2 = \ldots = \mu_k$
alt. hypothesis:	H_A: NOT H_0
test statistic:	$F = \dfrac{MSG}{MSE}$
decision rule:	*reject* H_0 *if* $F > F_{N-k}^{k-1}(\alpha)$

MSG is an estimate of the variability among groups, and MSE is an estimate of the variability within groups.

In ANOVA we assume 'variance homogeneity', which means that the within-group variance is constant across groups. This can be expressed as $\sigma_1^2 = \sigma_2^2 = \ldots = \sigma_k^2 = \sigma^2$, where σ_i^2 denotes the unknown variance of the i-th population. The common variance, σ^2, is estimated by s^2, a weighted average of the k sample variances:

$$s^2 = \frac{(n_1-1)\ s_1^2 + (n_2-1)\ s_2^2 + \ldots + (n_k-1)\ s_k^2}{(n_1 + n_2 + \ldots + n_k) - k} .$$

Since s_i^2 is the estimated variance within Group i, s^2 represents an average within-group variation over all groups. In ANOVA, s^2 is called the 'mean-square-error', or MSE, and its numerator is the 'sum-of-squares for error', or SSE. The 'error' is the deviation of each observation from its group mean. If SSE is expressed as the sum of squared errors,

$$SSE = \sum_{i=1}^{k} \sum_{j=1}^{n_i} (y_{ij} - \overline{y}_i)^2 \quad ,$$

it is seen that the pooled variance, s^2, is just SSE/(N-k). The denominator, N-k, where $N = n_1 + n_2 + ... + n_k$ is the total sample size over all samples, is known as the degrees-of-freedom (d.f.) associated with the error.

The variability among groups may be measured by the deviation of the average observation in each group from the overall average, $\overline{y}$. That is, the overall variance obtained by replacing each observation with its group mean ($\overline{y}_i$), represents the between-group variability, MSG. Its numerator is the 'sum-of-squares for groups', or SSG, computed as:

$$SSG = \sum_{i=1}^{k} n_i (\overline{y}_i - \overline{y})^2$$

where $\overline{y}$ is the mean of all N observations. Each group mean is treated like a single observation, so there are k-1 d.f. associated with the SSG. The mean-square for the GROUP effect is the sum-of-squares divided by its degrees-of-freedom, MSG = SSG / (k-1).

When the null hypothesis is true, the variation between groups should be the same as the variation within groups. Therefore, under H_0, the test statistic F should be close to 1 and has the F-distribution with k-1 upper degrees-of-freedom (d.f.) and N-k lower d.f. Tables of the F distribution can be consulted for the critical-F value to determine the rejection region, as illustrated in Example 5.1.

EXAMPLE 5.1-- "HAM-A Scores in GAD"

A new serotonin-uptake inhibiting agent, SN-X95, is being studied in subjects with general anxiety disorder (GAD). Fifty-two subjects diagnosed with GAD of moderate or greater severity consistent with the Diagnsostic and Statistical Manual, *3rd edition (DSMIIIR) were enrolled and randomly assigned to one of 3 treatment groups: 25 mg SN-X95, 100 mg SN-X95 or placebo. After 10 weeks of once-daily oral dosing in a double-blind fashion, a test based on the Hamilton Rating Scale for Anxiety (HAM-A) was administered. This test consists of 14 anxiety-related items (e.g., 'anxious mood', 'tension', 'insomnia', 'fears', etc.), each rated by the subject as 'not present', 'mild', 'moderate', 'severe' or 'very severe'. HAM-A test scores were found by summing the coded values over all 14 items using the numeric coding scheme of 0 for 'not present', 1 for 'mild', 2 for 'moderate', 3 for 'severe', 4 for 'very severe'. The data are presented in the following Table. Are there any differences in mean HAM-A test scores among the 3 groups?*

Lo-Dose		High Dose		Placebo	
Pat. No.	HAM-A	Pat. No.	HAM-A	Pat. No.	HAM-A
101	21	103	16	102	22
104	18	105	21	107	26
106	19	109	31	108	29
110	n/a	111	25	114	19
112	28	113	23	115	n/a
116	22	119	25	117	33
120	30	123	18	118	37
121	27	127	20	122	25
124	28	128	18	126	28
125	19	131	16	129	26
130	23	135	24	132	n/a
136	22	138	22	133	31
137	20	140	21	134	27
141	19	142	16	139	30
143	26	146	33	144	25
148	35	150	21	145	22
152	n/a	151	17	147	36
				149	32

SOLUTION

Patients who dropped out with no data (Nos. 110, 115, 132, 152) are excluded from the analysis. Arbitrarily assigning subscripts 1 for 'Lo-Dose', 2 for 'Hi-Dose' and 3 for 'Placebo', the group summary statistics for the HAM-A scores are:

| | -------------- GROUP -------------- | | | |
	Lo-Dose (i=1)	Hi-Dose (i=2)	Placebo (i=3)	Overall
$\bar{y}_i$	23.800	21.588	28.000	24.417
s_i	4.974	4.963	5.033	5.588
n_i	15	17	16	48

We compute:

$$SSG = \quad 15 \, (23.800 - 24.417)^2 +$$

$$17 \, (21.588 - 24.417)^2 +$$

$$16 \, (28.000 - 24.417)^2 \quad = \quad 347.1$$

with k = 3 groups, so that

$$MSG = SSG/(k-1) = 347.1 / 2 = 173.6.$$

$$SSE = \quad (21-23.800)^2 + (18-23.800)^2 + ... + (35-23.800)^2 +$$

$$(16-21.588)^2 + (21-21.588)^2 + ... + (17-21.588)^2 +$$

$$(22-28.000)^2 + (26-28.000)^2 + ... + (32-28.000)^2$$

$$= \quad 1120.5$$

with N-k = 48 - 3 = 45 degrees-of-freedom, so that MSE = 1120.5 / 45 = 24.9.

As a check on the calculations, we may also compute the MSE alternatively as the weighted average of the group variances:

$$MSE = \frac{14 \cdot (4.974^2) + 16 \cdot (4.963^2) + 15 \cdot (5.033^2)}{45} = 24.9 \quad .$$

The test summary, conducted at a significance level of $\alpha = 0.05$ is summarized as follows:

null hypothesis:	H_0: $\mu_1 = \mu_2 = \mu_3$
alt. hypothesis:	H_A: not H_0
test statistic:	$F = 173.6 / 24.9 = 6.97$
decision rule:	*reject H_0 if $F > F_{45}^2(0.05) = 3.2$*
conclusion:	since $6.97 > 3.2$, we reject H_0, and conclude that there is a significant difference in mean HAM-A scores among the 3 dose groups.

SAS Analysis of Example 5.1

We can analyze these data with the GLM procedure of SAS as shown in the SAS code and output on the next 3 pages.

The summary statistics (1) are first obtained for each dose group using PROC MEANS. The key to using PROC GLM is in correctly specifying the MODEL statement which lists the response variable on the left side of the equal sign and the model factors on the right. In the *One-Way ANOVA*, there is only one model factor, in this case Dose Group (variable=DOSEGRP). This must also be specified in the CLASS statement, indicating it is a classification factor rather than a numeric covariate.

The output shows the MSE (2), the MSG (3) and the F-test for the Dose Group effect of 6.97 (4), which corroborate the manual calculations. The p-value (5) of 0.0023 (<0.05) indicates that the mean HAM-A scores differ significantly among Dose Groups. Finally, the MEANS statement is used to obtain multiple comparison results (see DETAILS & NOTES).

```
* SAS Code for Example 5.1;

DATA GAD;
INPUT PATNO DOSEGRP $ HAMA @@;
CARDS;
101 LO 21   104 LO 18
106 LO 19   110 LO  .
112 LO 28   116 LO 22
120 LO 30   121 LO 27
124 LO 28   125 LO 19
130 LO 23   136 LO 22
137 LO 20   141 LO 19
143 LO 26   148 LO 35
152 LO  .   103 HI 16
105 HI 21   109 HI 31
111 HI 25   113 HI 23
119 HI 25   123 HI 18
127 HI 20   128 HI 18
131 HI 16   135 HI 24
138 HI 22   140 HI 21
142 HI 16   146 HI 33
150 HI 21   151 HI 17
102 PB 22   107 PB 26
108 PB 29   114 PB 19
115 PB  .   117 PB 33
118 PB 37   122 PB 25
126 PB 28   129 PB 26
132 PB  .   133 PB 31
134 PB 27   139 PB 30
144 PB 25   145 PB 22
147 PB 36   149 PB 32
; RUN;

PROC SORT DATA = GAD; BY DOSEGRP; RUN;
PROC MEANS MEAN STD N DATA = GAD;
BY DOSEGRP; VAR HAMA;
TITLE1 'One-Way ANOVA';
TITLE2 'EXAMPLE 5.1: HAM-A Scores in GAD';
RUN;

PROC GLM DATA = GAD; CLASS DOSEGRP;
MODEL HAMA = DOSEGRP;
MEANS DOSEGRP/T DUNCAN;
RUN;
```

```
            * SAS Output for Example 5.1


                              One-Way ANOVA
                      EXAMPLE 5.1: HAM-A Scores in GAD

                      Analysis Variable : HAMA

        ----------------------- DOSEGRP=HI -----------------------
                        Mean       Std Dev    N
                ------------------------------------
                 21.5882353    4.9630991    17
                ------------------------------------


        ----------------------- DOSEGRP=LO ----------------------- (1)
                        Mean       Std Dev    N
                ------------------------------------
                 23.8000000    4.9742192    15
                ------------------------------------


        ----------------------- DOSEGRP=PB -----------------------
                        Mean       Std Dev    N
                ------------------------------------
                 28.0000000    5.0332230    16
                ------------------------------------



                      General Linear Models Procedure
                          Class Level Information

                     Class     Levels    Values
                     DOSEGRP      3       HI LO PB

                Number of observations in data set = 52
```

NOTE: Due to missing values, only 48 observations can be used in this
      analysis.

Dependent Variable: HAMA

Source	DF	Sum of Squares	Mean Square	F Value	Pr > F
Model	2	347.14902	173.57451	6.97	0.0023
Error	45	1120.51765	24.90039		
Corrected Total	47	1467.66667	(2)		

R-Square	C.V.	Root MSE	HAMA Mean
0.236531	20.43698	4.9900	24.417

Source	DF	Type I SS	Mean Square	F Value	Pr > F
DOSEGRP	2	347.14902	173.57451	6.97	0.0023

Source	DF	Type III SS	Mean Square	F Value	Pr > F
DOSEGRP	2	347.14902	173.57451	6.97	0.0023
			(3)	(4)	(5)

*   SAS Output for Example 5.1 - continued

One-Way ANOVA
EXAMPLE 5.1: HAM-A Scores in GAD

General Linear Models Procedure

T tests (LSD) for variable: HAMA

NOTE: This test controls the type I comparisonwise error rate not
      the experimentwise error rate.

Alpha= 0.05 df= 45 MSE= 24.90039
Critical Value of T= 2.01
Least Significant Difference= 3.558
WARNING: Cell sizes are not equal.
Harmonic Mean of cell sizes= 15.95828

Means with the same letter are not significantly different.

T Grouping	Mean	N	DOSEGRP
A	28.000	16	PB
B	23.800	15	LO
B			
B	21.588	17	HI

Duncan's Multiple Range Test for variable: HAMA

NOTE: This test controls the type I comparisonwise error rate,
      not the experimentwise error rate

Alpha= 0.05 df= 45 MSE= 24.90039
WARNING: Cell sizes are not equal.
Harmonic Mean of cell sizes= 15.95828

Number of Means   2   3
Critical Range   3.558 3.742

Means with the same letter are not significantly different.

Duncan Grouping	Mean	N	DOSEGRP
A	28.000	16	PB
B	23.800	15	LO
B			
B	21.588	17	HI

DETAILS & NOTES

▸ The parameters associated with the F-distribution are the 'upper' and 'lower' degrees-of-freedom. Many elementary statistical texts provide tables of critical 'F-values' associated with a fixed significance level (usually 0.10, 0.05, 0.01) for various combinations of values for the upper and lower degrees-of-freedom. F-values or associated probabilities for known degrees-of-freedom can also be found using most statistical programs. In SAS, the function FINV($1-\alpha$,udf,ldf), where udf and ldf represent the upper and lower degrees-of-freedom, respectively, is used to obtain the critical F-values for a significance level of α.

▸ When conducting analysis-of-variance, a traditional and widely used method of summarizing the results is by using an 'ANOVA table'. The ANOVA summary identifies each source of variation, the degrees-of-freedom, the sum-of-squares, the mean-square and the F statistic. This is a conventional way of organizing results for analyses which use many factors. In Example 5.1, we have only one model factor (Dose Group), but it is still convenient to use the ANOVA table format to summarize the results. The ANOVA table for this example is as follows:

ANOVA

Source	d.f	SS	MS	F
DOSE GROUP	2	347.15	173.57	6.97 *
Error	45	1120.52	24.90	
Total	47	1467.67		

* Significant ($p < 0.05$)

▸ *One-Way ANOVA* requires the assumptions of (i) normally distributed data, (ii) independent samples from each group, and (iii) variance homogeneity among groups. The *Kolmogorov-Smirnoff Test* for normality and *Bartlett's Test* for variance homogeneity are 2 of a number of formal tests available for determining whether the sample data are consistent with these assumptions. Often, histograms or other depictions of the data will provide an informal but convenient means of identifying departures from normality.

In the event of significant preliminary tests which identify departures from the assumptions, a data transformation may be appropriate. Logarithmic and rank transformations are popular transformations used in clinical data analysis. The *Kruskal-Wallis Test* (Chapter 12) may be used as an alternative to the *One-Way ANOVA* when normality cannot be assumed.

► *MULTIPLE COMPARISONS*
When comparing more than 2 means ($k > 2$), a significant F-test indicates that at least one pair of means differs, but which pair (or pairs) is not identified by ANOVA. When we reject the null hypothesis of equal means, further analysis must be undertaken to discover where the differences lie. Multiple comparison procedures are available for comparing each pair of group means.

There are many approaches to multiple comparisons, but we will confine our attention to only one very simple approach and one very commonly used approach. For more information on these procedures, the reader is referred to an excellent review paper on multiple comparisons [D'Agostino et al, 1993], or the SAS manual.

The simplest approach to multiple comparisons is to conduct pairwise t-tests for each pair of treatments. This method uses the approach of the *Two-Sample t-Test* discussed in Chapter 4, but rather than using the pooled standard deviation of only the 2 groups being compared, the pooled standard deviation of all k groups is used (i.e., square-root of the MSE from the ANOVA). This procedure can be carried out in SAS using the 'T' option in the MEANS statement of the GLM procedure.

Another approach which is widely used is called 'Duncan's Multiple Range Test'. Special tables, available in many statistical texts, are needed to conduct this test manually. The results can be printed by SAS using the 'DUNCAN' option of the MEANS statement in PROC GLM.

As seen in the SAS output of Example 5.1, the 'T' and 'DUNCAN' results are the same, i.e., both the active groups have a signficantly smaller mean HAM-A score than placebo, while no difference is found between the low and high dose active groups.

The biggest drawback of using pairwise t-tests is the effect on the overall significance level, as described in Chapter 2. If each pairwise test is conducted at a significance level of $\alpha=0.05$, the chance of having at least one erroneous conclusion among all the comparisons performed increases with the number of groups, k. With 6 pairwise comparisons (k=4), for example, the overall error rate may be as high as $1 - (1 - 0.05)^6 = 0.265$. Approaches to multiple comparisons that control the overall error rate have been developed, and it is important to consider the use of these methods when the study uses a larger number of groups.

▸ More generalized comparisons among the group means can also be made by testing whether specific linear combinations of the group means differ from zero. These new hypotheses are called 'linear contrasts'. As an example, consider a study with 4 groups consisting of a placebo and 3 active dose levels. A contrast to compare the average response of the 3 active dose groups to the placebo response can be formed and tested by setting up an appropriate linear contrast.

▸ Multiple comparison results can sometimes be contrary to our intuition. For example, let $\bar{y}_A < \bar{y}_B < \bar{y}_C$, and suppose the analysis determines that the Group A mean is not statistically different from that of Group B, which is not different from C. One might infer that there is no difference among any of the 3 groups, while in fact, there may be a significant difference between Groups A and C. Remember that 'no difference' means 'insufficient evidence to detect a difference'.

▸ Sometimes, when a significant F-test for groups is found, it is preferable to report the confidence intervals for the group mean responses rather than perform multiple comparisons. A 95% confidence interval for the mean of Group i is found by:

$$\bar{y}_i \pm t_{0.025,N-k} \cdot \sqrt{\frac{MSE}{n_i}} \quad .$$

In Example 5.1, a 95% confidence interval for the Hi dose group is

$$21.588 \pm 2.014 \cdot \sqrt{\frac{24.9}{17}} = [19.2 - 24.0]$$

Similarly, 95% confidence intervals can be found for the Low dose group [21.2 - 26.4] and for the Placebo group [25.5 - 30.5]. Such intervals are often depicted graphically in medical journal articles.

▸ 95% confidence intervals can also be obtained for the mean difference between any pair of groups (say Group i vs. Group j) using the formula:

$$(\overline{y}_i - \overline{y}_j) \pm t_{0.025, N-k} \sqrt{MSE \left(\frac{1}{n_i} + \frac{1}{n_j}\right)} \quad .$$

In Example 5.1, a 95% confidence interval for the difference in mean HAM-A scores between the Placebo and Low dose groups is

$$(28.00 - 23.80) \pm 2.014 \cdot \sqrt{24.9 \left(\frac{1}{16} + \frac{1}{15}\right)}$$

or,   [0.59 *to* 7.81]   .

A confidence interval for the difference in means which does not contain zero is indicative of significantly different means.

▸ If there are only two groups (k = 2), the p-value for Group effect using ANOVA is the same as that of a *Two-Sample t-Test*. The F and t-distributions enjoy the relationship that, with 1 upper degree-of-freedom, the F statistic is the square of the t-statistic. When k = 2, the MSE computed as a pooled combination of the group sample means is identical to the pooled variance, s_p^2, used in the *Two-Sample t-Test* (Chapter 4).

▸ Manual computations (with a hand calculator) can be facilitated with standard computing formulas as follows:

$$G_i = \sum_j y_{ij} \qquad (Total\ for\ Group\ i)$$

$$G = \sum_i G_i \qquad (Overall\ Total)$$

$$C = \frac{G^2}{N} \qquad (Correction\ factor)$$

$$TOT(SS) = \sum_i \sum_j y_{ij}^2 - C \qquad (Total\ sum-of-squares)$$

$$SSG = \sum_i \frac{G_i^2}{n_i} - C \qquad (Sum-of-squares\ for\ Groups)$$

$$SSE = TOT(SS) - SSG \qquad (Sum-of-squares\ for\ Error)$$

▸ SAS computes the sum-of-squares in four ways. These are called the Type I, II, III and IV sums-of-squares. Computational differences among these types depend on the model used and the missing value structure. For the *One-Way ANOVA*, all four types of sums-of-squares are identical, so it does not matter which we select. SAS prints out the Type I and III results as default. These different types of sums-of-squares are discussed in Chapter 6 and Appendix D.

CHAPTER 6
TWO-WAY ANOVA

INTRODUCTION

Two-Way ANOVA is a method for simultaneously analyzing two factors affecting a response. As in *One-Way ANOVA*, there is a Group effect, such as treatment group or dose level. *Two-Way ANOVA* also includes another identifiable source of variation called a *blocking factor*, whose variation can be separated from the error variation to give more precise group comparisons. For this reason the *Two-Way ANOVA* layout is sometimes called a '*randomized block design*'.

Because clinical studies often use factors such as study center, gender, diagnostic group or disease severity as a blocking factor, *Two-Way ANOVA* is one of the most common ANOVA methods used in clinical data analysis.

The basic ideas underlying the *Two-Way ANOVA* are illustrated in Appendix C.2.

SYNOPSIS

In general, the layout has g (g $\geq$ 2) levels of a 'GROUP' factor and b (b $\geq$ 2) levels of a 'BLOCK' factor. An independent sample of measurements is taken from each of the gxb cells formed by the GROUP-BLOCK combinations. Let n_{ij} represent the number of measurements taken in Group i and Block j ('Cell i-j') and N be the number of measurements over all gxb cells. Let y_{ijk} denote the k-th response in Cell i-j (k = 1, 2, ..., n_{ij}).

The general entries in a *Two-Way ANOVA* summary table are represented as follows:

ANOVA

Source	d.f	SS	MS	F
GROUP (G)	g-1	SSG	MSG	F_G = MSG/MSE
BLOCK (B)	b-1	SSB	MSB	F_B = MSB/MSE
G x B (interaction)	(g-1)(b-1)	SSGB	MSGB	F_{GB} = MSGB/MSE
Error	N-gb	SSE	MSE	
Total	N-1	TOT(SS)		

'SS' represents a sum of squared deviations associated with the factor listed under 'Source'. These are computed in a similar manner as illustrated in Chapter 5 for the *One-Way ANOVA*.

The mean-square (MS) is found by dividing the SS by the degrees-of-freedom (d.f.), and represents a measure of variability associated with the factor. When there is no effect due to the specified factor, this variability reflects measurement error variability, σ^2, which is also estimated by MSE.

The F-values are ratios of the effect mean-squares to the mean-square-error, MSE. Under the null hypothesis of no effect, the F-ratio should be close to one. These F-values are used as the test statistics for testing the null hypothesis of no mean differences among the levels of the factor.

The F-test for GROUP (F_G) tests the primary hypothesis of no GROUP effect. Denoting the mean for the i-th group by μ_i, the test summary is:

null hypothesis: H_0: $\mu_1 = \mu_2 = \ldots = \mu_g$

alt. hypothesis: H_A: NOT H_0

test statistic:

$$F_G = \frac{MSG}{MSE}$$

decision rule:

$$\text{reject } H_0 \text{ if } F_G > F_{N-gb}^{g-1}(\alpha)$$

The F-test for the Block effect (F_B) provides a secondary test used in a similar manner to determine if the mean responses differ among blocking levels. A significant Block effect will usually result in a smaller error variance (MSE) and greater precision for testing the primary hypothesis of "no Group effect" than if the Block effect were ignored.

The "Group x Block" factor (G x B) represents the statistical interaction between the two main effects. If the F-test for interaction is significant, this would indicate that trends across Groups differ among the levels of the Blocking factor. This is usually the first test of interest in a *Two-Way ANOVA* since the test for Group effects may not be meaningful in the presence of a significant interaction. If the interaction is significant, further analysis may be required, such as application of *One-Way ANOVA* to compare groups within each level of the blocking factor.

In *Two-Way ANOVA*, we assume that the samples within each cell are normally distributed with the same variance. We can estimate this common variance, σ^2, by the mean-square-error, MSE, which is a pooled combination of the cell sample variances, s_{ij}^2, as follows:

$$s^2 = \frac{\sum_{i=1}^{g} \sum_{j=1}^{b} (n_{ij}-1) \cdot s_{ij}^2}{N - g \cdot b} \quad .$$

The numerator of this quantity is the sum-of-squares for error, SSE, based on N-gb degrees-of-freedom.

Generally, the effect sums-of-squares are computed in a manner similar to that illustrated for the *One-Way ANOVA*. For example, the sum-of-squares for GROUP (SSG), representing the variability among Group levels, is based on the sum of squared deviations of the Group means from the overall mean. Likewise, the sum-of-squares for BLOCK (SSB), representing the variability among the Block levels, is based on the sum of squared deviations of the Block means from the overall mean. The interaction sum-of-squares (SS(GB)) is based on the sum of squared deviations of the cell means from the overall mean. Computations are illustrated in Example 6.1.

EXAMPLE 6.1 -- "Hemoglobin Changes in Anemia"

A new synthetic erythropoietin-type hormone, Rebligen, used to treat chemotherapy-induced anemia in cancer patients was tested in a study of 48 adult cancer patients undergoing chemotherapeutic treatment. Half the patients received low dose administration of Rebligen via intramuscular injection 3 times at 2-day intervals, and half received a placebo in a similar fashion. Patients were stratified according to their type of cancer: cervical, prostate or colorectal. For admission, patients were required to have a baseline hemoglobin less than 10 mg/dl and a decrease in hemoglobin of at least 1 mg/dl following the last chemotherapy. Changes in hemoglobin (in mg/dl) from pre-first-injection to 1 week after last-injection, as shown in the table which follows, were obtained for analysis. Does Rebligen have any effect on the hemoglobin levels?

Cancer Type	--- ACTIVE ---		-- PLACEBO --	
	PAT. No.	Hgb Change	PAT. No.	Hgb Change
CERVICAL	1	1.7	2	2.3
	3	-0.2	4	1.2
	6	1.7	5	-0.6
	7	2.3	8	1.3
	10	2.7	9	-1.1
	12	0.4	11	1.6
	13	1.3	14	-0.2
	15	0.6	16	1.9
PROSTATE	22	2.7	21	0.6
	24	1.6	23	1.7
	26	2.5	25	0.8
	28	0.5	27	1.7
	29	2.6	30	1.4
	31	3.7	32	0.7
	34	2.7	33	0.8
	36	1.3	35	1.5
COLORECTAL	42	-0.3	41	1.6
	45	1.9	43	-2.2
	46	1.7	44	1.9
	47	0.5	48	-1.6
	49	2.1	50	0.8
	51	-0.4	53	-0.9
	52	0.1	55	1.5
	54	1.0	56	2.1

SOLUTION

We use a *Two-Way ANOVA*, with main effects 'TREATMENT' and 'CANCER TYPE', and the interaction TREATMENT-by-TYPE. TREATMENT has two levels: Active and Placebo; TYPE has three levels: Cervical, Prostate and Colorectal. Of primary interest is whether the Active group has any effect on hemoglobin relative to any effects shown by the Placebo group.

We first obtain the summary statistics depicted in a table of cell and marginal means as follows:

| Cancer Type | ----------- Treatment Group ------------ | | Row Mean |
	ACTIVE	PLACEBO	n
CERVICAL	1.313 (0.988) 8	0.800 (1.258) 8	1.056 16
PROSTATE	2.200 (1.004) 8	1.150 (0.469) 8	1.675 16
COLORECTAL	0.825 (0.998) 8	0.400 (1.707) 8	0.613 16
Column Mean n	1.446 24	0.783 24	1.115 48

[Entries are Cell mean (S.D.) and sample size]

The sum-of-squares for the main effects, Treatment and Cancer Type are computed as follows:

$$SS(TRT) = 24(1.446 - 1.115)^2 + 24(0.783 - 1.115)^2 = 5.27$$

$$SS(TYPE) = 16(1.056 - 1.115)^2 + 16(1.675 - 1.115)^2 + 16(0.613 - 1.115)^2 = 9.11 \quad .$$

The interaction sum-of-squares can be computed as:

$$SS(TRT\text{-}by\text{-}TYPE) =$$
$$8(1.313 - 1.115)^2 + 8(0.800 - 1.115)^2 +$$
$$8(2.200 - 1.115)^2 + 8(1.150 - 1.115)^2 +$$
$$8(0.825 - 1.115)^2 + 8(0.400 - 1.115)^2 -$$
$$SS(TRT) - SS(TYPE) =$$
$$0.92 \quad .$$

The total sum-of-squares is simply the numerator of the sample variance of all observations:

$$SS(TOT) = (1.7 - 1.115)^2 + (-0.2 - 1.115)^2 + \ldots + (2.1 - 1.115)^2$$
$$= 69.18.$$

Finally, the error sum-of-squares, SSE, can be found by subtracting the sum-of-squares of each of the effects from the total sum-of-squares:

$$SSE = SS(TOT) - SS(TRT) - SS(TYPE) - SS(TRT\text{-}by\text{-}TYPE) =$$
$$69.18 - 5.27 - 9.11 - 0.92 = 53.88.$$

As a check, we can also compute SSE from the cell standard deviations:

$$SSE = 7(0.988)^2 + 7(1.258)^2 + 7(1.004)^2 +$$
$$7(0.469)^2 + 7(0.998)^2 + 7(1.707)^2 = 53.88.$$

We may now complete the ANOVA table and compute the F-statistics as follows:

ANOVA

Source	d.f	SS	MS	F	p-Value
TREATMENT (TRT)	1	5.27	5.27	4.11	0.049*
CANCER (TYPE)	2	9.11	4.55	3.55	0.038 *
TRT-by-TYPE	2	0.92	0.46	0.36	0.702
Error	42	53.88	1.28		
Total	47	69.18			

* Significant ($p < 0.05$)   (p-values obtained from SAS)

At a significance level of α, the F-statistic is compared with the critical F-value which can be obtained from widely tabulated F-tables, or from SAS using the FINV(1-α,U,L) function. The 'upper' degrees of freedom (U) correspond to that of the MS in the numerator; the error d.f. (corresponding to MSE) is used as the 'lower' degrees-of-freedom (L).

The ANOVA summary indicates a non-significant interaction suggesting that the differences between Treatment levels are consistent over Cancer Types. The F-test for TREATMENT is significant (p = 0.049), indicating that the mean hemoglobin response for the Active group differs from that of the Placebo group 'averaged' over all Cancer Types.

The CANCER TYPE effect is also significant at the 0.05 level suggesting differing mean response levels among the Cancer Types. Such information might be useful in designing future studies or in guiding further analyses.

<u>SAS Analysis of Example 6.1</u>

The SAS code and output for analyzing these data with the *Two-Way ANOVA* are shown on the next three pages. The cell summary statistics are first printed out using PROC MEANS (1). The GLM procedure is used with the main effects, Treatment (TRT) and Cancer Type (TYPE), specified as class variables in the CLASSES statement and as factors in the MODEL statement. The interaction is also included in the MODEL statement.

For a balanced layout like this example (same sample size in each cell), the SAS Types I, II, III and IV sums-of-squares are identical. The Type III results included in the output (2) corroborate the results obtained by manual computations.

Since there are more than 2 levels of the Cancer Type effect, a significant finding may require further analyses to determine where the differences lie. To use pairwise t-tests for multiple comparsions, we include the MEANS statement with the T option after the MODEL statement in the SAS code. This provides comparisons between each pair of Cancer Types, as described in Chapter 5. As seen in the output (3), mean hemoglobin response differs significantly between the prostate and colerectal Types.

The LSMEANS statement is also included to illustrate another manner of obtaining pairwise comparisons. When the PDIFF option is used, SAS prints out a matrix of p-values for all pairwise comparisons (4). As indicated by a p-value less than

0.05, mean responses for the colerectal (#2 mean) and prostate (#3 mean) Types differ significantly (p = 0.0112).

```
* SAS Code for Example 6.1 ;

DATA HGBDS;
INPUT TRT $  TYPE $  PATNO HGBCH @@;
CARDS;
ACT C  1  1.7     ACT C  3 -0.2     ACT C  6  1.7
ACT C  7  2.3     ACT C 10  2.7     ACT C 12  0.4
ACT C 13  1.3     ACT C 15  0.6     ACT P 22  2.7
ACT P 24  1.6     ACT P 26  2.5     ACT P 28  0.5
ACT P 29  2.6     ACT P 31  3.7     ACT P 34  2.7
ACT P 36  1.3     ACT R 42 -0.3     ACT R 45  1.9
ACT R 46  1.7     ACT R 47  0.5     ACT R 49  2.1
ACT R 51 -0.4     ACT R 52  0.1     ACT R 54  1.0
PBO C  2  2.3     PBO C  4  1.2     PBO C  5 -0.6
PBO C  8  1.3     PBO C  9 -1.1     PBO C 11  1.6
PBO C 14 -0.2     PBO C 16  1.9     PBO P 21  0.6
PBO P 23  1.7     PBO P 25  0.8     PBO P 27  1.7
PBO P 30  1.4     PBO P 32  0.7     PBO P 33  0.8
PBO P 35  1.5     PBO R 41  1.6     PBO R 43 -2.2
PBO R 44  1.9     PBO R 48 -1.6     PBO R 50  0.8
PBO R 53 -0.9     PBO R 55  1.5     PBO R 56  2.1
; RUN;

PROC FORMAT;
VALUE $TYPFMT 'C' = 'CERVICAL   '
             'P' = 'PROSTATE   '
             'R' = 'COLORECTAL' ;
RUN;

PROC SORT DATA = HGBDS; BY TRT TYPE; RUN;
PROC MEANS MEAN STD N; VAR HGBCH; BY TRT TYPE;
FORMAT TYPE $TYPFMT.;
TITLE1 'Two-Way ANOVA';
TITLE2 'EXAMPLE 6.1: Hemoglobin Changes in Anemia';
RUN;

PROC GLM DATA = HGBDS; CLASSES TRT TYPE;
MODEL HGBCH = TRT TYPE TRT*TYPE;
MEANS TYPE / T;
LSMEANS TYPE / PDIFF STDERR;
FORMAT TYPE $TYPFMT.;
QUIT;
RUN;
```

```
*   SAS Output for Example 6.1


                              Two-Way ANOVA
                    EXAMPLE 6.1: Hemoglobin Changes in Anemia

                        Analysis Variable : HGBCH

                 -------------- TRT=ACT TYPE=CERVICAL ------------
                          Mean       Std Dev   N
                 ----------------------------------
                      1.3125000    0.9876921   8
                 ----------------------------------


                 -------------- TRT=ACT TYPE=PROSTATE ------------
                          Mean       Std Dev   N
                 ----------------------------------
                      2.2000000    1.0042766   8
                 ----------------------------------


                 ------------- TRT=ACT TYPE=COLORECTAL -----------
                          Mean       Std Dev   N
                 ----------------------------------
                      0.8250000    0.9982127   8              (1)
                 ----------------------------------


                 -------------- TRT=PBO TYPE=CERVICAL ------------
                          Mean       Std Dev   N
                 ----------------------------------
                      0.8000000    1.2581165   8
                 ----------------------------------


                 -------------- TRT=PBO TYPE=PROSTATE -----------
                          Mean       Std Dev   N
                 ----------------------------------
                      1.1500000    0.4690416   8
                 ----------------------------------


                 ------------- TRT=PBO TYPE=COLORECTAL ----------
                          Mean       Std Dev   N
                 ----------------------------------
                      0.4000000    1.7071279   8
                 ----------------------------------



                          General Linear Models Procedure
                             Class Level Information

                  Class    Levels   Values
                  TRT        2      ACT PBO
                  TYPE       3      CERVICAL COLORECTAL PROSTATE
                       Number of observations in data set = 48
```

Dependent Variable: HGBCH

Source	DF	Sum of Squares	Mean Square	F Value	Pr > F
Model	5	15.296042	3.059208	2.38	0.0543
Error	42	53.883750	1.282946		
Corrected Total	47	69.179792			

R-Square	C.V.	Root MSE	HGBCH Mean
0.221106	101.6229	1.1327	1.1146

Source	DF	Type III SS	Mean Square	F Value	Pr > F
TRT	1	5.2668750	5.2668750	4.11	0.0491
TYPE	2	9.1129167	4.5564583	3.55	0.0376
TRT*TYPE	2	0.9162500	0.4581250	0.36	0.7018

                                    (2)

* SAS Output for Example 6.1 - continued

Two-Way ANOVA
EXAMPLE 6.1: Hemoglobin Changes in Anemia

General Linear Models Procedure

T tests (LSD) for variable: HGBCH

NOTE: This test controls the type 1 comparisonwise error rate not
the experimentwise error rate.

Alpha= 0.05 df= 42 MSE= 1.282946
Critical Value of T= 2.02
Least Significant Difference= 0.8082

Means with the same letter are not significantly different.

T Grouping		Mean	N	CANCTYPE	
	A	1.6750	16	PROSTATE	
	A				
B	A	1.0563	16	CERVICAL	(3)
B					
B		0.6125	16	COLORECTAL	

Least Squares Means

CANCTYPE	HGBCH LSMEAN	Std Err LSMEAN	Pr > |T| H0:LSMEAN=0	LSMEAN Number
CERVICAL	1.05625000	0.28316806	0.0006	1
COLORECTAL	0.61250000	0.28316806	0.0363	2
PROSTATE	1.67500000	0.28316806	0.0001	3

Pr > \|T\| H0: LSMEAN(i)=LSMEAN(j)

i/j	1	2	3	
1	.	0.2741	0.1298	
2	0.2741	.	0.0112	(4)
3	0.1298	0.0112	.	

NOTE: To ensure overall protection level, only probabilities
associated with pre-planned comparisons should be used.

To better understand the interaction effect, it is helpful to visualize the trends graphically. Usually, an interaction is indicated if the response profiles cross or have markedly different slopes among the levels of the blocking factor. Figures a, b and c below show no interaction, while Figures d, e and f depict an interaction between the GROUP and BLOCK main effects.

FIGURE 6-1: Effects Showing Interaction
and No Interaction

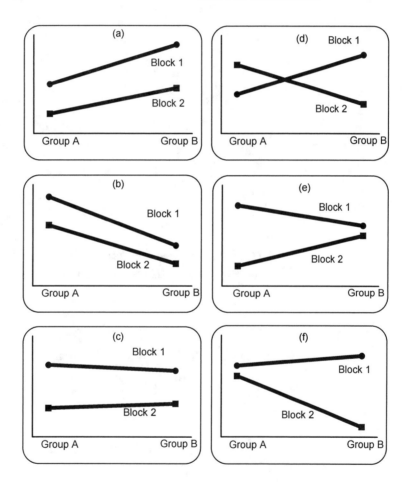

The next example shows the *Two-Way ANOVA* for an unbalanced layout with 3 treatment groups and a significant interaction.

EXAMPLE 6.2 -- "Memory Function"

Two investigators conducted a clinical trial to determine the effect of 2 doses of a new therapeutic agent on short-term memory function. Subjects were administered a single oral dose of test preparation and then asked to recall items one hour after exposure to a list consisting of 15 items. The number of items correctly identified are listed below. A placebo group was included as a control in a parallel-group design.

	--------------- DOSE GROUP ---------------					
CENTER	Placebo		30 mg		60 mg	
Dr. Abel	6	5	8	6	11	10
	5	6	12	9	7	12
	6	5	7	6	7	9
	8	5	8	11	11	15
	3	7			9	
	4	8				
Dr. Best	7	5	5	8	9	12
	4	9	6	6	12	14
	7	11	6	9	13	15
	6	4	5	11	9	12
	7	7	3	5	13	
	8					

SOLUTION

The summary statistics and ANOVA table are as follows:

	---------- DOSE GROUP ---------		
CENTER	Placebo	30 mg	60 mg
Abel	5.67	8.38	10.11
	(1.50)	(2.20)	(2.52)
	12	8	9
Best	6.82	6.40	12.11
	(2.09)	(2.32)	(2.03)
	11	10	9

[Entries are Mean, (S.D.), N]

This is an unbalanced layout, and the computation of the effect sums-of-squares as illustrated in Example 6.1 may not produce the most appropriate tests. With an unbalanced layout, the SAS Types I, II and III sums-of-squares differ, as discussed in Appendix D. We will focus only on the Type III results.

The SAS code for generating the *Two-Way ANOVA* is shown below, and the ANOVA summary table from the SAS output is as follows:

ANOVA

Source	d.f	SS	MS	F	p-Value
DOSE	2	251.42	125.71	28.43	0.0001 *
CENTER	1	2.23	2.23	0.50	0.481
CENTER-by-DOSE	2	39.77	19.88	4.50	0.016 *
Error	53	234.36	4.42		
Total	58	533.93			

* Significant (p < 0.05)

```
* SAS Code for Example 6.2 ;

DATA MEMRY;
INPUT DOSE $  CENTER $   Y @@;
CARDS;
 0 A   6    0 A   5    0 A   6    0 A   8    0 A   3
 0 A   4    0 A   5    0 A   6    0 A   5    0 A   5
 0 A   7    0 A   8    0 B   7    0 B   4    0 B   7
 0 B   6    0 B   7    0 B   8    0 B   5    0 B   9
 0 B  11    0 B   4    0 B   7   30 A   8   30 A  12
30 A   7   30 A   8   30 A   6   30 A   9   30 A   6
30 A  11   30 B   5   30 B   6   30 B   6   30 B   5
30 B   3   30 B   8   30 B   6   30 B   9   30 B  11
30 B   5   60 A  11   60 A   7   60 A   7   60 A  11
60 A   9   60 A  10   60 A  12   60 A   9   60 A  15
60 B   9   60 B  12   60 B  13   60 B   9   60 B  13
60 B  12   60 B  14   60 B  15   60 B  12
;
RUN;

PROC GLM DATA = MEMRY; CLASSES CENTER DOSE;
MODEL Y = DOSE CENTER CENTER*DOSE;
LSMEANS DOSE/PDIFF STDERR;
TITLE1 'Two-Way ANOVA';
TITLE2 'EXAMPLE 6.2: Memory Function';
QUIT;
RUN;
```

```
*   SAS Output for Example 6.2


                            Two-Way ANOVA
                      EXAMPLE 6.2: Memory Function



                     General Linear Models Procedure
                        Class Level Information

                       Class   Levels   Values
                       CENTER     2     A B
                       DOSE       3     0 30 60
                 Number of observations in data set = 59
```

Dependent Variable: Y

Source	DF	Sum of Squares	Mean Square	F Value	Pr > F
Model	5	299.57640	59.91528	13.55	0.0001
Error	53	234.35581	4.42181		
Corrected Total	58	533.93220			

R-Square	C.V.	Root MSE	Y Mean
0.561076	26.17421	2.1028	8.0339

Source	DF	Type I SS	Mean Square	F Value	Pr > F
DOSE	2	256.63027	128.31514	29.02	0.0001
CENTER	1	3.17780	3.17780	0.72	0.4004
CENTER*DOSE	2	39.76833	19.88416	4.50	0.0157

Source	DF	Type III SS	Mean Square	F Value	Pr > F	
DOSE	2	251.41973	125.70987	28.43	0.0001	(1)
CENTER	1	2.22730	2.22730	0.50	0.4810	
CENTER*DOSE	2	39.76833	19.88416	4.50	0.0157	(2)

```
                        Least Squares Means

        DOSE            Y         Std Err    Pr > |T|    LSMEAN
                      LSMEAN      LSMEAN    HO:LSMEAN=0   Number

         0         6.2424242    0.4388811     0.0001       1
        30         7.3875000    0.4987251     0.0001       2
        60        11.1111111    0.4956369     0.0001       3

              Pr > |T|  HO: LSMEAN(i)=LSMEAN(j)

               i/j    1        2        3
               1      .      0.0906   0.0001
               2    0.0906     .      0.0001
               3    0.0001   0.0001     .
```

NOTE: To ensure overall protection level, only probabilities associated with pre-planned comparisons should be used.

The DOSE effect is seen to be highly significant (1) indicating differences among the dose groups. However, whenever the interaction term is significant, caution must be used in the interpretation of the main effects. In this example, the F-value for CENTER-by-DOSE interaction is significant (2) indicating that the dose response is not the same for each study center. This interaction is depicted in Figure 6.2.

In the presence of such an interaction, we would typically perform analyses separately within each center. A *One-Way ANOVA* (Chapter 5) can be used to do this for Example 6.2. Such an analysis results in a significant DOSE effect for both centers with pairwise comparisons as follows:

| | ------- Pairwise Comparison -------- | | |
CENTER	Placebo vs. 30 mg	Placebo vs. 60 mg	30 mg vs. 60 mg
Dr. Abel	*	*	NS
Dr. Best	NS	*	*

* Significant (p < 0.05)   NS = not significant (p > 0.05)

FIGURE 6-2: Interaction in Example 6.2

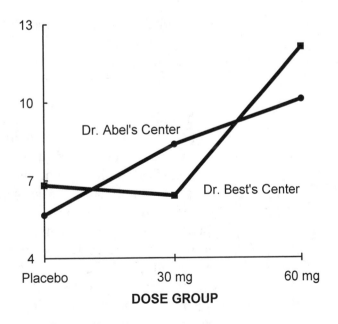

DETAILS & NOTES

▸ In Example 6.1, the main benefit of including Cancer Type as an ANOVA factor in the analysis is in improving the precision of the treatment comparisons by identifying the large variations among Cancer Types and removing them from the estimate of the error variation (MSE). Indeed, if a *One-Way ANOVA* had been used to compare treatments (ignoring Cancer Type), the result would be non-rejection of the hypothesis of equal treatment means based on an F-test of 3.79 ($p = 0.058$). This analysis produces an inflated estimate of the error variance of 1.39, compared with an MSE of 1.28 using the more appropriate *Two-Way ANOVA*.

▸ The computing methods shown in Example 6.1 are provided to show the deviations used in obtaining the effect sums-of-squares, but these equations are not recommended for practical use. Statistical packages obviate the need for manual calcuations. Without availability to such a computer program, computing formulas similar to those given for the *One-Way ANOVA* layout (Chapter 5) can be used with a hand calculator for finding the sums-of-squares in balanced designs.

▸ In clinical trials, there is almost always imbalance in two-way layouts, even if the study were designed as a balanced one. This might be due to patient dropouts, missed visits, data exclusion, or some other reason for missing data. In such cases, there may be more than one way to compute the sum-of-squares for the ANOVA effects, as seen by the different SAS types of sums-of-squares.

In the unbalanced case, the total sum-of-squares cannot be broken down as easily into additive components due to the sources of variation. A number of statistical methods have been devised to circumvent the problems which arise with sample size imbalance. The method of '*fitting constants*' and the method of '*weighted squares of means*' are traditionally used approaches which can be explored further by the interested reader [Bancroft, 1968]. Each method tests a slightly different hypothesis, as framed in terms of cell means. The method which should be used is that which corresponds most closely to the assumptions and hypotheses relevant to the given problem.

In SAS, Type III corresponds with the method of *weighted squares of means*, and is generally the method of choice for the analysis of clinical data. The hypothesis tested using Type III results is the equality of treatment group means, where each group mean is the unweighted average of the cell means comprising that group. That is, the group mean does not depend on the cell sample sizes (LS-mean), as is the case with the Type I and II methods. LS-Means are discussed in Appendix C.3, and interpretation of the various types of sums-of-squares is discussed in Appendix D.

▸ With an unbalanced layout, manual analysis using a hand-calculator becomes very tedious, regardless of which of the above methods is used. In developing the concept of analysis-of-variance in this and other chapters, calculations are demonstrated for balanced layouts to emphasize how the within- and between-group variability estimates arise and how the results are interpreted. Since computations are most efficient using matrix algebra, it is recommended that a computer package such as SAS be used in practice, especially for unbalanced layouts.

▸ In a multi-center trial, there may be differences among study centers due to such things as geography, climate, general population characteristics or specialty differences at specific centers. If we ignore these differences, the variation due to Study Centers will be included in the estimate of experimental error, or mean-square error (MSE). As we saw in Chapter 5 (*One-Way ANOVA*), potential treatment differences become obscured with large values of MSE. Therefore, we want to try to identify all important sources of variation which can be factored out of the experimental error to yield a more precise test for treatment effect. In the case of a multi-center study, 'Study Center' is usually considered an important factor in analyzing treatment differences because of known or suspected differences among centers.

▸ Sometimes inclusion of a block effect with a *Two-Way ANOVA* results in a <u>less</u> precise treatment comparison of the group means than by ignoring the blocking factor and using the *One-Way ANOVA*. Since the error degrees-of-freedom are reduced when including the Block variable as a source of variation in the ANOVA, the MSE may increase appreciably if among-block variation is small and the number of blocking levels is large. With an increased MSE, the F-test for GROUP is smaller due to the reduced degrees-of-freedom for error, so the precision of the group comparisons decreases. Thus, ANOVA should avoid including blocking factors with a large number of homogeneous levels.

▸ Pairwise comparisons of group means are often conducted using the 'PDIFF' option with the LSMEANS statement in SAS's GLM procedure as illustrated in Examples 6.1 and 6.2. This compares the LS-means of the levels of the factor specified in the LSMEANS statement using 't-test type' procedures. To avoid greatly altering the tests' significance levels, only pre-planned comparsions should be made. Multiple comparison procedures controlling for the overall significance level should be used when the number of comparisons becomes large.

▸ The MSE is an estimate of the variance among similar patients. Since patients are most similar within Group-by-Block cells, the MSE is an average or pooled variance over all cells of the within-cell variances. However, if each cell has only one measurement ($n_{ij} = 1$ for all i,j), the within cell variability cannot be estimated. In such cases, the analysis can proceed by assuming there is no interaction and using the interaction sum-of-squares as the SSE.

Even in layouts with cells having more than one measurement, if it is known or can be safely assumed that there is no interaction between main effects, the interaction can be ignored as a source in the ANOVA. The sum-of-squares for interaction is then absorbed into the SSE. While this increases the SSE, the number of degrees-of-freedom also increases. If the interaction effect is really insignificant, then increasing the degrees-of-freedom for MSE may more than offset the SSE increase with the net effect of perhaps gaining sensitivity in testing the main effects.

CHAPTER 7

REPEATED-MEASURES ANOVA

INTRODUCTION

'Repeated-measures' are measurements taken from the same patient at repeated time intervals. This situation arises frequently in clinical trials as many studies require that patients return for multiple visits during the trial, and response measurements are made at each.

These repeated response measurements can be used to characterize a response profile over time. One of the main questions the researcher may ask is whether the mean response profile for one treatment group is the same as for another treatment group or a placebo group. This situation may arise, for example, when trying to determine if the onset of effect or rate of improvement due to a new treatment is faster than that of a competitor's. Comparison of response profiles can be tested with a single F-test from a *Repeated-Measures ANOVA*.

Sample response profiles are shown in Figure 7-1 for 2 drug groups and 4 time periods.

SYNOPSIS

In general, we have g independent groups of patients each of whom are subjected to repeated measurements of the same response variable, y, at t time periods. Letting n_i represent the number of patients in Group i (i=1,2,...,g), the layout for g=3 groups is shown on the next page. In comparative trials, the groups often represent different parallel treatment groups or dose levels of a drug.

		--------- TIME ---------			
GROUP	PATIENT	1	2	...	t
1	101	y_{111}	y_{112}	...	y_{11t}
	102	y_{121}	y_{122}	...	y_{12t}
	...				
	n_1	y_{1n11}	y_{1n12}	...	y_{1n1t}
2	201	y_{211}	y_{212}	...	y_{21t}
	202	y_{221}	y_{222}	...	y_{22t}
	...				
	n_2	y_{2n21}	y_{2n22}	...	y_{2n2t}
3	301	y_{311}	y_{312}	...	y_{31t}
	302	y_{321}	y_{322}	...	y_{32t}
	...				
	n_3	y_{3n31}	y_{3n32}	...	y_{3n3t}

We note that the response may vary among groups, among patients within groups and among the different measurement times. Therefore, we include a GROUP effect, a PATIENT (within-GROUP) effect and a TIME effect as sources of variation in the ANOVA. The *Repeated-Measures ANOVA* also usually includes the GROUP-by-TIME interaction.

A significant interaction means that changes in response over Time differ among Groups, i.e., a significant difference in response profiles. When the profiles appear similar among Groups, the F-test for the GROUP effect tests the equality of mean responses among groups, 'averaged' over time. This test using the *Repeated-Measures ANOVA* approach may be more sensitive to detecting group differences than using a *One-Way ANOVA* to compare Groups at a single time point.

An F-test for the TIME effect is also available with the *Repeated-Measures ANOVA*. This tests for the equality of mean responses among the various measurement times for all groups combined.

In the simplest case of *Repeated-Measures ANOVA* which is presented here, the GROUP and the evaluation TIME are cross-classified main effects. However, the samples are not independent among the GROUP-TIME cells, since measurements over time taken from the same patient are correlated. To account for this correlation, the PATIENT effect must be included as a source of variation in the ANOVA.

With $N = n_1 + n_2 + ... + n_g$, the ANOVA summary table takes the following form:

ANOVA

SOURCE	df	SS	MS	F
GROUP	g-1	SSG	MSG	F_G=MSG/MSP(G)
PATIENT(GROUP)	N-g	SSP(G)	MSP(G)	--
TIME	t-1	SST	MST	F_T=MST/MSE
GROUP*TIME	(g-1)(t-1)	SSGT	MSGT	F_{GT}=MSGT/MSE
Error	(N-g)(t-1)	SSE	MSE	--
Total	Nt-1	TOT(SS)		

For the balanced layout ($n_1 = n_2 = ... = n_g$), the sums-of-squares can be computed in a manner similar to those illustrated for the *Two-Way ANOVA*. These computations are demonstrated in Example 7.1. As usual, the mean-squares (MS) are found by dividing the sums-of-squares (SS) by the corresponding degrees-of-freedom (df).

FIGURE 7-1: Sample Profiles of Drug Response

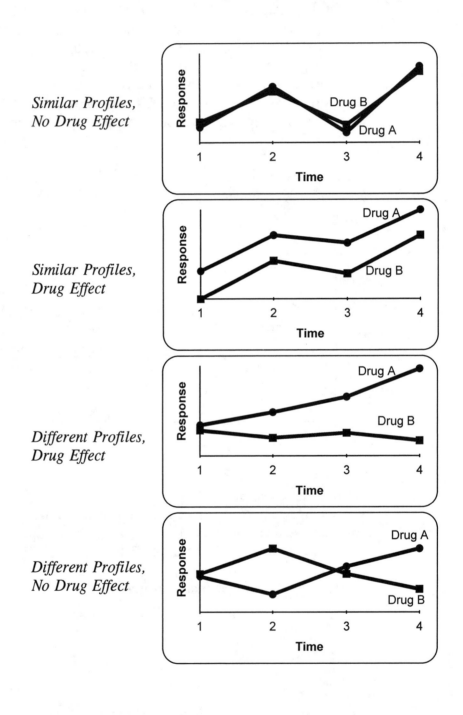

Similar Profiles,
No Drug Effect

Similar Profiles,
Drug Effect

Different Profiles,
Drug Effect

Different Profiles,
No Drug Effect

Variation from patient to patient is one type of random error, as estimated by the mean-square for PATIENT (within GROUP). If there is no difference among groups, the between-group variation merely reflects patient-to-patient variation. Therefore, under the null hypothesis of no GROUP effect, MSG and MSP(G) are independent estimates of the between-patient variability, so that F_G has the F-distribution with g-1 upper and N-g lower d.f.

If there is no TIME effect, the mean-square for TIME (MST) is an estimate of 'within-patient' variability, as is the error variation, MSE. The ratio of these independent estimates (F_T) is the F-statistic used to test the hypothesis of no TIME effect. Similarly, the interaction mean-square, also a 'within-patient' variation, is compared to the MSE to test for a significant GROUP-by-TIME interaction.

The following example is used to demonstrate the methods of the *Repeated-Measures ANOVA*.

EXAMPLE 7.1 -- "Arthritic Discomfort Following Vaccine"

A pilot study was conducted in 8 patients to evaluate the effect of a new vaccine on discomfort due to arthritic outbreaks. Four patients were randomly assigned to receive an active vaccine and 4 to receive a placebo. Patients were asked to return to the clinic monthly for 3 months and evaluate their comfort level with routine daily chores during the preceding month on a scale of 0 (no discomfort) to 10 (maximum discomfort). Eligibility criteria required patients to have a rating of at least an 8 in the month prior to vaccination. The rating data are shown below. Is there any evidence of a difference in response profiles between the active and placebo vaccines?

VACCINE	Pat. No.	VISIT		
		Month 1	Month 2	Month 3
Active	101	6	3	0
	103	7	3	1
	104	4	1	2
	107	8	4	3
Placebo	102	6	5	5
	105	9	4	6
	106	5	3	4
	108	6	2	3

SOLUTION

Using *Repeated-Measures ANOVA*, we identify VACCINE as the group effect and VISIT as the repeated factor. We will also include the PATIENT(within-VACCINE) and VACCINE-by-VISIT effects in the ANOVA. The sum-of-squares for each of these sources can be computed in the same manner as demonstrated previously (Chapters 5, 6). First, we obtain the marginal means, as shown below.

VACCINE	Pat. No.	Month 1	Month 2	Month 3	Mean
Active	101	6	3	0	3.000
	103	7	3	1	3.667
	104	4	1	2	2.333
	107	8	4	3	5.000
	Mean	6.25	2.75	1.50	3.500
	(S.D.)	(1.71)	(1.26)	(1.29)	
Placebo	102	6	5	5	5.333
	105	9	4	6	6.333
	106	5	3	4	4.000
	108	6	2	3	3.667
	Mean	6.50	3.50	4.50	4.833
	(S.D.)	(1.73)	(1.29)	(1.29)	
	Combined Mean	6.375	3.125	3.000	4.167

The VACCINE sum-of-squares is proportional to the sum of squared deviations of the group means from the overall mean:

$$SS(VACCINE) = [12 \cdot (3.500 - 4.167)^2] + [12 \cdot (4.833 - 4.167)^2] = 10.667 \quad .$$

This is based on 1 degree-of-freedom since there are 2 levels of the group factor VACCINE.

The sum-of-squares for VISIT, based on 2 degrees-of-freedom, and the VACCINE-by-VISIT interaction, also with 2 degrees-of-freedom, can be computed as follows:

$$SS(VISIT) = [8 \cdot (6.375 - 4.167)^2] \; +$$
$$[8 \cdot (3.125 - 4.167)^2] \; +$$
$$[8 \cdot (3.000 - 4.167)^2] = 58.583 \quad .$$

$$SS(VACCINE\text{-}by\text{-}VISIT) = [4 \cdot (6.25 - 4.167)^2] \; +$$
$$[4 \cdot (2.75 - 4.167)^2] \; +$$
$$[4 \cdot (1.50 - 4.167)^2] \; +$$
$$[4 \cdot (6.50 - 4.167)^2] \; +$$
$$[4 \cdot (3.50 - 4.167)^2] \; +$$
$$[4 \cdot (4.50 - 4.167)^2] \; -$$
$$SS(VACCINE) - SS(VISIT)$$

$$= 77.833 - 10.667 - 58.583$$
$$= 8.583 \quad .$$

The PATIENT(within VACCINE) sum-of-squares is found by replacing each of the patient's measurements with the mean response for that patient and summing the squared deviations from the vaccine group mean within which that patient is nested. Within each vaccine group, the factor PATIENT has 3 degrees-of-freedom, so for the two vaccine groups, we have 6 d.f. for PATIENT(VACCINE):

$$SS(PATIENT(VACCINE)) = [3 \cdot (3.00 - 3.500)^2] \; +$$
$$[3 \cdot (3.67 - 3.500)^2] \; +$$
$$[3 \cdot (2.33 - 3.500)^2] \; +$$
$$[3 \cdot (5.00 - 3.500)^2] \; +$$
$$[3 \cdot (5.33 - 4.833)^2] \; +$$
$$[3 \cdot (6.33 - 4.833)^2] \; +$$
$$[3 \cdot (4.00 - 4.833)^2] \; +$$
$$[3 \cdot (3.67 - 4.833)^2]$$

$$= 25.333 \quad .$$

The total sum-of-squares (23 d.f.) is found in the usual manner, summing the squared deviations of each observation from the overall mean:

$$SS(TOTAL) = [(6 - 4.167)^2] +$$
$$[(3 - 4.167)^2] +$$
$$[(0 - 4.167)^2] +$$
$$[(7 - 4.167)^2] +$$
$$... +$$
$$[(3 - 4.167)^2] +$$

$$= 115.333 \quad .$$

Finally, since this is a balanced layout, the error sum-of-squares (SSE) can be found by subtraction:

SSE = SS(TOTAL) -
       SS(VACCINE) -
          SS(PATIENT(VACCINE)) -
       SS(VISIT) -
          SS(VACCINE-by-VISIT)

$$= 115.333 - 10.667 - 25.333 - 58.583 - 8.583 = 12.167.$$

The ANOVA table can now be completed as shown below. The mean-squares for each effect are found by dividing the sum-of-squares (SS) by the degrees-of-freedom. The F-tests are the ratios of the effect mean-squares to the appropriate error associated with that effect.

ANOVA

SOURCE	df	SS	MS	F
VACCINE	1	10.667	10.667	2.53
PATIENT(VACCINE)	6	25.333	4.222	--
VISIT	2	58.583	29.292	28.89*
VACCINE-by-VISIT	2	8.583	4.292	4.23*
Error	12	12.167	1.014	--
Total	23	115.333		

* Significant ($p < 0.05$)

The F-test for the VACCINE effect is the ratio of the mean-square for VACCINE to the mean-square for PATIENT(VACCINE), F = 10.667/4.222 = 2.53. The F-values for VISIT and VACCINE-by-VISIT are found by the ratios of the mean-squares for these effects to the mean-square error (MSE = 1.014).

The hypothesis of similar response profiles over time between the vaccine groups is tested by the VACCINE-by-VISIT interaction. This is significant (F=4.23) when compared with the critical value of 3.89 found from the F-tables with 2 upper and 12 lower degrees-of-freedom and $\alpha = 0.05$. Further analyses can be performed by depicting the mean responses over time in graphical format and using linear contrasts to compare differences between vaccine groups in the changes from successive time points. A *One-Way ANOVA* can also be used to test for the VACCINE effect at each visit.

The VISIT effect is also seen to be significant. This means that the average responses for the combined vaccine groups differ among evaluation months. The F-test for the VACCINE effect can be interpreted as a comparison of mean responses between vaccine groups, 'averaged' over all measurement times. With a non-significant F-value of 2.53 and a significant interaction, further analyses as suggested above, are required prior to forming any conclusions with regard to the main effects.

SAS Analysis of Example 7.1

The SAS code for analyzing the data of Example 7.1 is shown on the following page. The input data set ARTHR is transformed to a new format with one observation per record in data set DISCOM. This data set is printed out using PROC PRINT, as shown in the output (1) on the subsequent pages.

The GLM procedure in SAS is applied to this data set using a MODEL statement which includes effects for Vaccine Group (VACGRP), Time (VISIT), and Patient (PAT) which is nested within Vaccine Group. These effects must be designated as classification variables in the CLASSES statement. The interaction is specified in the MODEL statement as VACGRP*VISIT.

As shown on the output, the MSE is computed as 1.01389 (2). Note that SAS automatically computes F-values for each model effect using the MSE as the denominator unless otherwise specified. The programmer must ask SAS to test the group effect (VACGRP) against the PATIENT(VACGRP) error using the TEST statement. The resulting F-value of 2.53 (3) is the appropriate F-test for the null hypothesis of no Vaccine Group effect. The F-value for VACGRP of 10.52 shown in the printout (4) is not meaningful for a *Repeated-Measures ANOVA*. The F-value of 4.16 for PAT(VACGRP) can also be ignored since this tests for a difference among patients within each group and will often be inconsequentially significant.

```
* SAS Code for Example 7.1 ;

DATA ARTHR;
INPUT VACGRP $  PAT MO1 MO2 MO3 ;
CARDS;
ACT 101 6 3 0
ACT 103 7 3 1
ACT 104 4 1 2
ACT 107 8 4 3
PBO 102 6 5 5
PBO 105 9 4 6
PBO 106 5 3 4
PBO 108 6 2 3
;
RUN;

DATA DISCOM; SET ARTHR;
KEEP VACGRP PAT VISIT SCORE;
 SCORE = MO1; VISIT = 1; OUTPUT;
 SCORE = MO2; VISIT = 2; OUTPUT;
 SCORE = MO3; VISIT = 3; OUTPUT;
RUN;

PROC PRINT DATA = DISCOM;
VAR VACGRP PAT VISIT SCORE;
TITLE1 'Repeated-Measures ANOVA';
TITLE2 'Example 7.1:  Arthritic Discomfort
    Following Vaccine';
RUN;

PROC GLM DATA = DISCOM;
CLASSES VACGRP PAT VISIT;
MODEL SCORE =
  VACGRP PAT(VACGRP) VISIT VACGRP*VISIT /SS3;
TEST H=VACGRP E=PAT(VACGRP);
QUIT; RUN;
```

```
*   SAS Output for Example 7.1


                         Repeated-Measures ANOVA
            Example 7.1:  Arthritic Discomfort Following Vaccine

              OBS     VACGRP     PAT     VISIT     SCORE

               1       ACT       101       1         6
               2       ACT       101       2         3
               3       ACT       101       3         0
               4       ACT       103       1         7
               5       ACT       103       2         3
               6       ACT       103       3         1
               7       ACT       104       1         4
               8       ACT       104       2         1
               9       ACT       104       3         2
              10       ACT       107       1         8
              11       ACT       107       2         4        (1)
              12       ACT       107       3         3
              13       PBO       102       1         6
              14       PBO       102       2         5
              15       PBO       102       3         5
              16       PBO       105       1         9
              17       PBO       105       2         4
              18       PBO       105       3         6
              19       PBO       106       1         5
              20       PBO       106       2         3
              21       PBO       106       3         4
              22       PBO       108       1         6
              23       PBO       108       2         2
              24       PBO       108       3         3



                        General Linear Models Procedure
                           Class Level Information

                  Class     Levels     Values

                  VACGRP       2       ACT PBO
                  PAT          8       101 102 103 104 105 106 107 108
                  VISIT        3       1 2 3
               Number of observations in data set = 24
```

Dependent Variable: SCORE

Source	DF	Sum of Squares	Mean Square	F Value	Pr > F
Model	11	103.16667	9.37879	9.25	0.0003
Error	12	12.16667	1.01389		
Corrected Total	23	115.33333	(2)		

R-Square	C.V.	Root MSE	SCORE Mean
0.894509	24.16609	1.0069	4.1667

Source	DF	Type III SS	Mean Square	F Value	Pr > F
VACGRP	1	10.666667	10.666667	10.52 (4)	0.0070
PAT(VACGRP)	6	25.333333	4.222222	4.16	0.0171
VISIT	2	58.583333	29.291667	28.89	0.0001
VACGRP*VISIT	2	8.583333	4.291667	4.23	0.0406

Tests of Hypotheses using the Type III MS for
PAT(VACGRP) as an error term

Source	DF	Type III SS	Mean Square	F Value	Pr > F
					(3)
VACGRP	1	10.666667	10.666667	2.53	0.1631

'MULTIVARIATE APPROACH'

The methodology demonstrated in Example 7.1 is a 'univariate' approach to repeated-measures analysis. In addition to normality and variance homogeneity, this approach requires the assumption of 'compound symmetry', which means that correlations between each pair of repeated measures are the same. This assumption is often not a valid one, especially if the time points are unequally spaced. Erroneous conclusions may result if the univariate approach is used under violation of the assumption of compound symmetry.

A 'multivariate approach' can be used to circumvent this problem. This approach uses the repeated measurements as multivariate response vectors, and is more robust when violations to the assumption of compound symmetry exist.

The SAS code needed to analyze Example 7.1 using the multivariate approach is shown below. Notice that this analysis uses the data set ARTHR, which is in the proper format for multivariate analysis.

```
* SAS Code for Example 7.1--Multivariate Approach ;

PROC PRINT DATA = ARTHR;
VAR VACGRP PAT MO1 MO2 MO3; RUN;

PROC GLM DATA = ARTHR; CLASS VACGRP;
MODEL MO1 MO2 MO3 = VACGRP / SS3;
REPEATED VISIT PROFILE / PRINTE SUMMARY;
TITLE3 '[Multivariate Approach]';
QUIT; RUN;
```

PROC PRINT is used to print out this data set, as shown in the SAS output (1).

The analysis uses the SAS GLM procedure, which can be used for the multivariate as well as the univariate approaches. When the PRINTE option is specified in the REPEATED statement, the SAS output includes a 'sphericity' test indicated as Mauchly's criterion applied to a set of orthogonal components. This test, based on a chi-square approximation, is used to test the assumption of compound symmetry. (Only part of the SAS GLM output is included here.) As shown (2), Mauchly's Criterion is not significant ($p = 0.8907$) using the data of Example 7.1.

* SAS Output for Example 7.1 -- Multivariate Approach

Repeated-Measures ANOVA
Example 7.1:   Arthritic Discomfort Following Vaccine
[Multivariate Approach]

OBS	VACGRP	PAT	MO1	MO2	MO3
1	ACT	1	6	3	0
2	ACT	3	7	3	1
3	ACT	4	4	1	2
4	ACT	7	8	4	3
5	PBO	2	6	5	5
6	PBO	5	9	4	6
7	PBO	6	5	3	4
8	PBO	8	6	2	3

(1)

General Linear Models Procedure
Repeated Measures Analysis of Variance

Test for Sphericity: Mauchly's Criterion = 0.8962875
Chisquare Approximation = 0.5474703 with 2 df   Prob > Chisquare = 0.7605

Applied to Orthogonal Components: (2)
Test for Sphericity: Mauchly's Criterion = 0.9547758
Chisquare Approximation = 0.2313939 with 2 df   Prob > Chisquare = 0.8907

Manova Test Criteria and Exact F Statistics for
the Hypothesis of no VISIT Effect
H = Type III SS&CP Matrix for VISIT   E = Error SS&CP Matrix

S=1   M=0   N=1.5

Statistic	Value	F	Num DF	Den DF	Pr > F
Wilks' Lambda	0.10207029	21.9929	2	5	0.0033
Pillai's Trace	0.89792971	21.9929	2	5	0.0033
Hotelling-Lawley Trace	8.79716981	21.9929	2	5	0.0033
Roy's Greatest Root	8.79716981	21.9929	2	5	0.0033

(3)

Manova Test Criteria and Exact F Statistics for
the Hypothesis of no VISIT*VACGRP Effect
H = Type III SS&CP Matrix for VISIT*VACGRP   E = Error SS&CP Matrix

S=1   M=0   N=1.5

Statistic	Value	F	Num DF	Den DF	Pr > F
Wilks' Lambda	0.44444444	3.1250	2	5	0.1317
Pillai's Trace	0.55555556	3.1250	2	5	0.1317
Hotelling-Lawley Trace	1.25000000	3.1250	2	5	0.1317
Roy's Greatest Root	1.25000000	3.1250	2	5	0.1317

(4)

Tests of Hypotheses for Between Subjects Effects

Source	DF	Type III SS	Mean Square	F Value	Pr > F
VACGRP	1	10.666667	10.666667	2.53	0.1631
Error	6	25.333333	4.222222		

(5)

When there is no evidence to contradict the assumption of compound symmetry, as in this case, the univariate results previously obtained can and should be used. The multivariate approach is known to produce overly conservative results when the compound symmetry assumption is satisfied. The output confirms this, as both the VISIT (3) and the VISIT*VACGRP (4) effects have less significance (i.e., greater p-values) than obtained by the univariate approach, namely 0.0033 vs. 0.0001 for VISIT and 0.1317 vs. 0.0406 for VISIT*VACGRP.

Four multivariate methods due to Wilks, Pillai, Hotelling and Roy are used to obtain the F-test statistic for these within-patient effects. Note that the test for the group effect (VACGRP) is the same as in the univariate analysis (5).

Additional factors can also be used in the *Repeated-Measures ANOVA*. Example 7.2 shows how Study Center can be used as a blocking effect in an unbalanced repeated-measures layout. This example also further illustrates the multivariate approach.

EXAMPLE 7.2 --"Treadmill Walking Distance in Intermittent Claudication"
Patients were randomly assigned to receive either a new drug, Novafylline, thought to reduce the symptoms of intermittent claudication, or placebo in a 4-month double-blind study. The primary measurement of efficacy is the walking distance on a treadmill until discontinuation due to claudication pain. Thirty-eight patients in 2 study centers underwent treadmill testing at baseline (Month-0) and at each of 4 monthly followup visits with the treadmill walking distances (in meters) shown on the next page. Is there any distinction in exercise tolerance between patients receiving Novafylline and those on placebo? (100-series patient numbers are from Center 1, 200-series from Center 2).

| Pat. No. | \multicolumn{5}{c}{------------------ Novafylline Group ------------------} Treatment Month | | | | | Pat. No. | \multicolumn{5}{c}{------------------ Placebo Group ------------------} Treatment Month | | | | |

Pat. No.	\multicolumn{5}{c}{Treatment Month}	Pat. No.	\multicolumn{5}{c}{Treatment Month}
	0	1	2	3	4		0	1	2	3	4
101	190	212	213	195	248	103	187	177	200	190	206
102	98	137	185	215	225	106	205	230	172	196	232
104	155	145	196	189	176	108	165	142	195	185	170
105	245	228	280	274	260	109	256	232	252	326	292
107	182	205	218	194	193	112	197	182	160	210	185
110	140	138	187	195	205	114	134	115	150	165	170
111	196	185	185	227	180	115	196	166	166	188	205
113	162	176	192	230	215	119	167	144	176	155	158
116	195	232	199	185	200	121	98	102	89	128	130
117	167	187	228	192	210						
118	123	165	145	185	215	201	167	175	122	162	125
120	105	144	119	168	165	203	123	136	147	130	135
						206	95	102	154	105	112
202	161	177	162	185	192	207	181	177	140	212	230
204	255	242	330	284	319	210	237	232	245	193	245
205	144	195	180	184	213	212	144	172	163	158	188
208	180	218	224	165	200	213	182	202	254	185	173
209	126	145	173	175	140	216	165	140	153	180	155
211	175	155	154	164	154	217	196	195	204	188	178
214	227	218	245	235	257						
215	175	197	195	182	193						

SOLUTION

We first prepare a summary table showing mean walking distances (in meters) and sample sizes, shown as follows:

Treatment	Center	\multicolumn{5}{c}{Month}				
		0	1	2	3	4
ACTIVE	1	163.2	179.5	195.6	204.1	207.7
		12	12	12	12	12
	2	180.4	193.4	207.9	196.8	208.5
		8	8	8	8	8
	COMB-INED	170.1	185.1	200.5	201.2	208.0
		20	20	20	20	20
PLACEBO	1	178.3	165.6	173.3	193.7	194.2
		9	9	9	9	9
	2	165.6	170.1	175.8	168.1	171.2
		9	9	9	9	9
	COMB-INED	171.9	167.8	174.6	180.9	182.7
		18	18	18	18	18
	TOTAL	38	38	38	38	38

Due to the sample size imbalance, the methods illustrated in Example 7.1 for manually computing the sums-of-squares can not be used. In such cases, the Type III sums-of-squares are most efficiently computed using matrix algebra with a program such as SAS. We use the GLM procedure with the multivariate approach for this example.

The SAS code for this analysis is shown on the next page. Patients are nested within each TREATMENT-by-CENTER cell, so that the factors TREATMENT, CENTER and TREATMENT-by-CENTER all represent between-patient effects. The F-tests for these effects, therefore, are based on the PATIENT(within TREATMENT-by-CENTER) 'error'.

The repeated-measures are specified as dependent variables on the left side of the equality sign in the MODEL statement, while the between-patient effects are specified on the right. SAS must be informed that these dependent variables are repeated-measures. This is done with the REPEATED statement, which labels the time factor as 'MONTH'. The PRINTE option is used to obtain the sphericity test for compound symmetry.

The SAS output for this example is shown in the following pages. Only selected portions of the entire output are reproduced here.

Unless suppressed with the NOUNI option of the MODEL statement, SAS prints out the results of a *Two-Way ANOVA* for each time point (1), denoted by dependent variables: WD0, WD1, WD2, WD3 and WD4. These results indicate no signficant TREATMENT or CENTER main effects and no TREATMENT-by-CENTER interaction at any of the individual measurement times ($p > 0.05$ for each) (2).

The multivariate analysis indicates a significant test (3) for compound symmetry ($p = 0.0103$) which invalidates the univariate approach demonstrated in Example 7.1. The MONTH and MONTH-by-TREATMENT effects are significant based on the multivariate tests (shown as "Wilks' Lambda", "Pillai's Trace", "Hotelling-Lawley Trace", and "Roy's Greatest Root"). These tests all yield the same F-values for each effect involving MONTH for this data set. The p-value of 0.0182 (4) for the MONTH-by-TREATMENT interaction indicates that the response profiles differ between groups. This difference is depicted in Figure 7-2, which shows the mean response at each month for the 2 treatment groups.

The TREATMENT effect, with an F-value of 2.11, is not significant (5) when 'averaged' over all measurement times (p=0.1556). The CENTER and TREATMENT-by-CENTER effects are also non-significant (5). The time effect (MONTH) is significant (6) for the combined treatment groups and study centers (p=0.0011). However, in light of the significant interaction indicating a treatment profile difference, further analyses should be conducted.

In the REPEATED statement (SAS code), "CONTRAST(1)" is specified, along with the SUMMARY option. These request that SAS provide an analysis of the *changes* in mean response from the first time period used. Since the first time period is Month 0 referring to baseline (prior to medication), the "CONTRAST(1)" option provides between treatment group comparisons of the mean changes from baseline to each time point (7). These results indicate a significant difference between the active and placebo groups in mean walking distance changes from baseline at each of the 4 followup months.

```
* SAS Code for Example 7.2 ;

DATA WDVIS;
INPUT TREATMNT $  PAT WD0 WD1 WD2 WD3 WD4;
CENTER = INT(PAT/100);
CARDS;
ACT 101 190 212 213 195 248
ACT 102  98 137 185 215 225
ACT 104 155 145 196 189 176
    (more data lines)...
PBO 216 165 140 153 180 155
PBO 217 196 195 204 188 178
;
RUN;

PROC GLM DATA = WDVIS; CLASSES TREATMNT CENTER;
MODEL WD0 WD1 WD2 WD3 WD4 =
      TREATMNT CENTER TREATMNT*CENTER / SS3;
REPEATED MONTH CONTRAST(1) / PRINTE SUMMARY;
TITLE1 'Repeated-Measures ANOVA';
TITLE2 'Example 7.2:  Treadmill Walking Distance
                in Intermittent Claudication';
QUIT;
RUN;
```

FIGURE 7-2: Mean Walking Distances for Example 7.2

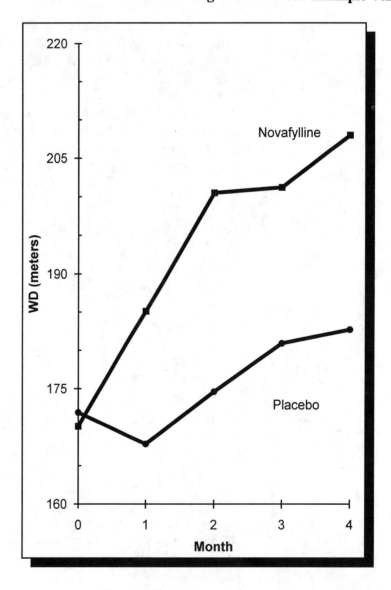

```
        * SAS Output for Example 7.2


                      Repeated-Measures ANOVA
     Example 7.2:  Treadmill Walking Distance in Intermittent Claudication
   ANOVA Results Using Multivariate Approach with Change From Month-0 as Cont

                     General Linear Models Procedure
                      Class Level Information                      (1)

                    Class    Levels    Values

                    TREATMNT    2     ACT PBO
                    CENTER      2     1 2
               Number of observations in data set = 38
```

Dependent Variable: WD0

Source	DF	Sum of Squares	Mean Square	F Value	Pr > F
Model	3	2190.1308	730.0436	0.40	0.7545
Error	34	62181.7639	1828.8754		
Corrected Total	37	64371.8947			

R-Square	C.V.	Root MSE	WD0 Mean
0.034023	25.01668	42.765	170.95

Source	DF	Type III SS	Mean Square	F Value	Pr > F
TREATMNT	1	0.2800	0.2800	0.00	0.9902
CENTER	1	45.5918	45.5918	0.02	0.8755
TREATMNT*CENTER	1	2088.3875	2088.3875	1.14	0.2928

(2) aligns with CENTER row.

Dependent Variable: WD1

Source	DF	Sum of Squares	Mean Square	F Value	Pr > F
Model	3	3825.5928	1275.1976	0.87	0.4642
Error	34	49611.9861	1459.1761		
Corrected Total	37	53437.5789			

R-Square	C.V.	Root MSE	WD1 Mean
0.071590	21.59429	38.199	176.89

Source	DF	Type III SS	Mean Square	F Value	Pr > F
TREATMNT	1	3215.5202	3215.5202	2.20	0.1469
CENTER	1	788.9467	788.9467	0.54	0.4672
TREATMNT*CENTER	1	201.7209	201.7209	0.14	0.7123

(2) aligns with CENTER row.

Dependent Variable: WD2

Source	DF	Sum of Squares	Mean Square	F Value	Pr > F
Model	3	7128.9686	2376.3229	1.08	0.3693
Error	34	74577.3472	2193.4514		
Corrected Total	37	81706.3158			

R-Square	C.V.	Root MSE	WD2 Mean
0.087251	24.88399	46.834	188.21

Source	DF	Type III SS	Mean Square	F Value	Pr > F
TREATMNT	1	6860.0220	6860.0220	3.13	0.0860
CENTER	1	504.3553	504.3553	0.23	0.6346
TREATMNT*CENTER	1	225.2155	225.2155	0.10	0.7506

(2) aligns with CENTER row.

* SAS Output for Example 7.2 (continued)

Repeated-Measures ANOVA
Example 7.2:   Treadmill Walking Distance in Intermittent Claudication

General Linear Models Procedure
Dependent Variable: WD3

Source	DF	Sum of Squares	Mean Square	F Value	Pr > F
Model	3	7086.0892	2362.0297	1.47	0.2391
Error	34	54499.3056	1602.9208		
Corrected Total	37	61585.3947			

R-Square	C.V.	Root MSE	WD3 Mean
0.115061	20.90104	40.036	191.55

Source	DF	Type III SS	Mean Square	F Value	Pr > F	
TREATMNT	1	3542.7168	3542.7168	2.21	0.1463	
CENTER	1	2512.2867	2512.2867	1.57	0.2191	(2)
TREATMNT*CENTER	1	771.2115	771.2115	0.48	0.4926	

Dependent Variable: WD4

Source	DF	Sum of Squares	Mean Square	F Value	Pr > F
Model	3	8437.1959	2812.3986	1.45	0.2450
Error	34	65863.7778	1937.1699		
Corrected Total	37	74300.9737			

R-Square	C.V.	Root MSE	WD4 Mean
0.113554	22.45275	44.013	196.03

Source	DF	Type III SS	Mean Square	F Value	Pr > F	
TREATMNT	1	5975.4050	5975.4050	3.08	0.0880	
CENTER	1	1141.2258	1141.2258	0.59	0.4481	(2)
TREATMNT*CENTER	1	1319.2903	1319.2903	0.68	0.4150	

Repeated Measures Level Information

Dependent Variable	WD0	WD1	WD2	WD3	WD4
Level of MONTH	1	2	3	4	5

Partial Correlation Coefficients from the Error SS&CP Matrix / Prob > |r|

DF = 34	WD0	WD1	WD2	WD3	WD4
WD0	1.000000	0.881446	0.778029	0.781755	0.742002
	0.0001	0.0001	0.0001	0.0001	0.0001
WD1	0.881446	1.000000	0.703789	0.663442	0.754124
	0.0001	0.0001	0.0001	0.0001	0.0001
WD2	0.778029	0.703789	1.000000	0.695239	0.724997
	0.0001	0.0001	0.0001	0.0001	0.0001
WD3	0.781755	0.663442	0.695239	1.000000	0.826616
	0.0001	0.0001	0.0001	0.0001	0.0001
WD4	0.742002	0.754124	0.724997	0.826616	1.000000
	0.0001	0.0001	0.0001	0.0001	0.0001

Test for Sphericity: Mauchly's Criterion = 0.3190188
Chisquare Approximation = 37.036211 with 9 df   Prob > Chisquare = 0.0000

Applied to Orthogonal Components: (3)
Test for Sphericity: Mauchly's Criterion = 0.5139265
Chisquare Approximation = 21.578963 with 9 df   Prob > Chisquare = 0.0103

```
*   SAS Output for Example 7.2 (continued)


                     Repeated-Measures ANOVA
    Example 7.2:  Treadmill Walking Distance in Intermittent Claudication

            Manova Test Criteria and Exact F Statistics for
                    the Hypothesis of no MONTH Effect
          H = Type III SS&CP Matrix for MONTH    E = Error SS&CP Matrix

                          S=1     M=1     N=14.5
Statistic                 Value           F        Num DF    Den DF   Pr > F

Wilks' Lambda             0.56579676     5.9475        4        31    0.0011
Pillai's Trace            0.43420324     5.9475        4        31    0.0011   (6)
Hotelling-Lawley Trace    0.76741911     5.9475        4        31    0.0011
Roy's Greatest Root       0.76741911     5.9475        4        31    0.0011


            Manova Test Criteria and Exact F Statistics for
                 the Hypothesis of no MONTH*TREATMNT Effect
      H = Type III SS&CP Matrix for MONTH*TREATMNT    E = Error SS&CP Matrix

                          S=1     M=1     N=14.5
Statistic                 Value           F        Num DF    Den DF   Pr > F

Wilks' Lambda             0.68930532     3.4932        4        31    0.0182
Pillai's Trace            0.31069468     3.4932        4        31    0.0182   (4)
Hotelling-Lawley Trace    0.45073593     3.4932        4        31    0.0182
Roy's Greatest Root       0.45073593     3.4932        4        31    0.0182


            Manova Test Criteria and Exact F Statistics for
                 the Hypothesis of no MONTH*CENTER Effect
      H = Type III SS&CP Matrix for MONTH*CENTER    E = Error SS&CP Matrix

                          S=1     M=1     N=14.5
Statistic                 Value           F        Num DF    Den DF   Pr > F

Wilks' Lambda             0.81294393     1.7833        4        31    0.1574
Pillai's Trace            0.18705607     1.7833        4        31    0.1574
Hotelling-Lawley Trace    0.23009714     1.7833        4        31    0.1574
Roy's Greatest Root       0.23009714     1.7833        4        31    0.1574


            Manova Test Criteria and Exact F Statistics for
              the Hypothesis of no MONTH*TREATMNT*CENTER Effect
          H = Type III SS&CP Matrix for MONTH*TREATMNT*CENTER
                        E = Error SS&CP Matrix

                          S=1     M=1     N=14.5
Statistic                 Value           F        Num DF    Den DF   Pr > F

Wilks' Lambda             0.88498645     1.0072        4        31    0.4188
Pillai's Trace            0.11501355     1.0072        4        31    0.4188
Hotelling-Lawley Trace    0.12996081     1.0072        4        31    0.4188
Roy's Greatest Root       0.12996081     1.0072        4        31    0.4188



            Tests of Hypotheses for Between Subjects Effects

Source              DF    Type III SS   Mean Square   F Value    Pr > F

TREATMNT             1      15215.68      15215.68      2.11     0.1556
CENTER               1        141.58        141.58      0.02     0.8894   (5)
TREATMNT*CENTER      1       3864.29       3864.29      0.54     0.4693

Error               34     245350.66       7216.20
```

```
              *   SAS Output for Example 7.2 (continued)


                          Repeated-Measures ANOVA
        Example 7.2:  Treadmill Walking Distance in Intermittent Claudication

                        General Linear Models Procedure
                       Repeated Measures Analysis of Variance
                       Analysis of Variance of Contrast Variables

    MONTH.N represents the contrast between the nth level of MONTH and the 1st

    Contrast Variable: MONTH.2

    Source              DF    Type III SS   Mean Square   F Value    Pr > F

    MEAN                 1    1035.12545    1035.12545      2.54     0.1205
    TREATMNT             1    3275.81362    3275.81362      8.03     0.0077  (7)
    CENTER               1     455.22581     455.22581      1.12     0.2984
    TREATMNT*CENTER      1     992.00000     992.00000      2.43     0.1283

    Error               34   13878.44444     408.18954

    Contrast Variable: MONTH.3

    Source              DF    Type III SS   Mean Square   F Value    Pr > F

    MEAN                 1    9854.88351    9854.88351     10.88     0.0023
    TREATMNT             1    6947.95878    6947.95878      7.67     0.0090  (7)
    CENTER               1     246.66846     246.66846      0.27     0.6051
    TREATMNT*CENTER      1     941.98029     941.98029      1.04     0.3150

    Error               34   30794.47222     905.71977

    Contrast Variable: MONTH.4

    Source              DF    Type III SS   Mean Square   F Value    Pr > F

    MEAN                 1   13127.4951    13127.4951      17.39     0.0002
    TREATMNT             1    3605.9897     3605.9897       4.78     0.0358  (7)
    CENTER               1    3234.7531     3234.7531       4.29     0.0461
    TREATMNT*CENTER      1     321.4198      321.4198       0.43     0.5184

    Error               34   25663.0139      754.7945

    Contrast Variable: MONTH.5

    Source              DF    Type III SS   Mean Square   F Value    Pr > F

    MEAN                 1   20601.2370    20601.2370      21.18     0.0001
    TREATMNT             1    6057.4951     6057.4951       6.23     0.0176  (7)
    CENTER               1    1643.0220     1643.0220       1.69     0.2025
    TREATMNT*CENTER      1      87.9252       87.9252       0.09     0.7655

    Error               34   33074.7639      972.7872
```

DETAILS & NOTES

▶ The computing methods demonstrated in Example 7.1 apply only to balanced designs (i.e., same number of patients per group). This demonstration is used to show which deviations are represented by each of the effect sum-of-squares, and is not recommended in practice. Even if a suitable computer package is unavailable, easier computing formulas are available for manual computations [see e.g., Winer, 1971]. For unbalanced layouts, the SAS Type III results are generally recommended.

▶ For the balanced case, the *Repeated-Measures ANOVA* error sum-of-squares (SSE) is simply the sum of the SSE's found by using *Two-Way ANOVA*'s (with no interaction) *within* each treatment group. In Example 7.1, the *Two-Way ANOVA* tables within each Vaccine Group are as follows:

ANOVA	Active Group				Placebo Group			
Source	*df*	*SS*	*MS*	*F*	*df*	*SS*	*MS*	*F*
PATIENT	3	11.667	3.889	3.41	3	13.667	4.556	5.12*
VISIT	2	48.500	24.250	21.29*	2	18.667	9.333	10.50*
Error	6	6.833	1.139		6	5.333	0.889	
Total	11	67.000			11	37.667		

* Significant ($p < 0.05$)

SSE for the *Repeated-Measures ANOVA* is $6.833 + 5.333 = 12.167$ based on $6 + 6 = 12$ degrees-of-freedom. Similarly, the SS(PATIENT) can be added to obtain the SS(PATIENT(GROUP)) for the repeated-measures ANOVA: $11.667 + 13.667 = 25.333$ with $3 + 3 = 6$ degrees-of-freedom. Note that the within-patient sum-of-squares, SS(VISIT), are not additive.

▶ The multivariate approach to *Repeated-Measures ANOVA* using SAS makes the within-patient tests using four criteria: Wilks' Lambda, Pillai's Trace, Hotelling-Lawley Trace and Roy's Greatest Root. Each of these methods uses multivariate statistical analysis to obtain an F-test of significance for the given factor based on complex functions of sums-of-squares. The differences among these tests depend on the alternative hypothesis. Wilk's Lambda, for example, may be the most powerful test to use under some alternatives and the least powerful of the four under others. A comparison of these tests suggests that Pillai's Trace may be the most appropriate one for use under a wide range of applications. The reader is referred to other references for further discussion of these comparisons [Hand & Taylor, 1982]. In any case, when there are only two groups (g=2), all four tests yield the same results, as shown in Examples 7.1 and 7.2.

▸ The univariate approach to *Repeated-Measures ANOVA* may still be used even under violations to the assumption of compound symmetry by applying an adjustment to the analysis. A correction factor, called the Greenhouse-Geiser epsilon (ε), can be computed as a function of the variances and covariances of the repeated measurements. The adjustment is made by multiplying each of the d.f. in the ANOVA table by ε to obtain adjusted d.f. The Greenhouse-Geiser adjusted p-values are printed in the SAS output (G-G) (these are not shown in the SAS output for Examples 7.1 and 7.2). When the sphericity test is highly significant, results may differ between the adjusted univariate approach and the multivariate approach, in which case, the multivariate approach is recommended.

▸ When there is a significant profile difference among groups, further analyses are required to determine at what time points these differences occur. Using the SUMMARY option of the REPEATED statement in the SAS GLM procedure will produce ANOVA's at various sets of time points. Specifying CONTRAST(1) will give the same results as if ANOVA were conducted on the changes in the response measure from the first time point, as illustrated in Example 7.2. This can be useful if the first time point is a baseline value.

Alternatively, using the SAS term PROFILE in the REPEATED statement provides the results as if ANOVA were conducted on the changes between *successive* time points. This might be useful, for example, in determining at what time point the responses of two treatment groups first begin to converge or diverge. Other contrasts can also be used with SAS (see SAS manual for details).

▸ The error variation for between-group comparisons (averaged over time) is estimated by the mean-square for PATIENTS-within-GROUP (MSP(G)) with N-g d.f. The within-patient error variation (over all groups) is estimated by MSE, with (N-g)(t-1) d.f. The error variation within the Group-by-Time cells is the pooled combination of these 2 sometimes disparate error estimates, namely,

$$\hat{\sigma}^2_{cell} = \frac{SSP(G) + SSE}{(N-g) + (N-g)(t-1)} = \frac{SSP(G) + SSE}{t \cdot (N-g)} .$$

This within-cell error variation is the within-time, among-patient variation, averaged over all time points. That is, if MSE_j represents the MSE from a *One-Way ANOVA* conducted at time period j, the within-cell variance of the repeated-measures layout is the average of these MSE's:

$$\hat{\sigma}^2_{cell} = \frac{\sum_{j=1}^{t} MSE_j}{t} .$$

This within-cell error variation can be used to compare cell means (e.g., Group i vs. Group j) for a specific time point or to form 95% confidence intervals for the cell means.

▸ The *Repeated-Measures ANOVA* is not recommended when there are many missing values. A repeated-measures layout with 2 time periods is similar to the paired-difference situation (Chapter 3). Patients with a missing value at one of the 2 time periods may contribute information regarding between-patient variability, but nothing regarding patient response profile (within-patient variability). Similar problems occur when patients have missing data in layouts with more than 2 time periods.

When there are missing values, *Repeated-Measures ANOVA* using SAS confounds hypotheses regarding treatment effects with other model effects resulting in complex hypotheses and interpretation difficulties. Unless the analyst can clearly restate the statistical hypothesis in clinical terms, *Repeated-Measures ANOVA* should be avoided when the data set is plagued with much missing data (one or two missing values in a large study should not present interpretation difficulties).

Often, estimates can be computed for missing values, and these can then be used in the analysis as if they were observed. The simplest estimate and one that is often used in clinical trials is the patient's observation from the previous time point. This has been referred to as the 'last-observation-carried-forward' technique [Gillings & Koch, 1991]. Other estimates of missing values may be based on averages of adjacent values, or on row and column means.

The multivariate approach using SAS eliminates patients with missing values from the analysis. If there are many missing values, and it is not feasible to use estimates or to eliminate the patients with only partial data, group profile comparisons may not be possible. In such cases, the most appropriate analysis may be separate ANOVA's at each time point.

▸ The term 'Time' has been used in this chapter to describe the study visit or time of measurement of the response variable during a trial. This is perhaps the most common repeated-measures situation, especially for comparative drug studies. In general, however, the repeated factor need not refer to time at all. The repeated factor could be a set of experimental conditions, each applied to the same set of patients in random order, such as subjecting each patient to each dose level of a test drug. The dose levels in this example represent the repeated measure, and the 'profiles' are the dose-response curves.

The *cross-over* design is such an example which can be analyzed with the *Repeated-Measures ANOVA*. In the popular two-period cross-over, the Treatment (say A or B) is the repeated-factor, since both treatments A and B are given to each patient. The Sequence Group, representing the order in which patients receive the treatments (A-B or B-A), would represent the 'GROUP' effect. Patients are nested within Sequence Group, and the analysis would be carried out as in Example 7.1. A significant Treatment-by-Sequence Group interaction would suggest a 'period effect', in which case, the analyst would perform separate analyses for each treatment period using the *Two-Sample t-Test*.

▸ With only one group (g=1), the repeated-measures layout is identical to that of a randomized block design. In this case, the analysis is carried out as described in Chapter 6 using the repeated factor as the 'Group' effect and patient as the 'blocking' factor.

CHAPTER 8
LINEAR REGRESSION

INTRODUCTION

Regression analysis is used to analyze the relationship between a response, y, and a quantitative factor, x. Knowledge of this relationship may be important for predicting unmeasured responses from a known x-value.

Examples where regression analysis might be useful in clinical data analysis include the modelling of blood pressue response (y) on the dose of a new antihypertensive drug (x), cholesterol level (y) on patient's age (x), pain relief (y) on time after dosing with an anti-inflammatory treatment (x), or degree of wound healing (y) on the baseline surface area of a burn wound (x).

While one might consider a number of potential relationships between x and y, we confine our attention here only to linear relationships. Simple *Linear Regression* methodology provides an estimate of the best-fitting line through a set of data points, (x_1,y_1), $(x_2,y_2),\ldots,(x_n,y_n)$. We may then determine the significance of the linear relationship or correlation, predict future responses and make inferences regarding the slope of the regression line.

SYNOPSIS

Given a number of observed values of a normally distributed response variable $(y_1, y_2,\ldots, y_n)$, the mean, $\bar{y}$, represents the best estimate of a future, yet unobserved response. The idea behind regression analysis is to improve on this estimate by using the value of some related factor, x. If x and y have a known linear relationship, the best estimate of y will be a linear function of the known value, x.

A linear relationship between a response, y, and an independent variable x, can be expressed as:

$$y = \alpha + \beta x + \epsilon$$

where α is the intercept and β is the slope, as shown in Figure 8-1. Since the response is subject to random measurement error, y may differ in repeated sampling for the same value of x. The ϵ accounts for this random nature of the response, y.

FIGURE 8-1: Simple Linear Regression of y on x

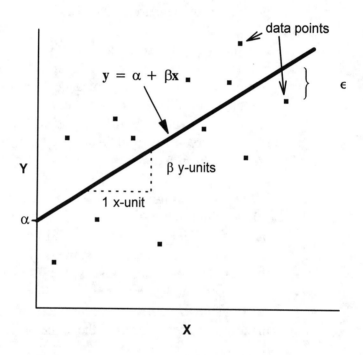

Typically, we have n pairs of coordinates, $\{(x_i, y_i)$, for i = 1, 2, ..., n\}$, and assume that the y_i's are independent, normally distributed and have the same variance, σ^2, for each x value. From these data we estimate the model parameters α and β by a and b, respectively, in such a manner that the resulting 'prediction equation',

$$\hat{y} = a + bx$$

is the 'best-fitting' line through the measured coordinates. In this sense, the prediction equation represents the best estimate of the unknown regression model.

We seek values for a and b such that the predicted response, $\hat{y}$, is as close as possible to the observed response, y, for all measured data points. One way to satisfy this requirement is to minimize the sum-of-squared differences between y and $\hat{y}$,

$$SSE = \sum_{i=1}^{n} (y_i - \hat{y}_i)^2 \quad .$$

This is known as the 'Least-Squares' criterion. SSE is the sum-of-squared 'errors' or deviations between the actual and predicted responses.

Let

$$S_{yy} = \sum_{i=1}^{n} (y_i - \bar{y})^2 = \sum_{i=1}^{n} y_i^2 - \frac{\left(\sum_{i=1}^{n} y_i\right)^2}{n}$$

$$S_{xx} = \sum_{i=1}^{n} (x_i - \bar{x})^2 = \sum_{i=1}^{n} x_i^2 - \frac{\left(\sum_{i=1}^{n} x_i\right)^2}{n}$$

and,

$$S_{xy} = \sum_{i=1}^{n} (x_i - \bar{x})(y_i - \bar{y}) = \sum_{i=1}^{n} x_i y_i - \frac{\left(\sum_{i=1}^{n} y_i\right) \cdot \left(\sum_{i=1}^{n} x_i\right)}{n} \quad .$$

The 'best-fitting' line based on the Least-Squares criterion is given by:

$$\hat{y} = a + bx \qquad where,$$

$$b = \frac{S_{xy}}{S_{xx}} \qquad and,$$

$$a = \bar{y} - b\bar{x} \qquad .$$

The best estimate of the variance, σ^2, is $s^2 = SSE/(n-2)$, where SSE can be calculated from the formula:

$$SSE = \frac{S_{xx} \cdot S_{yy} - S_{xy}^2}{S_{xx}}$$

based on n-2 degrees-of-freedom.

The main question posed by simple *Linear Regression* concerns the significance of the slope parameter. If the slope, β, is zero, then the value of x will not improve the prediction of y over the ordinary predictor, $\bar{y}$. A significant slope, β, indicating a linear relationship between x and y, means that knowledge of the x-values will significantly improve one's prediction ability.

The statistical test is based on a function of the slope estimate, b, which has the t-distribution when the null hypothesis of 'zero slope' is true. The test summary is as follows:

null hypothesis:	H_0: $\beta = 0$
alt. hypothesis:	H_A: $\beta \neq 0$
test statistic:	$t = \dfrac{b}{s / \sqrt{S_{xx}}}$
decision rule:	*reject H_0 if* $\mid t \mid > t_{\alpha/2,\ n-2}$

If the slope is meaningful, we can estimate the mean response at a given value of x, say x_0, with a 95% confidence interval by:

$$\hat{y}_{x_0} \pm t_{0.025,n-2} \cdot s \cdot \sqrt{\frac{1}{n} + \frac{(x_0 - \bar{x})^2}{S_{xx}}}$$

$$\text{where } \hat{y}_{x_0} = a + b \cdot x_0 \quad.$$

EXAMPLE 8.1 -- 'Anti-anginal Response vs. Disease History'

Treadmill stress tests were administered to patients with angina pectoris before and 4 weeks after once-daily dosing with an experimental anti-anginal medication. The investigator wanted to know if the improvement in exercise duration is related to the patient's disease history. Disease duration since initial diagnosis (in years) and percent-improvement in treadmill walking times are shown below for a study enrolling 20 patients. Is there a significant linear relationship between improvement on medication and disease duration?

Pat. No.	Disease Duration (yr) (x)	Response (%-Impr) (y)	Pat. No.	Disease Duration (yr) (x)	Response (%-Impr) (y)
1	1	40	11	1	60
2	1	90	12	4	0
3	3	30	13	2	50
4	2	30	14	2	110
5	1	80	15	3	20
6	5	60	16	3	70
7	1	10	17	5	-30
8	4	-10	18	3	20
9	2	50	19	1	40
10	6	40	20	6	0

SOLUTION

Using the formulas presented, we compute:

$$\sum x_i = 56 \qquad \sum y_i = 760 \qquad \sum x_i \cdot y_i = 1570$$
$$\sum x_i^2 = 212 \qquad \sum y_i^2 = 52{,}200 \qquad n = 20$$

so that,

$$S_{xx} = 212 - \frac{56^2}{20} = 55.2$$

$$S_{yy} = 52,200 - \frac{760^2}{20} = 23,320$$

$$S_{xy} = 1570 - \frac{56 \cdot 760}{20} = -558 \quad .$$

The estimated regression equation is found as follows:

$$b = \frac{-558}{55.2} = -10.109 \ , \qquad and$$

$$a = \frac{760}{20} - (-10.109) \cdot \frac{56}{20} = 66.304 \quad ,$$

which yield,

$$\hat{y} = 66.304 - 10.109x \quad .$$

In addition, we find:

$$SSE = \frac{(55.2)(23,320) - (-558)^2}{55.2} = 17,679.35 \qquad and,$$

$$s = \sqrt{\frac{17,679.35}{18}} = 31.34$$

The regression slope, representing the average change in y for a one unit change in x, is the best estimate of the rate of improvement in treadmill performance for each one-year increase in disease duration, i.e, -10.109%/year. The statistical significance is determined by the t-test, summarized as follows:

null hypothesis: H_0: $\beta = 0$
alt. hypothesis: H_A: $\beta \neq 0$

test statistic: $t = \dfrac{-10.109}{31.34/\sqrt{55.2}} = -2.40$

decision rule: *reject H_0 if $|t| > t_{0.025,\ 18}$*
                                          $(= 2.101)$

conclusion: Since $2.40 > 2.101$, we reject H_0 concluding that treadmill improvement has a significant linear relationship to disease duration.

The mean improvement in treadmill exercise time for the average patient with a 5-year history of angina is computed as

$$\hat{y}_5 = 66.304 - 10.109(5) = 15.76\%.$$

The 95% confidence interval for this mean is:

$$15.76 \pm 2.101 \cdot (31.34) \cdot \sqrt{\frac{1}{20} + \frac{(5-2.8)^2}{55.2}}$$

$$= 15.76 \pm 2.101 \cdot (11.629)$$

$$= 15.76 \pm 24.43$$

or (-8.67% *to* 40.19%). Since this interval contains zero, we would be inclined to conclude that the average treated patient with a 5 year history of angina does not have significant improvement in exercise tolerance.

SAS Analysis of Example 8.1

The SAS code and output for analyzing the data set of this example are shown on the following pages. A printout of the data set is first obtained using PROC PRINT (1), followed by the summary statistics for the x and y values using PROC MEANS (2).

For the regression analysis, we stick with the SAS GLM procedure, although PROC REG may also be used. When GLM is used without a CLASS statement, SAS assumes the independent variables in the MODEL statement are quantitative and performs a regression analysis.

The regression estimates, a and b, are printed in the 'Estimate' column of the output (3). Note the p-value for the t-test for slope is 0.0276 (4), confirming the significance of our manual analysis.

The P and CLM options specified after the MODEL statement request the predicted values based on the regression equation for each data point, along with 95% confidence intervals for the mean response at the corresponding x values. For x=5 (Observation Nos. 17 and 18), the predicted response (15.7608) has a corresponding 95% confidence interval of -8.67 to 40.19 (5), as in the manual calculations.

```
*   SAS Code for Example 8.1 ;

DATA ANGINA;
INPUT PAT X_DUR Y_IMPR @@;
CARDS;
   1 1  40       2 1  90       3 3  30
   4 2  30       5 1  80       6 5  60
   7 1  10       8 4 -10       9 2  50
  10 6  40      11 1  60      12 4   0
  13 2  50      14 2 110      15 3  20
  16 3  70      17 5 -30      18 3  20
  19 1  40      20 6   0
;
RUN;

PROC SORT DATA = ANGINA; BY X_DUR Y_IMPR; RUN;
PROC PRINT DATA = ANGINA;
  VAR PAT X_DUR Y_IMPR;
TITLE1 'Linear Regression & Correlation';
TITLE2 'Example 8.1:  Improvement in Angina vs.
        Disease Duration';
RUN;

PROC MEANS MEAN STD N; VAR X_DUR Y_IMPR;
RUN;

PROC GLM DATA = ANGINA;
MODEL Y_IMPR = X_DUR / P CLM SS3;
QUIT;
RUN;
```

* SAS Output for Example 8.1

Linear Regression & Correlation
Example 8.1: *Improvement in Angina vs. Disease Duration*

OBS	PAT	X_DUR	Y_IMPR	
1	7	1	10	
2	1	1	40	
3	19	1	40	
4	11	1	60	
5	5	1	80	
6	2	1	90	
7	4	2	30	
8	9	2	50	
9	13	2	50	(1)
10	14	2	110	
11	15	3	20	
12	18	3	20	
13	3	3	30	
14	16	3	70	
15	8	4	-10	
16	12	4	0	
17	17	5	-30	
18	6	5	60	
19	20	6	0	
20	10	6	40	

(2)

Variable	Mean	Std Dev	N
X_DUR	2.8000000	1.7044833	20
Y_IMPR	38.0000000	35.0338182	20

```
             * SAS Output for Example 8.1 (continued)


                       Linear Regression & Correlation
              Example 8.1:  Improvement in Angina vs. Disease Duration

                          General Linear Models Procedure
                        Number of observations in data set = 20

       Dependent Variable: Y_IMPR
                                      Sum of        Mean
       Source                DF       Squares      Square    F Value    Pr > F

       Model                  1     5640.6522    5640.6522     5.74     0.0276
       Error                 18    17679.3478     982.1860
       Corrected Total       19    23320.0000


                     R-Square          C.V.       Root MSE       Y_IMPR Mean
                (7)
                      0.241880      82.47328       31.340          38.000


       Source                DF   Type III SS   Mean Square   F Value    Pr > F
       X_DUR                  1     5640.6522     5640.6522     5.74     0.0276
                                                                (6)


                                         T for H0:     Pr > |T|    Std Error of
       Parameter           Estimate    Parameter=0                   Estimate

       INTERCEPT          66.30434783        4.83       0.0001     13.73346931
       X_DUR             -10.10869565       -2.40       0.0276      4.21820157
                             (3)                          (4)


       Obs'n   Observed   Predicted   Lower 95% CLM   Residual   Upper 95% CLM

         1      10.0000     56.1956      34.4879       -46.1956      77.9033
         2      40.0000     56.1956      34.4879       -16.1956      77.9033
         3      40.0000     56.1956      34.4879       -16.1956      77.9033
         4      60.0000     56.1956      34.4879         3.8043      77.9033
         5      80.0000     56.1956      34.4879        23.8043      77.9033
         6      90.0000     56.1956      34.4879        33.8043      77.9033
         7      30.0000     46.0869      29.7460       -16.0869      62.4278
         8      50.0000     46.0869      29.7460         3.9130      62.4278
         9      50.0000     46.0869      29.7460         3.9130      62.4278
        10     110.0000     46.0869      29.7460        63.9130      62.4278
        11      20.0000     35.9782      21.1491       -15.9782      50.8074
        12      20.0000     35.9782      21.1491       -15.9782      50.8074
        13      30.0000     35.9782      21.1491        -5.9782      50.8074
        14      70.0000     35.9782      21.1491        34.0217      50.8074
        15     -10.0000     25.8695       7.7076       -35.8695      44.0314
        16       0.0000     25.8695       7.7076       -25.8695      44.0314
        17     -30.0000     15.7608      -8.6702       -45.7608      40.1920    (5)
        18      60.0000     15.7608      -8.6702        44.2391      40.1920
        19       0.0000      5.6521     -26.3006        -5.6521      37.6049
        20      40.0000      5.6521     -26.3006        34.3478      37.6049


             Sum of Residuals                         -0.00000000
             Sum of Squared Residuals              17679.34782609
             Sum of Squared Residuals - Error SS       0.00000000
             Press Statistic                       22187.33121357
             First Order Autocorrelation              -0.05363544
             Durbin-Watson D                           1.91983119    (8)
```

DETAILS & NOTES

▸ The hypothesis of 'zero regression slope' is equivalent to the hyothesis that the covariate is not an important predictor of response. The covariate, x, can be viewed as an ANOVA model factor with 1 degree-of-freedom with the following ANOVA summary:

ANOVA

SOURCE	df	SS	MS	F
X	1	SSX	MSX	F_x = MSX/MSE
Error	n-2	SSE	MSE	
Total	n-1	TOT(SS)		

The SSX and MSX may be computed as

$$SSX = MSX = \frac{S_{xy}^{\,2}}{S_{xx}} \quad .$$

The F-value for the null hypothesis that the covariate is unimportant is F = MSX/MSE, with 1 upper and n-2 lower degrees-of-freedom. Algebraically, this is equivalent to the square of the t-test for the 'zero slope' hypothesis since,

$$F = \frac{MSX}{MSE} = \frac{\left(\frac{S_{xy}^{\,2}}{S_{xx}}\right)}{s^2} = \frac{\left(\frac{S_{xy}}{S_{xx}}\right)^2}{s^2/S_{xx}} = \left(\frac{b}{s/\sqrt{S_{xx}}}\right)^2 = t^2 \quad .$$

The F-value for the covariate effect in Example 8.1 is seen on the SAS output to be 5.74 (6), which is the square of the t-value (-2.40).

▸ Another equivalent method of making inferences about the covariate effect is with the correlation coefficient. A positive regression slope indicates a positive correlation, i.e, y increases as x increases. A negative slope indicates a negative correlation, i.e., y decreases as x increases. The Pearson-product-moment correlation coefficient is often used as a measure of the degree of linear correlation between two variables, x and y.

The correlation coefficient, ρ, is a unitless measure between -1 and +1. A correlation of +1 indicates a perfect positive correlation, a -1 indicates a perfect negative correlation and a 0 indicates no linear correlation. The population parameter, ρ, is estimated by the sample correlation coefficient, r:

$$r = \frac{S_{xy}}{\sqrt{S_{xx} \cdot S_{yy}}}$$

A t-test for significant correleation is:

null hypothesis:	H_0: $\rho = 0$
alt. hypothesis:	H_A: $\rho \neq 0$
test statistic:	$t = \dfrac{r \cdot \sqrt{n-2}}{\sqrt{1-r^2}}$
decision rule:	*reject H_0 if $\lvert t \rvert > t_{\alpha/2,\, n-2}$*

Expressing the slope, b, the standard deviation, s and the correlation coefficient, r in terms of S_{xx}, S_{yy} and S_{xy}, it is easy to show the t-test based on the correlation is identical to the t-test based on the slope. Note the equivalency of the hypotheses, H_0: $\beta = 0$ and H_0: $\rho = 0$.

The correlation coefficient for Example 8.1 is

$$r = -558 / \{55.2 \,(23{,}320)\}^{1/2} = -0.492.$$

The t-statistic for significant correlation is

$$t = \frac{(-0.492) \cdot \sqrt{18}}{\sqrt{1 - (-0.492)^2}} = -2.4$$

which is the same t-value computed from the slope estimate, b. The SAS output (7) prints r^2 (R-Square), which is a measure of goodness-of-fit.

▸ When estimating a mean response for a specified value of x, say x_0, the confidence interval will be smallest when x_0 is closest to the mean, $\bar{x}$, since the confidence interval width is a monotonically increasing function of $(x_0 - \bar{x})^2$. Such intervals can be computed for a number of x_0 values and plotted along with the regression equation to form confidence bands. Figure 8-2 below shows the confidence bands for Example 8.1.

FIGURE 8-2: 95% Confidence Bands for Example 8.1

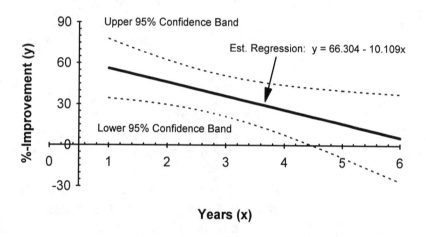

▸ The prediction equation can be used to estimate the response, y, for any value of the predictor, x, within the experimental region. The experimental region consists of the range of x-values from the data used to compute the regression estimates. Predicting a response, y for a value of x outside the experimental region is called 'extrapolation'. Extrapolation to a point x_e should not be used unless it can be safely assumed that x and y have the same linear relationship outside the experimental region at point x_e. Since this assumption may not often be met, extrapolation should be avoided in the face of any uncertainty about this assumption.

▸ A significant correlation implies a significant linear relationship between x and y, but does not imply causality. Conversely, a non-significant correlation does not imply that there is no causal (or other) relationship between x and y. There may in fact be a quadratic or parabolic relationship, or some other relationship between x and y resulting in no *linear* correlation. It is always a good idea to plot the data to obtain a visual impression of any relationship. Quadratic, cubic and higher order regression analyses can be performed quite easily by including these terms in the MODEL statement using the SAS GLM procedure (see SAS manual).

▸ Simple *Linear Regression* refers to a single response variable, y, modelled on a single predictor variable, x. Sometimes, several quantitative factors, x_1, x_2, x_3, ..., are thought to affect a response, y. These predictors along with the manner in which they interact can all be used to estimate a *multiple Linear Regression* equation of the form

$$y = a_0 + a_1x_1 + a_2x_2 + ... + a_kx_k$$

assuming k factors. Like the estimate b of β in the simple linear model, a_i is a coefficient determined by the amount of contribution x_i makes to the prediction of y.

For each regression model, SAS provides a measure of the 'goodness-of-fit' by r^2. The magnitude of changes in r^2 following the addition or deletion of predictors from the multiple linear regression model can provide insight as to which of the x_i's might be significant contributors in the prediction of the response, y. This technique is referred to as 'stepwise regression', and is described more fully in the SAS manual.

▸ One of the assumptions needed to perform regression analysis is a constant error variance over the experimental region. To investigate the validity of this assumption, one could look for a constant, horizontal pattern in the plot of the residuals (i.e., the difference between the observed and predicted values) against the x-values. If the residuals appear to increase or decrease with x, the assumption of variance homogeneity may be violated. If such is the case, the analyst may use a transformation of the data to attempt to stabilize the variance. Popular variance-stabilizing transformations include the natural logarithm, square-root and arcsin transformations.

▸ Another assumption of the regression procedures is that of independent observations. If x represents time, and the responses, y, represent measurements on the same experimental unit (e.g., patient) at various time points, the assumption of independence is violated. In such cases, use of *Repeated-Measures ANOVA* may be more appropriate.

A correlation over time is often referred to as 'autocorrelation' in time-series analysis. SAS can test for auto-correlation using the *Durbin-Watson test*. A value close to 2, such as 1.92 in the SAS output of Example 8.1 (8), indicates no significant auto-corrleation.

▸ For a particular value of x, say x_p, a 95% 'prediction interval' for the predicted response of a future observation is given by:

$$\hat{y}_{x_p} \pm t_{0.025,n-2} \cdot s \sqrt{1 + \frac{1}{n} + \frac{(x_p - \bar{x})^2}{S_{xx}}}$$

$$\text{where,} \quad \hat{y}_{x_p} = a + bx_p \quad .$$

Prediction bands can be established around the prediction equation in a manner similar to that described for confidence bands.

CHAPTER 9
ANALYSIS-of-COVARIANCE

INTRODUCTION

Analysis-of-Covariance, or ANCOVA, provides a method for comparing response means among 2 or more groups adjusted for a quantitative concomitant variable, or "covariate", thought to influence the response. We will confine our attention to cases in which the response (y) may be linearly related to the covariate (x). ANCOVA combines regression and ANOVA methods by fitting simple linear regression models within each group and comparing regressions among groups.

ANCOVA methods represent one of the most widely used statistical methods in clinical trials. Examples where ANCOVA might be applied include: (i) comparing cholesterol levels (y) between a treated and a reference group adjusted for age (x, in years), (ii) comparing scar healing (y) between conventional and laser surgery adjusted for excision size (x, in mm), or (iii) comparing exercise tolerance (y) in 3 dose levels of a treatment used for angina patients adjusted for smoking habits (x, in cigarettes/day).

ANCOVA can often increase the precision of comparisons of the group means by including the covariate (x) as a source of variation, thereby decreasing the estimated error variance. ANCOVA is particularly useful when the values of the covariate differ among the groups. When this occurs and the response is linearly related to the covariate, covariance adjustments can lead to markedly different conclusions than those obtained using the unadjusted ANOVA methods.

SYNOPSIS

Suppose we have k groups with n_i independent x-y points in Group i (i = 1, 2, ..., k), as depicted in the following layout.

GROUP 1		GROUP 2		...	GROUP k	
x	y	x	y		x	y
x_{11}	y_{11}	x_{21}	y_{21}	...	x_{k1}	y_{k1}
x_{12}	y_{12}	x_{22}	y_{22}	...	x_{k2}	y_{k2}
x_{13}	y_{13}	x_{23}	y_{23}	...	x_{k3}	y_{k3}
...	...	...	...	...	...	...
x_{1n1}	y_{1n1}	x_{2n2}	y_{2n2}	...	x_{knk}	y_{knk}

As with ANOVA, we assume independent groups with a normally distributed response measure, y, and variance homogeneity. In addition, we assume the regression slopes are the same for each group, i.e., $\beta_1 = \beta_2 = ... = \beta_k = \beta$. The mean response within each group depends on the covariate, resulting in a model for the i-th group mean as:

$$\mu_i = \alpha_i + \beta x \quad .$$

For each group, we may compute $\bar{x}$, $\bar{y}$, S_{xx}, S_{yy} and S_{xy} using the formulas of Chapter 8. Let $\bar{x}_i$, $\bar{y}_i$, $S_{xx(i)}$, $S_{yy(i)}$ and $S_{xy(i)}$ represent these quantities, respectively, for Group i (i = 1, 2, ..., k). Also, compute S_{xx}, S_{yy} and S_{xy} for all groups combined (ignoring group). The estimated regression line for Group i is

$$\hat{y} = a_i + bx \qquad (for \ i = 1,2,...,k)$$

where a_i and b are the Least-Squares estimates computed as:

$$b = \frac{\sum_i S_{xy_{(i)}}}{\sum_i S_{xx_{(i)}}} \quad and,$$

$$a_i = \bar{y}_i - b\bar{x}_i \quad .$$

With $N = n_1 + n_2 + \ldots + n_k$, the ANOVA table summarizing the significance of the sources of variation is as follows:

ANOVA

SOURCE	df	SS	MS	F
GROUP	k-1	SSG	MSG	F_G = MSG/MSE
X (covariate)	1	SSX	MSX	F_X = MSX/MSE
Error	N-k-1	SSE	MSE	
Total	N-1	TOT(SS)		

The sums-of-squares (SS) can be found from the following computing formulas:

$$TOT(SS) = S_{yy}$$

$$SSE = \frac{\left(\sum_i S_{xx_{(i)}}\right)\left(\sum_i S_{yy_{(i)}}\right) - \left(\sum_i S_{xy_{(i)}}\right)^2}{\left(\sum_i S_{xx_{(i)}}\right)}$$

$$SSG = \frac{(S_{xx})(S_{yy}) - (S_{xy})^2}{S_{xx}} - SSE$$

$$SSX = \sum_i S_{yy_{(i)}} - SSE \quad .$$

Note that when k=1 (one group), SSG = 0 and the computing formulas are identical to those used for *Linear Regression* in Chapter 8.

The mean-squares are the SS's divided by the d.f.'s. Of primary interest is the comparison of the group means adjusted to a common value of the covariate, say x_0. Letting μ_{i0} represent the mean of Group i for $x = x_0$, the test can be summarized as follows:

null hypothesis:	H_0: $\mu_{10} = \mu_{20} = \ldots = \mu_{k0}$
alt. hypothesis:	H_A: NOT H_0
test statistic:	$F_G = MSG/MSE$
rejection region:	*reject H_0 if $F_G > F_{N-k-1}^{k-1}(\alpha)$*

Notice that the hypothesis is equivalent to the equality of intercepts among groups,

$$H_0: \alpha_1 = \alpha_2 = \ldots = \alpha_k \, ,$$

and the test does not depend on the actual value of x_0 selected.

This test may result in improved precision for the group means comparisons over *One-Way ANOVA* methods if the slope, β, differs from zero. To determine whether the covariate has a significant effect on the response, we use the F_X ratio to test for zero regression slope using the following test summary:

null hypothesis:	H_0: $\beta = 0$
alt. hypothesis:	H_A: $\beta \neq 0$
test statistic:	$F_X = MSX/MSE$
rejection region:	*reject H_0 if $F_X > F_{N-k-1}^{1}(\alpha)$*

EXAMPLE 9.1 -- "Triglyceride Changes Adjusted for Glycemic Control"

A new cholesterol-lowering supplement Fibralo, *was studied in a double-blind study against a marketed reference agent,* Gemfibrozil, *in 34 non-insulin dependent diabetic (NIDDM) patients. One of the study's objectives was to compare the mean decrease in triglyceride levels between groups. Degree of glycemic control, measured by hemoglobin A_{1c} levels (HbA_{1c}) was thought to be an important factor in the responsiveness to the treatment. This covariate was measured at the start of the study, and is shown below with the percent-changes in triglycerides from pretreatment to the end of the 10 week trial. Is there a difference in mean responses between supplements?*

	FIBRALO GROUP			*GEMFIBROZIL* GROUP	
Pat. No.	HbA_{1c} ng/ml (X)	Triglyceride %-Change (Y)	Pat. No.	HbA_{1c} ng/ml (X)	Triglyceride %-Change (Y)
2	7.0	5	1	5.1	10
4	6.0	10	3	6.0	15
7	7.1	-5	5	7.2	-15
8	8.6	-20	6	6.4	5
11	6.3	0	9	5.5	10
13	7.5	-15	10	6.0	-15
16	6.6	10	12	5.6	-5
17	7.4	-10	14	5.5	-10
19	5.3	20	15	6.7	-20
21	6.5	-15	18	8.6	-40
23	6.2	5	20	6.4	-5
24	7.8	0	22	6.0	-10
27	8.5	-40	25	9.3	-40
28	9.2	-25	26	8.5	-20
30	5.0	25	29	7.9	-35
33	7.0	-10	31	7.4	0
			32	5.0	0
			34	6.5	-10

SOLUTION

To apply ANCOVA using HbA_{1c} as a covariate, we first obtain some summary results from the data as follows:

	Fibralo (Group 1)	Gemfibrozil (Group 2)	Combined
Σx	112.00	119.60	231.60
Σx^2	804.14	821.64	1625.78
Σy	-65.00	-185.00	-250.00
Σy^2	4575.00	6475.00	11050.00
Σxy	-708.50	-1506.50	-2215.00
$\bar{x}$	7.0000	6.6444	6.8118
$\bar{y}$	-4.0625	-10.2778	-7.3529
n	16	18	34

Using the formulas of Chapter 8, we compute for the *Fibralo* group (i=1):

$$S_{xx(1)} = 804.14 - (112)^2/16 = 20.140$$

$$S_{yy(1)} = 4575.00 - (-65)^2/16 = 4310.938$$

$$S_{xy(1)} = -708.50 - (112)(-65)/16 = -253.500 \quad .$$

Similarly for the *Gemfibrozil* group (i=2), we obtain:

$$S_{xx(2)} = 26.964$$

$$S_{yy(2)} = 4573.611$$

$$S_{xy(2)} = -277.278 \quad .$$

Finally, for the combined data (ignoring groups), we compute:

$$S_{xx} = 48.175$$

$$S_{yy} = 9211.765$$

$$S_{xy} = -512.059 \quad .$$

The sums-of-squares can now be obtained as:

$$TOT(SS) = 9211.8$$

$$SSE =$$

$$\frac{(20.140 + 26.964)(4310.938 + 4573.611) - [-253.500 - 277.278)]^2}{(20.140 + 26.964)}$$

$$= 2903.6$$

$$SSG = \frac{(48.175)(9211.765) - (-512.059)^2}{48.175} - 2903.6 = 865.4$$

$$SSX = (4310.938 + 4573.611) - 2903.6 = 5980.9$$

and the ANOVA summary table can be completed as follows:

ANCOVA

SOURCE	df	SS	MS	F
TREATMENT	1	865.4	865.4	9.2 *
X (HbA1c)	1	5980.9	5980.9	63.8 *
Error	31	2903.7	93.7	
Total	33	9211.8		

* Significant (p < 0.05); critical F-value = 4.16

The F-statistics are formed as the ratios of effect mean-squares (MS) to the MSE (93.7). Each F-statistic is compared with the critical F value with 1 upper and 31 lower degrees-of-freedom. The critical F-value for $\alpha = 0.05$ is 4.16.

The significant covariate effect (F=63.8) indicates that the triglyceride response has a significant linear relationship with HbA_{1c}. The significant F-value for TREATMENT indicates that the mean triglyceride response adjusted for glycemic control differs between treatment groups.

Application of the *One-Way ANOVA* (Chapter 5) to compare treatment group means, ignoring the covariate, results in the following ANOVA table:

ANOVA

SOURCE	d.f.	SS	MS	F
TREATMENT	1	327.22	327.22	1.18
Error	32	8884.55	277.64	
Total	33	9211.76		

The rejection region for the TREATMENT effect based on a significance level of $\alpha = 0.05$ includes F-values greater than 4.15, the critical F-value with 1 upper and 32 lower d.f. With an F of only 1.18, we cannot reject the hypothesis of equal means. We therefore must conclude that no difference in mean response betweeen treatment groups is evident based on this test.

One reason the ANCOVA produces a significant treatment group difference while ANOVA does not is a large reduction in MSE, (from 277.6 to 93.7). This results in greater precision of the treatment group comparison.

Another reason for this difference is due to an increase in the difference between means by using the adjusted values, as we further explore. We estimate the common slope, β, as,

$$b = [(-253.500) + (-277.278)]/[20.140 + 26.964]$$
$$= -11.268 \ ,$$

and the intercepts (a_i's) as:

$$a_1 = (\ -4.0625) - (-11.268)(7.0000) = 74.81$$

$$a_2 = (-10.2778) - (-11.268)(6.6444) = 64.59 \ ,$$

yielding the estimated regression equations:

$$\textit{Fibralo Group}: \qquad \hat{y} = 74.81 - 11.268x$$

$$\textit{Gemfibrozil Group}: \qquad \hat{y} = 64.59 - 11.268x \qquad .$$

The adjusted mean responses for each group are the values of the estimated regression equations evaluated at the overall mean of the covariate, $\bar{x} = 6.8118$, as follows:

Fibralo: $74.81 - 11.268(6.8118) = -1.9$

Gemfibrozil: $64.59 - 11.268(6.8118) = -12.2$.

These means differ considerably from the unadjusted means already computed. The summary table of means can be expressed as:

Mean Response	*Fibralo* Group	*Gemfibrozil* Group	p-Value
Unadjusted	-4.1%	-10.3%	0.2858
Adjusted	-1.9%	-12.2%	0.0048 *

* Significant (p < 0.05)	(p-values from SAS output)

Triglycerides decrease by a mean of 11.27% for every one ng/ml increase in HbA_{1c}, and this rate of change is seen to be significant. Notice that the mean HbA_{1c} level is slightly higher in the *Fibralo* group compared with the *Gemfibrozil* group (7.00 v. 6.64). The unadjusted mean responses are those which lie on the regression lines corresponding to the mean of the covariate for each group, as shown in Figure 9-1. By insisting that we compare the mean responses of the 2 groups at the same value of the covariate ($\bar{x} = 6.81$) requires using a smaller x value for the *Fibralo* group (resulting in a smaller triglyceride decrease), and a larger x value for the *Gemfibrozil* group (resulting in a larger triglyceride decrease). The end result is a larger difference in response means based on the adjusted values compared with the unadjusted values.

FIGURE 9-1: ANCOVA-Adjusted Means for Example 9.1

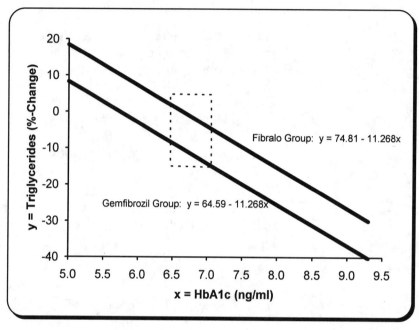

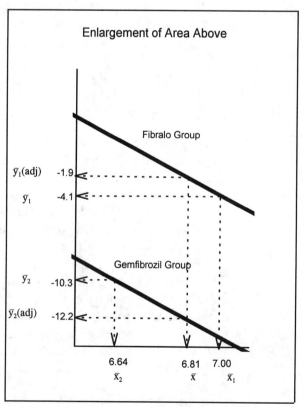

SAS Analysis of Example 9.1

The SAS code for performing this analysis is shown on the next page, followed by the SAS output. The PRINT, PLOT and MEANS procedures are used to provide a data listing (1), a scatterplot of the data (2) and basic summary statistics (3).

The GLM procedure is used to conduct the ANCOVA, using the treatment group (TRT) effect as a class variable and HGBA1C as a numeric covariate. The sums-of-squares, mean-squares and F-tests all corroborate the manual calculations (4).

The SOLUTION option is used with the GLM MODEL statement to obtain the estimates for the regression equations. The slope estimate, b, is -11.268 (5). The intercept estimates are found by adding each treatment group effect to the intercept estimate:

$$a_1 = 64.59 + 10.22 = 74.81, \text{ and}$$

$$a_2 = 64.59 + 0.00 = 64.59 \quad (6).$$

The LSMEANS statement instructs SAS to printout the adjusted mean responses at the common covariate mean (7).

The data set is also analyzed using the *One-Way ANOVA*, ignoring the covariate (9). These results, as discussed previously, show a non-significant treatment effect ($p = 0.2858$).

```
* SAS Code for Example 9.1 ;

DATA TRI;
INPUT TRT $ PAT HGBA1C TRICHG @@;
CARDS;
FIB  2 7.0   5    FIB  4 6.0  10
FIB  7 7.1  -5    FIB  8 8.6 -20
FIB 11 6.3   0    FIB 13 7.5 -15
       (more data lines)...
GEM 29 7.9 -35    GEM 31 7.4   0
GEM 32 5.0   0    GEM 34 6.5 -10
; RUN;
PROC SORT DATA = TRI;
BY TRT HGBA1C TRICHG; RUN;

 ** Print data set ;
PROC PRINT DATA = TRI;
VAR TRT PAT HGBA1C TRICHG;
TITLE1 'Analysis of Covariance';
TITLE2 'Example 9.1: Triglyceride Changes
        in Diabetics';
RUN;

 ** Plot data, by group ;
PROC PLOT VPERCENT=45 DATA = TRI;
PLOT TRICHG*HGBA1C=TRT; RUN;

 ** Obtain summary statistics for each group ;
PROC MEANS MEAN STD N DATA = TRI;
BY TRT; VAR HGBA1C TRICHG; RUN;

 ** Use glycemic control as covariate ;
PROC GLM DATA = TRI; CLASSES TRT;
MODEL TRICHG = TRT HGBA1C / SS3 SOLUTION;
LSMEANS TRT/PDIFF STDERR;
RUN;

 ** Compare groups with ANOVA, ignoring
       the covariate ;
PROC GLM DATA = TRI; CLASSES TRT;
MODEL TRICHG = TRT / SS3; RUN;
```

```
        * SAS Output for Example 9.1

                         Analysis of Covariance
          Example 9.1:  Triglyceride Changes in Diabetics

               OBS    TRT    PAT    HGBA1C    TRICHG

                1     FIB    30     5.0        25
                2     FIB    19     5.3        20
                3     FIB     4     6.0        10
                4     FIB    23     6.2         5
                5     FIB    11     6.3         0
                6     FIB    21     6.5       -15
                7     FIB    16     6.6        10
                8     FIB    33     7.0       -10
                9     FIB     2     7.0         5
               10     FIB     7     7.1        -5
               11     FIB    17     7.4       -10
               12     FIB    13     7.5       -15
               13     FIB    24     7.8         0
               14     FIB    27     8.5       -40
               15     FIB     8     8.6       -20
               16     FIB    28     9.2       -25        (1)
               17     GEM    32     5.0         0
               18     GEM     1     5.1        10
               19     GEM    14     5.5       -10
               20     GEM     9     5.5        10
               21     GEM    12     5.6        -5
               22     GEM    10     6.0       -15
               23     GEM    22     6.0       -10
               24     GEM     3     6.0        15
               25     GEM    20     6.4        -5
               26     GEM     6     6.4         5
               27     GEM    34     6.5       -10
               28     GEM    15     6.7       -20
               29     GEM     5     7.2       -15
               30     GEM    31     7.4         0
               31     GEM    29     7.9       -35
               32     GEM    26     8.5       -20
               33     GEM    18     8.6       -40
               34     GEM    25     9.3       -40
```

Plot of TRICHG*HGBA1C.   Symbol is value of TRT.

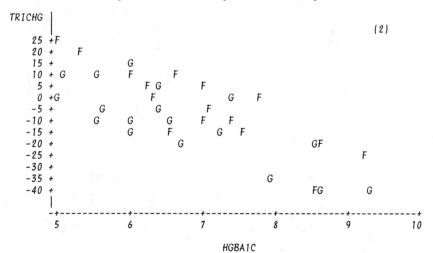

```
TRICHG  |
                                                      (2)
    25 +F
    20 +     F
    15 +          G
    10 + G     G    F        F
     5 +          F G       F
     0 +G             F         G    F
    -5 +         G       F
   -10 +   G   G     G     F   F
   -15 +        G     F     G   F
   -20 +            G               GF
   -25 +                                F
   -30 +
   -35 +                     G
   -40 +                          FG      G
        |
        -+------------+------------+------------+------------+------------+
         5            6            7            8            9           10
                                 HGBA1C
```

```
                 * SAS Output for Example 9.1 (continued)



                             Analysis of Covariance
                 Example 9.1:  Triglyceride Changes in Diabetics

           ----------------------- TRT=FIB -----------------------
                     Variable        Mean        Std Dev   N
           --------------------------------------------------------
                     HGBA1C        7.0000000    1.1587349  16
                     TRICHG       -4.0625000   16.9527530  16
           --------------------------------------------------------


           ----------------------- TRT=GEM ----------------------- (3)
                     Variable        Mean        Std Dev   N
           --------------------------------------------------------
                     HGBA1C        6.6444444    1.2594220  18
                     TRICHG      -10.2777778   16.4023153  18
           --------------------------------------------------------



                        General Linear Models Procedure
                           Class Level Information

                      Class    Levels   Values
                      TRT        2       FIB GEM
                 Number of observations in data set = 34

Dependent Variable: TRICHG
                                       Sum of       Mean
Source                     DF         Squares      Square    F Value    Pr > F

Model                       2       6308.0753    3154.0376    33.67     0.0001
Error                      31       2903.6894      93.6674
Corrected Total            33       9211.7647

                 R-Square          C.V.        Root MSE          TRICHG Mean

                 0.684785       -131.6234        9.6782            -7.3529


Source                     DF   Type III SS  Mean Square   F Value    Pr > F

TRT         (4)             1      865.3635     865.3635      9.24     0.0048
HGBA1C                      1     5980.8592    5980.8592     63.85     0.0001


                                     T for H0:    Pr > |T|   Std Error of
Parameter           Estimate        Parameter=0               Estimate

INTERCEPT         64.59251309 B         6.70      0.0001     9.64331471
TRT      FIB      10.22171475 B (6)     3.04      0.0048     3.36293670
         GEM       0.00000000 B          .          .           .
HGBA1C          -11.26810398 (5)       -7.99      0.0001     1.41014344   (8)

NOTE: The X'X matrix has been found to be singular and a generalized
      inverse was used to solve the normal equations.  Estimates
      followed by the letter 'B' are biased, and are not unique
      estimators of the parameters.



                              Least Squares Means

        TRT       TRICHG       Std Err    Pr > |T|     Pr > |T| H0:
                  LSMEAN       LSMEAN    H0:LSMEAN=0  LSMEAN1=LSMEAN2
                                (9)
        FIB      -1.9414451   2.4340646    0.4312        0.0048      (7)
        GEM     -12.1631599   2.2933414    0.0001
```

```
              * SAS Output for Example 9.1 (continued)


                            Analysis of Covariance
                  Example 9.1:  Triglyceride Changes in Diabetics
                                                                    (9)
                         General Linear Models Procedure
                            Class Level Information

                          Class    Levels    Values

                           TRT        2      FIB GEM
                   Number of observations in data set = 34


        Dependent Variable: TRICHG
                                      Sum of          Mean
        Source                DF      Squares        Square    F Value    Pr > F

        Model                  1    327.21609      327.21609     1.18     0.2858
        Error                 32   8884.54861      277.64214
        Corrected Total       33   9211.76471

                     R-Square          C.V.       Root MSE            TRICHG Mean

                     0.035522       -226.6113       16.663               -7.3529


        Source                DF    Type III SS   Mean Square   F Value    Pr > F
        TRT                    1     327.21609     327.21609      1.18     0.2858
```

DETAILS & NOTES

▸ The standard error of the slope estimate, b, is given by

$$s_b = \sqrt{\dfrac{MSE}{\sum_i S_{xx_{(i)}}}} \quad .$$

Since "*a significant covariate effect*" means the same as "*a non-zero slope*", an alternate but equivalent test to the F-test for the covariate effect is the t-test as follows:

null hypothesis:	H_0: $\beta = 0$
alt. hypothesis:	H_A: $\beta \neq 0$
test statistic:	$t = \dfrac{b}{s_b}$
decision rule:	reject H_0 if $\mid t \mid > t_{\alpha/2,\ N-k-1}$

In Example 9.1, we have MSE = 93.67, so that

$$s_b = \sqrt{\frac{93.67}{20.140 + 26.964}} = 1.410 \quad .$$

The t-statistic is computed as

$$t = (-11.27) / 1.41 = -7.99,$$

based on 31 degress-of-freedom, as shown on the SAS output (8). Note that the square of the t-statistic is the F-statistic, $(-7.99)^2 = 63.8$, based on 1 upper and 31 lower d.f.

▸ Differences in adjusted response means are the same regardless of the value of the covariate, x, since the slopes are assumed to be equal among groups. In Example 9.1, the estimated difference in adjusted response means at x_0 is:

$$(74.81 - 11.27x_0) - (64.59 - 11.27x_0) = 10.22 ,$$

regardless of what value x_0 takes. This is not the case if the slopes differ among groups.

If the assumption of equal slopes within each group is not valid, the ANCOVA methods described here cannot be used. One method of testing for equal slopes is to use an 'interaction' factor between GROUP and X in the SAS MODEL statement, e.g.,

```
MODEL Y = GROUP X GROUP*X;        .
```

A significant interaction effect (GROUP*X) implies that the differences among group levels change for different X values, i.e, different slopes. ANCOVA should not be used if a preliminary test results in significantly different slopes among groups.

▸ A 95% confidence interval for the adjusted mean response in Group i (i = 1, 2, ..., k) is given by:

$$(a_i + b\bar{x}) \pm t_{0.025,N-k-1} \cdot s \cdot \sqrt{\frac{1}{n_i} + \frac{(\bar{x}_i - \bar{x})^2}{S_{xx}}}$$

where, $s = \sqrt{MSE}$ *from the ANOVA table .*

For Example 9.1, a 95% confidence interval for the adjusted mean responses for each treatment group are as follows:

Fibralo Group:

$$(74.81 - 11.268 \cdot 6.8118) \pm$$

$$2.04 \cdot \sqrt{93.67} \cdot \sqrt{\frac{1}{16} + \frac{(7.0000 - 6.8118)^2}{48.175}} =$$

$$-1.95 \pm 4.96 \quad or, \quad [-6.91 \ to \ 3.01]$$

Gemfibrozil Group:

$$(64.59 - 11.268 \cdot 6.8118) \pm$$

$$2.04 \cdot \sqrt{93.67} \cdot \sqrt{\frac{1}{18} + \frac{(6.6444 - 6.8118)^2}{48.175}} =$$

$$-12.17 \pm 4.68 \quad or, \quad [-16.85 \ to \ -7.49]$$

Note that the confidence interval widths (4.96 and 4.68) can be easily computed as $t \cdot SEM$ where t is the critical t-value, 2.04, and SEM is the standard error of the LS-mean from the SAS output (9).

▸ A 95% confidence interval for the difference in adjusted mean responses between 2 groups, say Group *u* and Group *v*, is given by:

$$(a_u - a_v) \pm t_{0.025,N-k-1} \cdot s \cdot \sqrt{\frac{1}{n_u} + \frac{1}{n_v} + \frac{(\bar{x}_u - \bar{x}_v)^2}{S_{xx}}} \quad .$$

For Example 9.1, a 95% confidence interval for the difference in adjusted means between the *Fibralo* and *Gemfibrozil* groups is:

$$(74.81 - 64.59) \quad \pm$$

$$2.04 \cdot \sqrt{93.7} \cdot \sqrt{\frac{1}{16} + \frac{1}{18} + \frac{(7.0000 - 6.6444)^2}{48.175}} \quad =$$

$$10.22 \pm 6.86 \quad or, \quad [3.36 \ to \ 17.08]$$

▸ Note that the standard errors of the adjusted group means and mean differences are smallest when $\bar{x}_i = \bar{x}$ for all i (= 1, 2, ..., k). In this case, the standard error is the same as that of the unadjusted case (see Chapter 5).

▸ As shown in the output, the adjusted F-tests in SAS are found with the Type III sums-of-squares. The Type I results depend on the order in which the factors are specified in the MODEL statement (see Appendix D). When the TREATMENT effect is specified <u>before</u> the covariate in the GLM MODEL statement, the Type I sum-of-squares represents the unadjusted sum-of-squares for TREATMENT (ignoring the covariate). While this is the same sum-of-squares obtained with the *One-Way ANOVA*, the corresponding F-test is <u>not</u> the same F-test as for the unadjusted TREATMENT effect since the 'covariate-adjusted' MSE is used as a divisor.

▸ The ANCOVA methods described here combine simple linear regression analysis with the *One-Way ANOVA*. Analysis-of-covariance methodology can also be applied with the two-way and higher-order ANOVA layouts. Furthermore, as simple linear regression can be extended to multiple regression when there is more than one covariate, simple linear covariance analysis can be extended to include multiple covariates. Models involving numerous classification factors combined with multiple numeric covariates can be developed, and such complex models can easily be analyzed using SAS's GLM procedure.

CHAPTER 10
The WILCOXON SIGNED-RANK TEST

INTRODUCTION

The *Wilcoxon Signed-Rank Test* is a non-parametric analog of the *One-Sample t-Test* (Chapter 3). This test can be used to make inferences about a population mean or median, without requiring the assumption of normally distributed data. As its name implies, the *Wilcoxon Signed-Rank Test* is based on the ranks of the data.

One of the most common applications of the *Signed-Rank Test* in clinical trials is to compare responses between correlated or paired data, such as testing for significant pre- to poststudy changes of a non-normally distributed evaluation measurement. The layout is the same as that for the paired-difference t-test (Chapter 3).

SYNOPSIS

Given a sample, y_1, y_2, ..., y_n, of n non-zero differences or changes (zero's are ignored), let r_i represent the rank of $|y_i|$ (when ranked lowest to highest). Let $R^{(+)}$ represent the sum of the ranks associated with the positive values of the y_i's, and $R^{(-)}$ represent the sum of the ranks associated with the negative values of the y_i's. The test statistic is based on the smaller of $R^{(+)}$ and $R^{(-)}$. The hypothesis of 'no mean difference' is rejected if this statistic is larger than the critical value found from a special set of tables.

To avoid the requirement of special table values, we use an approximation to this test based on the t-distribution as follows.

Let

$$S = (R^{(+)} - R^{(-)})/2 \quad , \text{ and}$$

$$V = \{n(n+1)(2n+1)\}/24.$$

The approximate test can be summarized as follows:

null hypothesis:	H_0: $\theta = 0$
alt. hypothesis:	H_A: $\theta \neq 0$
test statistic:	$T = \dfrac{S \cdot \sqrt{n-1}}{\sqrt{n \cdot V - S^2}}$
decision rule:	reject H_0 if $|T| > t_{\alpha/2, n-1}$

θ represents the unknown population mean, median or other location parameter. When H_0 is true, T has an approximate Student-t distribution with n-1 degrees-of-freedom. Widely available t-tables can be used to determine the rejection region.

When there are tied data values, the averaged rank is assigned to the corresponding r_i values. A small adjustment to V for tied data is appropriate, as follows: suppose there are g groups of tied values. For the j-th such group, compute $c_j = m(m-1)(m+1)$, where m is the number of tied values for that group. The correction factor of $C = c_1 + c_2 + \ldots + c_g$ is used to adjust V as follows:

$$V = \{n(n+1)(2n+1) - C/2\} / 24.$$

EXAMPLE 10.1 -- "Rose Bengal Staining in KCS"

A study enrolling 24 patients diagnosed with keratitis sicca (KCS) was conducted to determine the effect of a new ocular wetting agent, 'Oker-Rinse', in improvement of the ocular dryness based on Rose Bengal staining scores. Patients were instructed to use Oker-Rinse in one eye (assigned at random) and Hypotears® as a control in the other eye 4-times per day for 3 weeks. Rose-Bengal staining scores were measured as a score of 0, 1, 2, 3 or 4 in each of 4 areas of the eye: cornea, limbus, lateral conjuntiva and medial conjunctiva. Higher scores represent a greater number of devitalized cells, a condition associated with KCS. The overall scores for each eye, shown below, were obtained by adding the scores over the 4 areas. Is there evidence of a difference between the 2 test preparations in overall Rose-Bengal staining scores?

Pat No.	Hypo-Tears®	Oker-Rinse	Pat No.	Hypo-Tears®	Oker-Rinse
1	15	8	13	8	10
2	10	3	14	10	2
3	6	7	15	11	4
4	5	13	16	13	7
5	10	2	17	6	1
6	15	12	18	6	11
7	7	14	19	9	3
8	5	8	20	5	5
9	8	13	21	10	2
10	12	3	22	9	8
11	4	9	23	11	5
12	13	3	24	8	8

SOLUTION ▬▬▬▬▬▬▬▬▬▬▬▬▬▬▬▬

Since each patient receives both treatments, we have a matched-pairs setup. The analysis is performed on the differences in Rose-Bengal scores between the treatment groups. The data may be plotted to reveal that the differences have a bimodal distribution (2 peaks), which is not consistent with an assumption of normality. Indeed, a formal test for normality (see SAS results later) indicates a significant departure from this assumption. Therefore, use of the paired-difference t-test should be passed up in favor of the *Wilcoxon Signed-Rank Test*.

We wish to test the hypothesis that θ, the average difference in Rose Bengal scores between the treatment groups, is zero. The differences in scores and ranks of their absolute values are shown below.

The average rankings for tied differences are used. For example, a difference of ± 1 occurs twice (Pat. 3 and 22) so the average of the ranks 1 and 2 ($= 1.5$) is used. Also note that the zero differences are omitted from the rankings leaving n = 22, not 24.

Pat No.	Differ-ence	Rank	Pat No.	Differ-ence	Rank
1	7	14.5	13	-2	3
2	7	14.5	14	8	18.5
3	-1	1.5	15	7	14.5
4	-8	18.5	16	6	11
5	8	18.5	17	5	7.5
6	3	4.5	18	-5	7.5
7	-7	14.5	19	6	11
8	-3	4.5	20	0	--
9	-5	7.5	21	8	18.5
10	9	21	22	1	1.5
11	-5	7.5	23	6	11
12	10	22	24	0	--

We compute:

$$R^{(+)} = (14.5 + 14.5 + 18.5 + 4.5 + 21 + 22 + 18.5 +$$
$$14.5 + 11 + 7.5 + 11 + 18.5 + 1.5 + 11)$$

$$= 188.5, \quad \text{and,}$$

$$R^{(-)} = (1.5 + 18.5 + 14.5 + 4.5 + 7.5 + 7.5 + 3 + 7.5)$$
$$= 64.5$$

so that,

$$S = (188.5 - 64.5)/2 = 62.0 .$$

To apply the correction factor for ties, we note 6 groups of ties with the frequencies (m's): 2, 2, 4, 3, 4 and 4, as summarized below. Thus, $c_1 = 2(1)(3) = 6$, $c_2 = 6$, $c_3 = 4(3)(5) = 60$, $c_4 = 3(2)(4) = 24$, $c_5 = 60$ and $c_6 = 60$, yielding C = 216.

Tie Group (i)	|Difference|	# ties (m)	$c_i =$ m(m-1)(m+1)
1	1	2	6
2	3	2	6
3	5	4	60
4	6	3	24
5	7	4	60
6	8	4	60
			C=216

Finally,

$$V = \{n(n+1)(2n+1) - C/2\} / 24$$

$$= \{22(23)(45) - 108\} / 24 = 944.25 .$$

The test is summarized as follows:

null hypothesis: $H_0: \theta = 0$
alt. hypothesis: $H_A: \theta \neq 0$

test statistic:

$$T = \frac{S \cdot \sqrt{n-1}}{\sqrt{n \cdot V - S^2}}$$

$$= \frac{62 \cdot \sqrt{21}}{\sqrt{(22 \cdot 944.25) - 62^2}} = 2.184$$

decision rule: reject H_0 if $|T| > t_{0.025,21} = 2.080$

conclusion: Since 2.184 > 2.080, reject H_0, and conclude that there is a significant difference in Rose Bengal scores between treatments.

SAS Analysis of Example 10.1

In the above test summary, the SAS function PROBT can be used to obtain the p-value associated with a t statistic of 2.184 based on 21 d.f, namely p = 0.0405.

The SAS code and output for executing this analysis is shown on the next page. The *Wilcoxon Signed-Rank Test* is performed in SAS using PROC UNIVARIATE. The NORMAL procedure option is used to provide a test for normality based on the *'Shapiro-Wilk Test'*. This test is rejected with a p-value of 0.0305 (1), indicating that the data cannot be assumed to have come from a normal distribution. This result makes the paired-difference *One-Sample t-Test* (Chapter 3) inappropriate for this analysis.

From the output, the Signed-Rank statistic is confirmed to be 62 (2) with a p-value of 0.0405 (3).

SAS uses the t-approximation to the *Wilcoxon Signed-Rank Test* if n is greater than 20. For $n \leq 20$, SAS computes the exact probability.

```
* SAS Code for Example 10.1 ;

DATA KCS;
INPUT PAT HYPOTEAR OKERINSE @@;
  DIFF = HYPOTEAR - OKERINSE;
CARDS;
  1 15  8     2 10  3      3  6  7      4  5 13
  5 10  2     6 15 12      7  7 14      8  5  8
  9  8 13    10 12  3     11  4  9     12 13  3
 13  8 10    14 10  2     15 11  4     16 13  7
 17  6  1    18  6 11     19  9  3     20  5  5
 21 10  2    22  9  8     23 11  5     24  8  8
;
RUN;

PROC UNIVARIATE NORMAL DATA = KCS; VAR DIFF;
TITLE1 'The Wilcoxon-Signed-Rank Test';
TITLE2 'EXAMPLE 10.1:  Rose Bengal Staining in KCS';
RUN;
```

```
* SAS Output for Example 10.1


                    The Wilcoxon-Signed-Rank Test
              Example 10.1:  Rose Bengal Staining in KCS

                        Univariate Procedure

    Variable=DIFF
                              Moments
                  N            24   Sum Wgts       24
                  Mean    2.291667   Sum           55
                  Std Dev 5.668212   Variance  32.12862
                  Skewness -0.40114  Kurtosis  -1.28593
                  USS          865   CSS       738.9583
                  CV       247.3401  Std Mean  1.157019
                  T:Mean=0 1.980665  Pr>|T|      0.0597
                  Num ^= 0      22   Num > 0        14
                  M(Sign)       3    Pr>=|M|     0.2863
              (2) Sgn Rank      62   Pr>=|S|     0.0405  (3)
                  W:Normal 0.907533  Pr<W        0.0305  (1)


                        Quantiles(Def=5)
                  100% Max      10     99%          10
                   75% Q3        7     95%           9
                   50% Med       4     90%           8
                   25% Q1      -2.5    10%          -5
                    0% Min      -8      5%          -7
                                        1%          -8


                  Range         18
                  Q3-Q1        9.5
                  Mode          -5


                           Extremes
                  Lowest    Obs    Highest    Obs
                    -8(      4)       8(       5)
                    -7(      7)       8(      14)
                    -5(     18)       8(      21)
                    -5(     11)       9(      10)
                    -5(      9)      10(      12)
```

DETAILS & NOTES

▸ The *Wilcoxon Signed-Rank Test* is considered a non-parametric test because it makes no assumptions regarding the distribution of the population from which the data are collected. This appears to be a tremendous advantage over the *t-test*, so why not use the *Signed-Rank Test* in all situations?

First, the *t-test* has been shown to be a more powerful test in detecting true differences when the data *are* normally distributed. Since the normal distribution occurs quite often in nature, the *t-test* is the method of choice for a wide range of applications. Secondly, analysts often feel more comfortable reporting a *t-test* whenever it is appropriate, especially to a non-statistician, since many clinical research professionals have become familiar with the terminology. One reason the *t-test* has enjoyed popular usage is its robustness under deviations to the underlying assumptions. Finally, the *Wilcoxon Signed-Rank Test* <u>does</u> require the assumption of a symmetrical underlying distribution. When the data are highly skewed or otherwise non-symmetrical, an alternative to the *Signed-Rank Test*, such as the *Sign Test* (discussed in Chapter 12), can be used.

▸ Let $R_i = r_i$ if $y_i > 0$ and $R_i = -r_i$ if $y_i < 0$. It can be shown that the T statistic discussed is equivalent to performing a *One-Sample t-Test* (Chapter 3) on the R_i's, that is the ranked data adjusted by the appropriate sign. This procedure is sometimes referred to as performing a *t-test* on the 'rank-transformed' data.

▸ An alternative approximation to the *Signed-Rank Test* for large samples is the Z-test. The test statistic is taken to be $S' = $ smaller of $\{R^{(+)}, R^{(-)}\}$. S' has mean and variance:

$$\mu_{S'} = \frac{n \cdot (n+1)}{4} \qquad and,$$

$$\sigma^2_{S'} = \frac{n \cdot (n+1) \cdot (2n+1)}{24} \qquad .$$

Under H_0,

$$Z = \frac{S' - \mu_{S'}}{\sigma_{S'}}$$

has an approximate normal distribution with mean 0 and variance 1. The Z test-statistic is compared with the tabled value of $Z_{\alpha/2}$ for a 2-tailed test ($=1.96$ for $\alpha = 0.05$).

For the data of Example 10.1, we compute:

$$S' = 64.5$$

$$\mu_{S'} = \frac{22 \cdot 23}{4} = 126.5 \quad ,$$

$$\sigma_{S'} = \sqrt{\frac{22 \cdot 23 \cdot 45}{24}} = 30.8$$

so that

$$Z = (64.5 - 126.5) / 30.8 = -2.013.$$

At p = 0.05, we reject H_0 since 2.013 > 1.96. The SAS function PROBNORM can be used to obtain the actual p-value of 0.044.

▸ The *One-Sample t-Test* is often used with larger samples, regardless of the distribution of the data. This is because the *Central Limit Theorem* states that the sample mean, $\bar{y}$, is normally distributed for large n, no matter what distribution the underlying data have. Usually, for n > 30, we can safely use the *One-Sample t-Test* of Chapter 3, ignoring distributional assumptions, providing the distribution is symmetric. The *Wilcoxon Signed-Rank Test* and the *t-Test* become closer as n gets larger. For non-symmetrical distributions, the mean, median and other measures of central tendency may have widely disparate values. The *t-test* should be used only if the mean is the appropriate measure of central tendency for the population being studied.

▸ The procedure shown here is for a two-tailed test. For a 1-tailed test, the same procedures shown in Chapter 3 for the *One-Sample t-Test* can be used. If SAS is used, the p-value associated with the *Signed-Rank Test* can be halved for an approximate one-tailed test.

CHAPTER 11

The WILCOXON RANK-SUM TEST

INTRODUCTION

The *Wilcoxon Rank-Sum Test* is a non-parametric analog of the *Two-Sample t-Test* (Chapter 4). This test, based on ranks of the data, can be used to compare location parameters, such as the mean or median, between two independent populations without the assumption of normally distributed data.

Although the *Wilcoxon Rank-Sum Test* was developed for use with continuous numeric data, the test is also applied to the analysis of ordered categorical data. In clinical data analysis, this test is often useful, for example, for comparing patient global assessments or severity ratings between two treatment groups.

SYNOPSIS

The data are collected as 2 independent samples of size n_1 and n_2, denoted by y_{11}, y_{12}, ..., y_{1n_1} and y_{21}, y_{22}, ..., y_{2n_2}. The data are ranked, from lowest to highest, over the combined samples, and the test statistic is based on the sum of ranks for the first group.

Let r_{1j} = rank of y_{1j} ($j = 1, 2, ..., n_1$) and r_{2j} = rank of y_{2j} ($j = 1, 2, ..., n_2$), and compute:

$$R_1 = \sum_{j=1}^{n_1} r_{1j} \quad\quad and \quad\quad R_2 = \sum_{j=1}^{n_2} r_{2j} \quad .$$

The hypothesis of equal means would be supported by similar average ranks between the two groups, i.e., if R_1/n_1 is close to R_2/n_2. R_1 is compared to a critical value obtained from a special set of tables based on Wilcoxon rank-sum exact probabilities to determine the appropriate rejection region. Such tables can be found in many intermediate statistical books or non-parametric statistical references.

Lack of availability of these tables may somewhat limit the usefulness of this test. However, the requirement for special tables can often be circumvented by using a normal approximation for larger samples. It has been shown that the normal approximation for the *Rank-Sum Test*, discussed below, is excellent for samples as small as 8 per group.

With $N = n_1 + n_2$, the sum of the ranks $(1+2+...+N)$ can be expressed as $N(N+1)/2$. When the hypothesis of equality is true (H_0), we would expect the proportion of this sum from Sample 1 to be about n_1/N and the proportion from Sample 2 to be about n_2/N. That is, the expected value of R_1 under H_0 is

$$\mu_{R_1} = \left(\frac{n_1}{N}\right) \cdot \left(\frac{N(N+1)}{2}\right) = \frac{n_1 \cdot (N+1)}{2} \quad .$$

Additionally, the variance of R_1 can be computed as

$$\sigma^2_{R_1} = \frac{n_1 \cdot n_2}{12}(N+1) \quad .$$

If there are tied data values, the average rank is assigned to the corresponding r_{ij} values. Suppose there are g groups of tied values. For the k-th such group, compute $c_k = m(m^2-1)$, where m is the number of tied values for that group. We can make a small adjustment to the variance using a correction factor $C = c_1 + c_2 + ... + c_g$, as follows:

$$\sigma^2_{R_1} = \frac{n_1 \cdot n_2}{12}\left(N+1 - \frac{C}{N(N-1)}\right) \quad .$$

The test statistic, using a 0.5 continuity correction, is based on an approximate normal distribution, summarized as follows:

---

null hypothesis: H_0: $\theta_1 = \theta_2$
alt. hypothesis: H_A: $\theta_1 \neq \theta_2$

test statistic: $Z = \dfrac{|R_1 - \mu_{R_1}| - 0.5}{\sigma_{R_1}}$

decision rule: reject H_0 if $|Z| > Z_{\alpha/2}$

---

where θ_1 and θ_2 represent the mean, median or other location parameters for the two populations.

EXAMPLE 11.1 -- "Global Evaluations of *Seroxatene* in Back Pain"

In previous studies of a new anti-depressant, Seroxatene, researchers noticed that patients with low back pain experienced a decrease in radicular pain after 6-8 weeks of daily treatment. A new study was conducted in 28 patients to determine whether this phenomenon is a drug-related response or coincidental. Patients with MRI-confirmed disk herniation and symptomatic leg pain were enrolled and randomly assigned to receive Seroxatene or placebo for 8 weeks. At the end of the study, patients were asked to provide a global rating of their pain, relative to baseline, on a coded improvement scale as follows:

-------- Deterioration ---------				--------- Improvement --------		
Marked	Mod-erate	Slight	No Change	Slight	Mod-erate	Marked
-3	-2	-1	0	+1	+2	+3

Data are shown in the following table. Is there evidence that Seroxatene *has any effect on radicular back pain?*

| ------ Seroxotene Group ------- | | | | -------- Placebo Group --------- | | | |
Pat. No.	Score	Pat. No.	Score	Pat. No.	Score	Pat. No.	Score
2	0	16	-1	1	3	15	0
3	2	17	2	4	-1	18	-1
5	3	20	-3	7	2	19	-3
6	3	21	3	9	3	23	-2
8	-2	22	3	11	-2	25	1
10	1	24	0	13	1	28	0
12	3	26	2				
14	3	27	-1				

SOLUTION

With a situation involving a two-sample comparison of means, we might first consider the *Two-Sample t-Test* or the *Wilcoxon Rank-Sum Test*. Since the data are ordered categorical responses, the assumption of normality is dubious, so we will apply the *Rank-Sum Test*, as shown below.

Tied values are identified as follows:

Response (y)	No. of ties (m)	Ranks	Average Rank	$c_k = m(m^2-1)$
-3	2	1,2	1.5	6
-2	3	3,4,5	4	24
-1	4	6,7,8,9	7.5	60
0	4	10,11,12,13	11.5	60
+1	3	14,15,16	15	24
+2	4	17,18,19,20	18.5	60
+3	8	21,22,23,24, 25,26,27,28	24.5	504

$$C = 738$$

With $n_1 = 16$, $n_2 = 12$ and $N = 28$, the ranked values (r's) of the responses (y's) are as follows:

----- Seroxotene Group -----				------- Placebo Group --------			
Pat. No.	Score Rank	Pat. No.	Score Rank	Pat. No.	Score Rank	Pat. No.	Score Rank
2	11.5	16	7.5	1	24.5	15	11.5
3	18.5	17	18.5	4	7.5	18	7.5
5	24.5	20	1.5	7	18.5	19	1.5
6	24.5	21	24.5	9	24.5	23	4
8	4	22	24.5	11	4	25	15
10	15	24	11.5	13	15	28	11.5
12	24.5	26	18.5				
14	24.5	27	7.5				

We compute:

$$R_1 = 11.5 + 18.5 + 24.5 + ... + 7.5 = 261, \qquad \text{and}$$

$$R_2 = 24.5 + 7.5 + 18.5 + ... + 11.5 = 145.$$

As a check, we note that $R_1 + R_2 = N(N+1)/2 = 406$. We further compute:

$$\mu_{R_1} = \frac{16 \cdot (29)}{2} = 232 \qquad and,$$

$$\sigma^2_{R_1} = \frac{(16)(12)}{12} \cdot \left(29 - \frac{738}{(28)(27)}\right) = 448.38 \qquad .$$

The test summary, based on a normal approximation at a significance level of $\alpha = 0.05$, becomes:

null hypothesis: H_0: $\theta_1 = \theta_2$
alt. hypothesis: H_A: $\theta_1 \neq \theta_2$

test statistic: $$Z = \frac{|R_1 - \mu_{R_1}| - 0.5}{\sigma_{R_1}}$$

$$= \frac{(261 - 232) - 0.5}{\sqrt{448.38}} = 1.346$$

decision rule: reject H_0 if $|Z| > 1.96$

conclusion: Since 1.346 is not > 1.96, we do not reject H_0, concluding that there is insufficient evidence of a difference between *Seroxatene* and placebo in global back pain evaluations.

SAS Analysis of Example 11.1

Interpolation of Appendix A.1 results in a 2-tailed p-value of 0.178 for the Z-statistic of 1.346. (The p-value can also be found from the SAS function PROBNORM).

The *Wilcoxon Rank-Sum Test* is performed in SAS using the NPAR1WAY procedure with the option WILCOXON, as shown in the SAS code which follows. The sum of ranks for either group can be used to compute the test statistic. Our manual calculations use $R_1 = 261$, while SAS uses $R_2 = 145$. When the smaller is used, a negative Z-value will result (1). In either case, for a 2-tailed test, $|Z| = 1.346$ with a p-value of 0.178 (2).

The output of this procedure also gives the results of the analysis using the *Kruskal-Wallis* Chi-square approximation (3), which is discussed in the next chapter.

```
* SAS Code for Example 11.1 ;

DATA RNKSM;
INPUT TRT $ PAT SCORE @@;
CARDS;
SER  2   0    SER  3   2    SER  5   3
SER  6   3    SER  8  -2    SER 10   1
SER 12   3    SER 14   3    SER 16  -1
SER 17   2    SER 20  -3    SER 21   3
SER 22   3    SER 24   0    SER 26   2
SER 27  -1    PBO  1   3    PBO  4  -1
PBO  7   2    PBO  9   3    PBO 11  -2
PBO 13   1    PBO 15   0    PBO 18  -1
PBO 19  -3    PBO 23  -2    PBO 25   1
PBO 28   0
; RUN;

PROC NPAR1WAY WILCOXON DATA = RNKSM;
CLASS TRT; VAR SCORE;
TITLE1 'The Wilcoxon Rank-Sum Test';
TITLE2 'Example 11.1:  Seroxatene in Back Pain';
RUN;
```

*SAS Output for Example 11.1

The Wilcoxon Rank-Sum Test
Example 11.1: Seroxatene in Back Pain

N P A R 1 W A Y   P R O C E D U R E
Wilcoxon Scores (Rank Sums) for Variable SCORE
Classified by Variable TRT

TRT	N	Sum of Scores	Expected Under H0	Std Dev Under H0	Mean Score
SER	16	261.0	232.0	21.1750077	16.3125000
PBO	12	145.0	174.0	21.1750077	12.0833333

Average Scores were used for Ties
Wilcoxon 2-Sample Test (Normal Approximation)
(with Continuity Correction of .5)

(1)   S= 145.000   Z= -1.34593   Prob > |Z| =   0.1783 (2)

T-Test approx. Significance =   0.1895

Kruskal-Wallis Test (Chi-Square Approximation)
(3)   CHISQ= 1.8756   DF= 1   Prob > CHISQ=   0.1708

DETAILS & NOTES

▸ The term 'mean' is used loosely in this chapter referring to the appropriate location parameter. Since the mean is not always the best measure of a distribution's center, the location parameter may refer to some other measure such as one of the measures of central tendency described in Chapter 1.

For symmetric distributions, the population mean and median are the same. For skewed distributions with long tails to the right, the median is usually smaller than the mean, and considered a better measure of the distributional 'center' or location. The geometric mean is also smaller than the arithmetic mean and is often used as a location parameter for exponentially distributed data. The *Wilcoxon Rank-Sum Test* tests for a location or positional shift in distributions without the need to identify the best measure of central tendency. Thus, the parameter θ is simply a symbol generically denoting a distribution's location.

▸ Although we need make no assumptions regarding the actual distributions of the data, the *Wilcoxon Rank-Sum Test* does assume the two population distributions have the same shape and differ only by a possible shift in location. Thus, we assume the same dispersion, which is analogous to the assumption of variance homogeneity required of the *Two-Sample t-Test*. Unlike the *Wilcoxon Signed-Rank Test*, we need not assume the data come from a symmetric distribution.

▸ The test statistic, R_1, has a symmetric distribution about its mean, $n_1(N+1)/2$. Because of this symmetry, the 1-tailed p-value is easily obtained by halving the two-tailed p-value.

▸ The *Mann-Whitney U-test* is another non-parametric test for comparing location parameters based on 2 independent samples. Mathematically, it can be shown that the *Mann-Whitney test* is equivalent to the *Wilcoxon Rank-Sum Test*.

▸ Note that the approximate test statistic, Z, can be computed from R_2 instead of R_1. When using R_2, the mean and standard deviation (μ_R, σ_R) are computed by reversing n_1 and n_2 in the formulas given.

▸ Another approximation to the *Wilcoxon Rank-Sum Test* is the use of the *Two-Sample t-Test* on the ranked data. In SAS, the RANK procedure can first be used to rank the data, followed by PROC TTEST. A comparison of this procedure with the standard *Wilcoxon Rank-Sum Test* is discussed by Conover and Iman [1981].

▸ The assumption of normality can be tested using the SAS procedure NPAR1WAY. If this is rejected, the *Wilcoxon Rank-Sum Test* is preferrable to the *Two-Sample t-Test*.

CHAPTER 12
The KRUSKAL-WALLIS TEST

INTRODUCTION

The *Kruskal-Wallis Test* is a non-parametric analogue of *One-Way ANOVA* (Chapter 5). This method is used to compare population location parameters (mean, median, etc.) among 2 or more groups based on independent samples. Unlike ANOVA, the assumption of normally distributed responses is not necessary. The *Kruskal-Wallis Test* is an extension of the *Wilcoxon Rank-Sum Test* (Chapter 11) to more than two groups, just as *One-Way ANOVA* is an extension of the *Two Sample t-Test*.

The *Kruskal-Wallis Test* is based on the ranks of the data. This test is often useful in clinical trials for comparing responses among 3 or more dose groups or treatment groups using samples of non-normally distributed response data.

SYNOPSIS

The data are collected as k (≥ 2) independent samples of size n_1, n_2, ... n_k, as follows:

Group 1	Group 2	...	Group k
y_{11}	y_{21}		y_{k1}
y_{12}	y_{22}		y_{k2}
...	...		...
y_{1n_1}	y_{2n_2}		y_{kn_k}

We wish to test the hypothesis of equal mean responses among groups (H_0). The data are ranked, from lowest to highest, over the combined samples, and the test statistic is a function of the ranks and sample sizes.

Letting r_{ij} = rank of y_{ij} (j = 1, 2, ..., n_i), we compute:

$$R_i = \sum_{j=1}^{n_i} r_{ij} \quad \textit{for } i = 1, 2, ..., k \quad .$$

The average rank of all N = n_1 + n_2 + ... + n_k observations is $\bar{R}$ = (N+1)/2. Therefore, when the null hypothesis is true, the average rank for each group, $\bar{R}_i$ = (R_i/n_i), should be close to this value, and the sum-of-squared deviations,

$$\sum_{i=1}^{k} n_i(\bar{R}_i - \bar{R})^2$$

should be small.

This form is recognizable as the familiar 'between-group' sum-of-squares used in the analysis-of-variance (Chapters 5, 6), after replacing the observed values with their ranks. The *Kruskal-Wallis Test* statistic is a function of this sum-of-squares, which simplifies algebraically to the quantity:

$$h^* = \frac{12}{N(N+1)} \cdot \left[\sum_{i=1}^{k} \frac{R_i^2}{n_i} \right] - 3(N+1) \quad .$$

When H_0 is true, h* has an approximate *chi-square* distribution with k-1 degrees-of-freedom.

As with other ranking procedures, when ties exist, the average rank of the tied values is assigned to the corresponding r_{ij} values. Suppose there are g categories of tied values. For the j-th such category, compute c_j = $m(m^2-1)$, where m is the number of tied values for that category. A small adjustment can be made to the test statistic using the correction factor C = c_1 + c_2 + ... + c_g. With θ representing the population location parameter, the test is summarized as follows:

null hypothesis: H_0: $\theta_1 = \theta_2 = \ldots = \theta_k$

alt. hypothesis: H_A: $\theta_i \neq \theta_j$ for at least one pair (i,j)

test statistic: $h = \dfrac{h^*}{\left[1 - \dfrac{C}{N(N^2-1)}\right]}$

decision rule: *reject H_0 if $h > \chi^2_{(k-1)}(\alpha)$*

$\chi^2_{k-1}(\alpha)$ represents the critical chi-square value based on k-1 degrees-of-freedom and a significance level of α. Critical chi-square values can be obtained from tables of the chi-square distribution, or with the PROBCHI function in SAS.

EXAMPLE 12.1 -- "Psoriasis Evaluation in 3 Groups"

A study comparing a low-dose (0.1%) and a high dose (0.2%) of a new non-steroidal anti-psoriasis medication was conducted using a parallel design, including a placebo group as control. Thirty-two patients were studied for 4 weeks of daily treatment. The primary efficacy response measure was the degree of psoriatic lesion reduction at study termination, rated on an ordinal scale as follows:

Coded Response Category	Reduction in Lesion Size	Coded Response Category	Reduction in Lesion Size
1	< 0%	5	26-50%
2	0%	6	51-75%
3	1-10%	7	76-99%
4	11-25%	8	100%

Based on the data shown in the following data table, is there any difference in response among the 3 groups?

0.1% Solution		0.2% Solution		Placebo	
Pat No.	Category Code	Pat No.	Category Code	Pat No.	Category Code
1	5	3	5	2	5
6	4	5	8	4	3
9	1	7	2	8	7
12	7	10	8	11	1
15	4	14	7	13	2
19	3	18	4	16	4
20	6	22	5	17	2
23	7	26	4	21	1
27	8	28	6	24	4
32	7	31	4	25	5
				29	4
				30	5

SOLUTION

This data set has an ordinal scale response with unequally spaced intervals. If we use *One-Way ANOVA*, the results may depend on the coding scheme used. Since the codes of 1-8 are arbitrary, the *Kruskal-Wallis Test* is appropriate since the results do not depend on the magnitude of the coded values, only their ranks.

We can summarize the data in a frequency table format which includes the ranks as follows:

Response Category	Code	---- Frequencies ---- 0.1%	0.2%	Pbo	Ranks	Ave. Rank	Total Frequency (m)	$c = m(m^2-1)$
<0%	1	1	0	2	1-3	2	3	24
0%	2	0	1	2	4-6	5	3	24
1-10%	3	1	0	1	7-8	7.5	2	6
11-25%	4	2	3	3	9-16	12.5	8	504
26-50%	5	1	2	3	17-22	19.5	6	210
51-75%	6	1	1	0	23-24	23.5	2	6
76-99%	7	3	1	1	25-29	27	5	120
100%	8	1	2	0	30-32	31	3	24
		10	10	12			32	C = 918

The table of ranks, along with the rank sums for each group, are as follows:

0.1% Solution		0.2% Solution		Placebo	
Pat No.	Category Rank	Pat No.	Category Rank	Pat No.	Category Rank
1	19.5	3	19.5	2	19.5
6	12.5	5	31	4	7.5
9	2	7	5	8	27
12	27	10	31	11	2
15	12.5	14	27	13	5
19	7.5	18	12.5	16	12.5
20	23.5	22	19.5	17	5
23	27	26	12.5	21	2
27	31	28	23.5	24	12.5
32	27	31	12.5	25	19.5
				29	12.5
				30	19.5
$R_1 = 189.5$ $(n_1 = 10)$		$R_2 = 194.0$ $(n_2 = 10)$		$R_3 = 144.5$ $(n_3 = 12)$	

We may now compute the test statistic as

$$h^* = \frac{12}{32(33)} \cdot \left[\frac{189.5^2}{10} + \frac{194.0^2}{10} + \frac{144.5^2}{12} \right] - 3(33)$$

$$= 4.348 \quad ,$$

and the test is summarized as follows:

null hypothesis: H_0: $\theta_1 = \theta_2 = \theta_3$

alt. hypothesis: H_A: not H_0

test statistic: $$h = \frac{4.348}{\left[1 - \dfrac{918}{32\,(32^2 - 1)}\right]}$$

$$= \frac{4.348}{0.972} = 4.473 \qquad .$$

decision rule: *reject H_0 if $h > \chi^2_2(0.05)$*

$$= 5.991$$

conclusion: Since 4.473 is not > 5.991, there is insufficient evidence to reject H_0, and we conclude that the data fail to reveal a statistical difference in psoriatic lesion reduction among the groups.

SAS Analysis of Example 12.1

In the above test summary, the SAS function PROBCHI can be used to obtain the p-value associated with the test statistic of 4.473 based on 2 d.f., namely p = 0.107.

The *Kruskal-Wallis Test* can be performed in SAS using the NPAR1WAY procedure with the option WILCOXON, as shown in the SAS code which follows. The output provides the rank sums for each group (1) and the chi-square statistic (2), which corroborate the manual calculations demonstrated. The p-value (3) is also printed out by SAS.

```
* SAS Code for Example 12.1 ;

DATA PSOR;
INPUT DOSE $ PAT SCORE @@;
CARDS;
0.1  1   5    0.1  6   4    0.1  9  '1    0.1 12   7
0.1 15   4    0.1 19   3    0.1 20   6    0.1 23   7
0.1 27   8    0.1 32   7    0.2  3   5    0.2  5   8
0.2  7   2    0.2 10   8    0.2 14   7    0.2 18   4
0.2 22   5    0.2 26   4    0.2 28   6    0.2 31   4
PBO  2   5    PBO  4   3    PBO  8   7    PBO 11   1
PBO 13   2    PBO 16   4    PBO 17   2    PBO 21   1
PBO 24   4    PBO 25   5    PBO 29   4    PBO 30   5
;
RUN;

PROC NPAR1WAY WILCOXON DATA = PSOR;
CLASS DOSE; VAR SCORE;
TITLE1 'The Kruskal-Wallis Test';
TITLE2 'Example 12.1:  Psoriasis Evaluation in 3
        Groups';
RUN;

PROC RANK DATA = PSOR OUT = RNK;
VAR SCORE; RANKS RNKSCORE;
RUN;

PROC GLM DATA = RNK; CLASSES DOSE;
MODEL RNKSCORE = DOSE / SS3;
RUN;
```

```
*   SAS Output for Example 12.1


                 The Kruskal-Wallis Test
         Example 12.1:  Psoriasis Evaluation in 3 Groups


                 N P A R 1 W A Y   P R O C E D U R E
            Wilcoxon Scores (Rank Sums) for Variable SCORE
                    Classified by Variable DOSE

                        Sum of    Expected      Std Dev       Mean
   DOSE        N        Scores    Under HO      Under HO      Score
                          (1)
   0.1        10      189.500000    165.0      24.2494180   18.9500000
   0.2        10      194.000000    165.0      24.2494180   19.4000000
   PBO        12      144.500000    198.0      25.3276911   12.0416667
                    Average Scores were used for Ties


          Kruskal-Wallis Test (Chi-Square Approximation)
             CHISQ= 4.4737   DF= 2   Prob > CHISQ=    0.1068
                  (2)                                 (3)
```

```
*  SAS Output for Example 12.1 - continued


                        The Kruskal-Wallis Test
             Example 12.1:  Psoriasis Evaluation in 3 Groups


                      General Linear Models Procedure
                         Class Level Information

                      Class     Levels     Values
                      DOSE        3        0.1 0.2 PBO
                 Number of observations in data set = 32

   Dependent Variable: RNKSCORE    RANK FOR VARIABLE SCORE
                                 Sum of          Mean
   Source              DF        Squares         Square    F Value    Pr > F

   Model                2       382.64583      191.32292     2.45     0.1044
   Error               29      2268.85417       78.23635
   Corrected Total     31      2651.50000


               R-Square          C.V.         Root MSE        RNKSCORE Mean

               0.144313        53.60686        8.8451            16.500


   Source              DF     Type III SS   Mean Square   F Value    Pr > F

   DOSE                 2       382.64583    191.32292      2.45      0.1044
                                                                        (4)
```

DETAILS & NOTES

▸ When k=2, the *Kruskal-Wallis* chi-square value has 1 d.f. This test is identical to the normal approximation used for the *Wilcoxon Rank-Sum Test* (Chapter 11). As noted in previous sections, a chi-square with 1 d.f. can be represented by the square of a standardized normal random variable. In the case of k=2, the h-statistic is the square of the *Wilcoxon Rank-Sum Z-test* (without the continuity correction).

▸ The effect of adjusting for tied ranks is to slightly increase the value of the test statistic, h. Therefore, omission of this adjustment results in a more conservative test.

▸ For small n_i's (< 5), the chi-square approximation may not be appropriate. Special tables for the exact distribution of h are available in many non-parametric statistics books. Such tables can be used to obtain the appropriate rejection region for small samples.

▸ Another approximate test based on the ranks is use of *One-Way ANOVA* methods on the ranked data. This approach is often used instead of the *Kruskal-Wallis Test*, as similar results can be expected. The SAS output for Example 12.1 shows the ANOVA results using the ranked data, resulting in a p-value (4) of 0.104 (compared with 0.107 for the chi-square approach).

▸ When the *Kruskal-Wallis Test* is significant, pairwise comparisons can be carried out with the *Wilcoxon Rank-Sum Test* for each pair of groups. However, the problem of overall error rate alteration must be considered for larger values of k. Techniques for multiple comparisons adjusted to an experiment-wise error rate are presented in a number of non-parametric statistics books (e.g., [Hollander & Wolfe, 1973]).

▸ When the distribution of the response data are unknown and cannot be assumed to be normal, the median (rather than the mean) is frequently used as a measure of location or central tendency. The median is computed as the middle value (for an odd number of observations) or the average of the 2 middle values (for an even number of observations). Approximate 95% confidence intervals for the median can be constructed using non-parametric methods developed by Hodges & Lehmann [Hollander & Wolfe, 1973].

▸ Using *ANOVA* methods based on the rank-transformed data is a common approach to analyzing data when the parametric assumptions may not be fulfilled. This method can also be used for a 2-way layout by first ranking the observations from lowest to highest across all treatment groups within each block, then using the usual *Two-Way ANOVA* methods (Chapter 6) on these ranks to test for significant treatment effects. Such a technique is often substituted for *Friedman's Test*, which is the non-parametric analog of the *Two-Way ANOVA*. Other types of layouts can be analyzed using similar approaches [Conover & Iman, 1981].

CHAPTER 13
The BINOMIAL TEST

INTRODUCTION

The *Binomial Test* is used to make inferences about a proportion or response rate based on a series of independent observations, each resulting in one of two possible mutually exclusive outcomes. The outcomes may be response to treatment or no response, cure or no cure, survival or death, or in general, *event* or *non-event*. These observations are 'binomial' outcomes if the chance of observing the *event* of interest is the same for each observation.

In clinical trials, a common use of the *Binomial Test* is in estimating a response rate, p, using the number of patients (X) who respond to an investigative treatment out of a total of n studied. Special cases of the *Binomial Test* include two commonly used tests in clinical data analysis, *McNemar's Test* (Chapter 15) and the *Sign Test* (discussed later in this chapter).

SYNOPSIS

The experiment consists of observing n independent observations, each with one of two possible outcomes: *event* or *non-event*. For each observation, the probability of the *event* is denoted by p ($0 < p < 1$).

The total number of *events* in n observations, X, follows the binomial probability distribution (Chapter 1). Intuitively, the sample proportion, X/n, would be a good estimate of the unknown population proportion, p. Statistically, it is the best estimate.

The general formula for a binomial probability is:

$$Pr(X=x) = \frac{n!}{x!(n-x)!} \cdot p^x(1-p)^{n-x}$$

where x can take integer values 0, 1, 2, ..., n. The symbol '!' is read 'factorial' and indicates multiplication by successively smaller integer values down to 1. Thus,

$$a! = (a)(a-1)(a-2) \ldots (3)(2)(1).$$

(For example, 5! = 5 x 4 x 3 x 2 x 1 = 120).

We wish to determine whether the population proportion, p, differs from a hypothesized value, p_0. If the unknown proportion, p, equals p_0, then the estimated proportion, X/n, should be close to p_0, i.e., X should be close to $n \times p_0$. When p differs from p_0, X may be much larger or smaller than $n \times p_0$. Therefore, we reject the null hypothesis if X is 'too large' or 'too small'.

The test summary is:

null hypothesis:	H_0: $p = p_0$
alt. hypothesis:	H_A: $p \neq p_0$
test statistic:	X = the number of *events* in n observations
decision rule:	reject H_0 if $X \leq X_L$ or $X \geq X_U$, where X_L and X_U are chosen to satisfy $Pr\{X_L < X < X_U\} \geq 1-\alpha$

Tables of binomial probabilities found in most introductory statistical texts, or the SAS function PROBBNML can be used to determine X_L and X_U. This method is demonstrated in Example 13.1. Another option, using a normal approximation, is discussed following this example.

EXAMPLE 13.1 -- "Genital Wart Cure Rate"

A company markets a therapeutic product for genital warts with a known cure rate of 40% in the general population. In a study of 25 patients with genital warts treated with this product, patients were also given high doses of vitamin C. As shown below, 14 patients were cured. Is this consistent with the cure rate in the general population?

Pat. No.	Cured?	Pat. No.	Cured?	Pat. No.	Cured?	Pat. No.	Cured?
1	YES	8	YES	15	YES	22	YES
2	NO	9	NO	16	NO	23	NO
3	YES	10	NO	17	NO	24	YES
4	NO	11	YES	18	YES	25	YES
5	YES	12	NO	19	YES		
6	YES	13	YES	20	NO		
7	NO	14	NO	21	YES		

SOLUTION

We let p represent the probability of a cure in any randomly selected patient with genital warts and treated concomitantly with the company's product plus Vitamin C. We want to know if this unknown rate differs from the established rate of $p_0 = 0.4$. Thus,

null hypothesis: H_0: $p = 0.4$

alt. hypothesis: H_A: $p \neq 0.4$

test statistic: $X = 14$ (the number cured out of the $n=25$ patients treated)

decision rule: reject H_0 if $X \leq 4$ or $X \geq 15$

conclusion: Since 14 does not lie in the rejection region, we do not reject the null hypothesis and conclude that there is insufficient evidence from this study to indicate that concomitant Vitamin C treatment has an effect on the product's cure rate.

With a nominal significance level of $\alpha = 0.05$, the limits of the rejection region, 4 and 15, are found from a table of binomial probabilities, satisfying $\Pr\{X \leq 4\} + \Pr\{X \geq 15\} \leq 0.05$. The actual significance level is 0.044.

NORMAL APPROXIMATION

A binomial response, X, can often be approximated by a normal distribution with mean $n \cdot p$ and variance $n \cdot p \cdot (1-p)$. The approximation improves as n gets larger or as p gets closer to 0.5. Based on this statistical principle, another way to establish the rejection region for $\alpha = 0.05$ and large n is by computing:

$$X_L = n \cdot p_0 - 1.96[n \cdot p_0 \cdot (1-p_0)]^{\frac{1}{2}} \quad , \quad \text{and}$$

$$X_U = n \cdot p_0 + 1.96[n \cdot p_0 \cdot (1-p_0)]^{\frac{1}{2}}.$$

Applying these formulas to Example 13.1, we obtain

$$X_L = 25(0.4) - 1.96[25(0.4)(0.6)]^{\frac{1}{2}} = 5.2 \quad , \quad \text{and}$$

$$X_U = 25(0.4) + 1.96[25(0.4)(0.6)]^{\frac{1}{2}} = 14.8.$$

Since X can only take integer values, the rejection region becomes $X \leq 5$ and $X \geq 15$. Because of the small sample size, this approximation produces a slightly larger lower rejection region yielding an actual significance level of 0.064 (based on exact binomial probabilities).

A more common form of the normal approximation to the binomial test uses as the test statistic the actual estimate of p, namely X/n. Under the assumption of approximate normality, the test summary becomes:

$$
\begin{array}{ll}
\text{null hypothesis:} & H_0\text{: } p = p_0 \\
\text{alt. hypothesis:} & H_A\text{: } p \neq p_0
\end{array}
$$

$$
\text{test statistic:} \quad Z = \frac{|\hat{p} - p_0| - \dfrac{1}{2n}}{\sqrt{\dfrac{p_0 \cdot (1 - p_0)}{n}}}
$$

$$
\left(\text{where } \hat{p} = \frac{X}{n}\right)
$$

$$
\text{decision rule:} \quad \text{reject } H_0 \text{ if } |Z| > Z_{\alpha/2}
$$

Since the binomial distribution is a discrete distribution (i.e., takes integer values), while the normal distribution is continuous, the $1/(2n)$ in the numerator of the test statistic is used as a 'continuity correction' to improve the approximation. When H_0 is true, Z has an approximate standard normal distribution. For the commonly used value of $\alpha = 0.05$, $Z_{0.025} = 1.96$.

In Example 13.1, the test statistic based on the normal approximation is as follows:

$$
Z = \frac{\left|\dfrac{14}{25} - 0.4\right| - \dfrac{1}{50}}{\sqrt{\dfrac{0.4 \cdot 0.6}{25}}} = \frac{0.140}{0.098} = 1.429 \quad .
$$

Since 1.429 is less than 1.96, the null hypothesis is not rejected.

DETAILS & NOTES

▸ The normal approximation to the binomial is generally a good approximation if

$$n \cdot p - 2\sqrt{n \cdot p \cdot (1-p)} \geq 0 \qquad and,$$
$$n \cdot p + 2\sqrt{n \cdot p \cdot (1-p)} \leq n$$

▸ An approximate 95% confidence interval for estimating the proportion, p, is given by

$$\hat{p} \pm 1.96 \cdot \sqrt{\frac{\hat{p} \cdot (1-\hat{p})}{n}}, \qquad where \ \hat{p} = \frac{X}{n}.$$

With X/n = 14/25 = 0.56 in Example 13.1, a 95% confidence interval for p is:

$$0.56 \pm 1.96 \ [(0.56 \times 0.44)/25]^{\frac{1}{2}} =$$

$$0.56 \pm 0.19 \ = \ [0.37 - 0.75].$$

▸ The SAS function, PROBBNML, can be used to obtain binomial probabilities for specified p and n. The actual significance level of 0.044 in Example 13.1 is found using a SAS statement which includes:

PROBBNML(0.4,25,4) + (1 - PROBBNML(0.4,25,14)).

The PROBNORM function can be used with the normal approximation to obtain p-values. The approximate p-value for Example 13.1 with a Z test statistic of 1.429 is found in SAS as p = 2*(1-PROBNORM(1.429)) = 0.136.

▸ When p_0 = 0.5, the *Binomial Test* is sometimes called the *Sign Test*. A common application of the *Sign Test* is in testing for pre- to posttreatment changes, given information only as to whether a measurement increases or decreases following treatment. The number of increases is a binomial random variable with $p = 0.5$ when the null hypothesis of no pre- to post- changes is true. The UNIVARIATE procedure of SAS can be used to conduct the *Sign Test* (see Chapter 16 for example).

▸ Because Example 13.1 tests for a difference from the hypothesized value in either direction, a two-tailed test is used. A one-tailed test would be used when it is desired to test whether the population proportion, p, is strictly <u>greater than</u> *or* strictly <u>less than</u> the threshhold level, p_0. We use the rejection region according to the alternative hypothesis as follows:

Type of Test	Alternative Hypothesis	Corresponding Rejection Region
two-tailed	H_A: $p \neq p_o$	reject H_0 if $Z > Z_{\alpha/2}$ or $Z < -Z_{\alpha/2}$
one-tailed (right)	H_A: $p > p_0$	reject H_0 if $Z > Z_\alpha$
one-tailed (left)	H_A: $p < p_0$	reject H_0 if $Z < -Z_\alpha$

CHAPTER 14
The CHI-SQUARE TEST

INTRODUCTION

The *Chi-Square Test* is used to compare two independent binomial proportions, p_1 and p_2. In the analysis of clinical data, the binomial proportions typically represent response rates, cure rates, survival rates or abnormality rates. We often wish to compare such 'response' rates between a treated group and a parallel control group.

The *Chi-Square Test* is an approximate test and may be used when the normal approximation to the binomial distribution is valid (see Chapter 13). A popular alternative, *Fisher's Exact Test*, is based on exact probabilities, and is often used when conditions for using the *Chi-Square Test* are not met.

SYNOPSIS

Observation is made of X_1 'responders' out of n_1 patients studied in one group, and X_2 'responders' out of n_2 patients in a second independent group, as shown in the following layout.

	Group 1	Group 2	Combined
No. of 'Responders'	X_1	X_2	X_1+X_2
No. of 'Non-Responders'	n_1-X_1	n_2-X_2	$N-(X_1+X_2)$
Total	n_1	n_2	$N = n_1 + n_2$

We assume that each of the n_i ($i = 1,2$) patients have the same chance, p_i, of responding, so that X_1 and X_2 are independent binomial random variables (see Chapter 13). The goal is to compare population 'response' rates (p_1 *vs.* p_2) based on these sample data. We compute,

$$NUM = \frac{(X_1 \cdot n_2 - X_2 \cdot n_1)}{N} , \qquad and$$

$$DEN = \frac{n_1 \cdot n_2 \cdot (X_1 + X_2) \cdot (N - X_1 - X_2)}{N^3} .$$

Assuming that the normal approximation to the binomial distribution is applicable (see 'DETAILS & NOTES'), the *Chi-Square Test* summary is:

null hypothesis:	H_0: $p_1 = p_2$
alt. hypothesis:	H_A: $p_1 \neq p_2$
test statistic:	$\chi^2 = \dfrac{NUM^2}{DEN}$
decision rule:	*reject H_0 if $\chi^2 > \chi^2_1(\alpha)$*

The rejection region is found by obtaining the critical chi-square value based on 1 degree-of-freedom, denoted as

$$\chi^2_1(\alpha) ,$$

from chi-square tables. For $\alpha = 0.05$, the critical chi-square value is 3.841.

This computing formula for the chi-square statistic can be shown to be equivalent to the more popular form:

$$\chi^2 = \sum_{i=1}^{4} \frac{(O_i - E_i)^2}{E_i}$$

where the O_i's and E_i's are the observed and expected cell frequencies, respectively, as follows:

i	O_i	E_i
1	X_1	$n_1(X_1+X_2)/N$
2	X_2	$n_2(X_1+X_2)/N$
3	n_1-X_1	$n_1(N-X_1-X_2)/N$
4	n_2-X_2	$n_2(N-X_1-X_2)/N$

EXAMPLE 14.1 -- "ADR Frequency with Antibiotic Treatment"

A study was conducted to monitor the incidence of gastro-intestinal (GI) adverse drug reacions (ADR's) of a new antibiotic used in lower respiratory tract infections (LRTI). Two parallel groups were included, one consisting of 66 LRTI patients receiving the new treatment and a reference group of 52 LRTI patients receiving erythromycin. Twenty-two patients in the test group and 28 in the control (erythromycin) group reported one or more GI complaints during 7 days of treatment. Is there evidence of a difference in GI side effect rates between the two groups?

SOLUTION

Define 'response' as the event of a patient developing one or more GI reactions during the study, and let p_1 and p_2 represent the probabilities that a randomly selected LRTI patient has such a 'response' when treated with the test drug and control, respectively. The data are normally presented in a 2-by-2 contingency table as follows:

	Test Drug	Control	Combined
No. of 'Responders'	22	28	50
No. of Non-'Responders'	44	24	68
Total	66	52	118

We compute:

$$NUM = \frac{(22 \cdot 52) - (28 \cdot 66)}{118} = -5.966 \; ,$$

$$DEN = \frac{66 \cdot 52 \cdot 50 \cdot 68}{118^3} = 7.102$$

At a significance level of 0.05, the test summary is:

null hypothesis: H_0: $p_1 = p_2$
alt. hypothesis: H_A: $p_1 \neq p_2$

test statistic: $\chi^2 = \frac{(-5.966)^2}{7.102} = 5.01$

decision rule: *reject H_0 if $\chi^2 > \chi^2_1(0.05)$*
                       $= 3.841$

conclusion: since $5.01 > 3.841$, we reject H_0 and conclude there is a signficant difference in the incidence of GI effects between treatement groups at a 0.05 level of significance.

SAS Analysis of Example 14.1

The SAS code for conducting the *Chi-Square Test* using PROC FREQ is shown on the next page   The WEIGHT statement is used to tell SAS that the response variable (CNT) represents the cell frequencies in the data set analyzed.

The output shows the chi-square statistic, 5.012 with a p-value of 0.025 (1).

```
*   SAS Code for Example 14.1 ;

DATA ADR;
INPUT GRP RESP $ CNT @@;
CARDS;
1 YES 22   1 _NO 44
2 YES 28   2 _NO 24
; RUN;

* GRP 1 = Test Drug,  GRP 2 = Control;
PROC FREQ DATA = ADR;
   TABLES RESP*GRP / CHISQ EXACT NOPERCENT NOROW;
WEIGHT CNT;
TITLE1 'The Chi-Square Test';
TITLE2 'Example 14.1: ADR Frequency with Antibiotic
        Treatment';
RUN;
```

```
*   SAS Output for Example 14.1


                        The Chi-Square Test
      Example 14.1:  ADR Frequency with Antibiotic Treatment

                        TABLE OF RESP BY GRP
              RESP      GRP

              Frequency|
              Col Pct  |      1|      2| Total
              ---------+--------+--------+
              YES      |     22 |     28 |    50
                       |  33.33 |  53.85 |
              ---------+--------+--------+
              _NO      |     44 |     24 |    68
                       |  66.67 |  46.15 |
              ---------+--------+--------+
              Total          66       52     118


            STATISTICS FOR TABLE OF RESP BY GRP

      Statistic                   DF    Value        Prob
      -----------------------------------------------------
      Chi-Square                   1    5.012   (1)  0.025
      Likelihood Ratio Chi-Square  1    5.027        0.025
      Continuity Adj. Chi-Square   1    4.207   (2)  0.040
      Mantel-Haenszel Chi-Square   1    4.969        0.026
      Fisher's Exact Test (Left)                     0.020
                         (Right)                     0.992
                         (2-Tail)                    0.039
      Phi Coefficient                   -0.206
      Contingency Coefficient            0.202
      Cramer's V                        -0.206

      Sample Size = 118
```

DETAILS & NOTES

▸ An equivalent test to the *Chi-Square Test* for comparing binomial proportions is based on the Z-test statistic as follows:

$$Z = \frac{\hat{p}_1 - \hat{p}_2}{\sqrt{\bar{p}(1-\bar{p}) \cdot (\frac{1}{n_1} + \frac{1}{n_2})}}$$

$$\left(where \ \hat{p}_i = \frac{X_i}{n_i} \quad and \quad \bar{p} = \frac{(X_1 + X_2)}{(n_1 + n_2)} \right)$$

When H_0 is true, Z has the standard normal distribution, and we reject H_0 if $|Z| > Z_{\alpha/2}$.

Since the square of a standard normal variable is a chi-square with 1 d.f., Z^2 has a chi-square distribution, and can be shown algebraically to be equivalent to the chi-square test statistic already introduced. In Example 14.1, the response rate estimates are found as follows:

	Test Group (i=1)	Control Group (i=2)	Combined
X_i	22	28	50
n_i	66	52	118
Est. of p	0.333	0.538	0.424

and the Z-test statistic is:

$$Z = \frac{0.333 - 0.538}{\sqrt{(0.424) \cdot (0.576) \cdot (\frac{1}{66} + \frac{1}{52})}}$$

$$= -2.238$$

Since 2.238 > 1.96, we reject H_0 based on the Z-statistic at a 0.05 level of significance.

Note that $Z^2 = (-2.238)^2 = 5.01$ is the chi-square value previously obtained. The critical chi-square values with 1 d.f. from the chi-square tables correspond to the square of the critical Z values from the normal tables. For $\alpha = 0.05$, we use critical values, $\chi^2(0.05) = 3.841 = 1.96^2 = (Z_{0.025})^2$.

► In conducting a two-sample binomial comparison using either the *Chi-Square Test* or the Z-statistic, the normal approximation to the binomial distribution must be valid. The tests described here may not be valid if X_i or n_i-X_i is small for i = 1 or 2. As a rule of thumb, the analyst should be wary of results using this approximate test if any cell frequency is less than 5. *Fisher's Exact Test* (Chapter 15) may be applicable for cases involving small cell frequencies.

The normal approximation to the binomial is generally a good approximation if

$$n_i \cdot p_i - 2\sqrt{n_i \cdot p_i \cdot (1-p_i)} \geq 0 \qquad and,$$
$$n_i \cdot p_i + 2\sqrt{n_i \cdot p_i \cdot (1-p_i)} \leq n_i$$

for i = 1 and i = 2.

For small values of n_1 and n_2, the normal approximation can be improved by adjusting the test statistic with a 'continuity correction', $C = 0.5(1/n_1 + 1/n_2)$. The adjustment is made by subtracting C from the numerator of the Z test statistic if the numerator is greater than zero, or by adding C to the numerator of Z if it is less than zero.

In Example 14.1, the Z statistic using the continuity correction is

$$Z = \frac{(0.333 - 0.538) + 0.5(\frac{1}{66} + \frac{1}{52})}{\sqrt{0.424 \cdot (0.576) \cdot (\frac{1}{66} + \frac{1}{52})}} = -2.05 \quad .$$

The continuity-corrected chi-square value is the square of this Z-value, $(-2.05)^2 = 4.21$. This adjusted value appears on the SAS output (2), with a p-value of 0.040.

▸ An approximate 95% confidence interval for the proportion, p_i, is given by

$$\hat{p}_i \pm 1.96 \cdot \sqrt{\frac{\hat{p}_i \cdot (1-\hat{p}_i)}{n_i}}, \quad where \; \hat{p}_i = \frac{X_i}{n}.$$

An approximate 95% confidence interval for the difference in proportions, $p_1 - p_2$, is given by

$$(\hat{p}_1 - \hat{p}_2) \pm 1.96 \cdot \sqrt{\frac{\hat{p}_1 \cdot (1-\hat{p}_1)}{n_1} + \frac{\hat{p}_2 \cdot (1-\hat{p}_2)}{n_2}}.$$

With $X_1/n_1 = 22/66 = 0.333$ and $X_2/n_2 = 28/52 = 0.538$ in Example 14.1, a 95% confidence interval for $p_1 - p_2$ is

$$0.333 - 0.538 \pm 1.96 \cdot \left(\frac{(0.333 \cdot 0.667)}{66} + \frac{(0.538 \cdot 0.462)}{52} \right)^{\frac{1}{2}} =$$

$$-0.21 \pm 0.18 = [-0.39 \; to \; -0.03]$$

▸ Because Example 14.1 tests for a difference from the hypothesized value in either direction, a two-tailed test is used. A one-tailed test would be used when it is desired to test whether one population proportion is strictly <u>greater than</u> *OR* strictly <u>less than</u> the other. We use the rejection region according to the alternative hypothesis as follows:

Type of Test	Alternative Hypothesis	Corresponding Rejection Region
two-tailed	H_A: $p_1 \neq p_2$	reject H_0 if $Z > Z_{\alpha/2}$ or $Z < -Z_{\alpha/2}$
one-tailed (right)	H_A: $p_1 > p_2$	reject H_0 if $Z > Z_{\alpha}$
one-tailed (left)	H_A: $p_1 < p_2$	reject H_0 if $Z < -Z_{\alpha}$

Note that the *Chi-Square Test* is a 2-tailed test since large chi-square values within the rejection region occur when Z is a very large positive *or* large negative value. To conduct a one-tailed *Chi-Square Test*, the nominal significance level, α, should be doubled when looking up the critical chi-square values. The critical values for a rejection region corresponding to a significance level of $\alpha = 0.05$ are:

Test	1-Tailed	2-Tailed
Z-Test	1.645	1.960
Chi-Square	2.706	3.841

The p-value for a *Chi-Square Test* in the SAS output corresponds to a 2-tailed test. The one-tailed p-value is found by halving this value.

▸ For the case of $n_1 = n_2$, a method for estimating sample sizes to detect a difference in response rates, $\Delta = p_1 - p_2$, is shown in Chapter 2.

▸ The *Chi-Square Test* can easily be extended to more than two treatment groups using a 2-by-g contingency table, where g is the number of groups. For example, if dichotomous responses were taken from patients in 4 parallel groups representing differing dose levels of a treatment, we might have a 2-by-4 table as follows:

Response	-------------- Dose Group --------------			
	10 mg	20 mg	40 mg	80 mg
Yes	X_{11}	X_{21}	X_{31}	X_{41}
No	X_{12}	X_{22}	X_{32}	X_{42}

Similarly, the *Chi-Square Test* may also be used when the number of response levels is more than 2. With two treatment groups, we use a k-by-2 table, where k is the number of response levels. For example, if active and placebo groups of patients had a response categorized as 'acute', 'chronic' or 'intermittent', the 3-by-2 table would be:

Response	Active	Placebo
Acute	X_{11}	X_{21}
Chronic	X_{12}	X_{22}
Intermittent	X_{13}	X_{23}

Note that the response levels need not be ordinal.

The general layout includes g groups and k response levels in a k-by-g contingency table, with a total of k·g cells. The null hypothesis is that of equal distributions among response levels across all groups, or more generally, independence of the row and column factors. The *Chi-Square Test* is based on the test statistic

$$\chi^2 = \sum_{i=1}^{kg} \frac{(O_i - E_i)^2}{E_i}$$

where O_i and E_i represent the observed and expected values, respectively, in the i-th cell. The expected value is computed under the assumption that the null hypothesis is true, found by dividing the product of the row and column totals for that cell by the total sample size, N. The test statistic is compared with the critical chi-square value with (k-1)x(g-1) degrees-of-freedom to obtain the decision rule. Caution must be used when cell sizes are small.

Chapter 15
FISHER's EXACT TEST

INTRODUCTION

Fisher's Exact Test is an alternative to the *Chi-Square Test* (Chapter 14) for comparing two independent binomial proportions, p_1 and p_2. This method is based on computing exact probabilities of observing a given result, or one more extreme, when the hypothesis of equal proportions is true. *Fisher's Exact Test* is useful when the normal approximation to the binomial may not be applicable, such as in the case of small cell sizes or extreme proportions.

SYNOPSIS

Using the same notation as in Chapter 14, we observe X_1 'responders' out of n_1 patients studied in one group, and X_2 'responders' of n_2 patients in a second independent group, as in the layout below:

	Group 1	Group 2	TOTAL
No. of 'Responders'	X_1	X_2	$X_1 + X_2$
No. of 'Non-Responders'	$n_1 - X_1$	$n_2 - X_2$	$N - (X_1 + X_2)$
TOTAL	n_1	n_2	$N = n_1 + n_2$

Given equal proportions, $p_1 = p_2$, the probability of observing the above configuration when the marginal totals are fixed, is found by the 'hypergeometric probability distribution' as:

$$prob = \frac{\binom{n_1}{X_1} \cdot \binom{n_2}{X_2}}{\binom{N}{X_1+X_2}} \quad, \qquad where \ \binom{a}{b} = \frac{a!}{b! \cdot (a-b)!}$$

is the combinatorial symbol representing 'the number of ways **b** items can be selected from a set of **a** items'. The symbol ! is read 'factorial' and $a! = a(a-1)(a-2)...(3)(2)(1)$. For example, $5! = (5)(4)(3)(2)(1) = 120$. The probability of the table configuration simplifies to,

$$prob = \frac{(X_1+X_2)! \cdot (N-X_1-X_2)! \cdot (n_1)! \cdot (n_2)!}{N! \cdot X_1! \cdot X_2! \cdot (n_1-X_1)! \cdot (n_2-X_2)!} \ .$$

The p-value for the test, Fisher's exact probability, is the probability of the observed configuration plus the sum of the probabilities of all other configurations with a more extreme result for fixed row and column totals.

EXAMPLE 15.1 -- "CHF Incidence in CABG after ARA"

A new adenosine-releasing agent (ARA) thought to reduce side effects in patients undergoing coronary artery bypass surgery (CABG) was studied in a pilot trial enrolling 35 patients who received active medication and 20 patients who received placebo. Followup observation revealed that 2 active and 5 placebo patients had shown symptoms of congestive heart failure (CHF) within 90 days post surgery. Is this evidence of a reduced rate of CHF for patients treated with the ARA compound?

SOLUTION ▬▬▬▬▬▬▬▬▬▬▬▬▬▬▬▬

Let p_1 and p_2 represent the CHF rates for the active and placebo groups, respectively. We wish to test for equal proportions vs. the one-tailed alternative, since we are looking for improvement in one direction.

$$H_0: \ p_1 = p_2$$
$$H_A: \ p_1 < p_2 \ .$$

The summary results are:

	Active Group (i=1)	Placebo Group (i=2)	Combined
X_i	2	5	7
n_i	35	20	55
Est. of p	0.057	0.250	0.127

The conditions for using the *Chi-square Test* are not met in this case because of the small cell sizes. We therefore use *Fisher's Exact Test*. The observed table and those with a more extreme result having the same row and column totals are shown as follows:

	Table 1 ACT	Table 1 PBO	Table 2 ACT	Table 2 PBO	Table 3 ACT	Table 3 PBO	ROW TOTAL
X	2	5	1	6	0	7	7
n-X	33	15	34	14	35	13	48
n	35	20	35	20	35	20	55

Under H_0, the probability for Table 1 is found by:

$$prob_1 = \frac{(7)! \cdot (48)! \cdot (35)! \cdot (20)!}{(55)! \cdot (2)! \cdot (5)! \cdot (33)! \cdot (15)!} = 0.046 \ .$$

Similarly, the probabilities for Tables 2 and 3 may be computed as $prob_2 = 0.007$ and $prob_3 = 0.000$, respectively. The exact one-tailed p-value is $p = 0.046 + 0.007 + 0.000 = 0.053$. Since this is greater than 0.05, we would not reject the hypothesis of equal proportions at a significance level of 0.05. (This is close to 0.05, however, and may give the researcher encouragement to conduct a larger study).

SAS Analysis of Example 15.1

Fisher's Exact Test can be carried out with SAS using the EXACT option with PROC FREQ, as shown in the sample code which follows. This example uses the WEIGHT statement since the summary results are input. If the data set containing the individual patient observations were used, the WEIGHT statement would be omitted.

Fisher's exact probability is printed under 'Prob' on the output, with a one-tailed value of 0.053 (1). Note that SAS prints out a warning against use of the *Chi-Square Test* when cell sizes are too small.

```
*   SAS Code for Example 15.1 ;

DATA CABG;
INPUT GRP RESP $ CNT  @@;
CARDS;
1 YES  2   1 _NO 33   2 YES  5   2 _NO 15
; RUN;

PROC FREQ DATA = CABG;
   TABLES RESP*GRP / EXACT NOPERCENT NOROW;
   WEIGHT CNT;
TITLE1 'Fisher''s Exact Test';
TITLE2 'Example 15.1:  CHF Incidence in CABG
           after ARA';
RUN;
```

```
*   SAS Output for Example 15.1


                   Fisher's Exact Test
         Example 15.1:  CHF incidence in CABG after ARA

                    TABLE OF RESP BY GRP

            RESP      GRP

            Frequency|
            Col Pct  |      1|      2| Total
            ---------+-------+-------+
            YES      |      2|      5|     7
                     |   5.71|  25.00|
            ---------+-------+-------+
            _NO      |     33|     15|    48
                     |  94.29|  75.00|
            ---------+-------+-------+
            Total          35      20      55


                 STATISTICS FOR TABLE OF RESP BY GRP

          Statistic                   DF    Value     Prob
          ---------------------------------------------------
          Chi-Square                   1    4.262     0.039
          Likelihood Ratio Chi-Square  1    4.103     0.043
          Continuity Adj. Chi-Square   1    2.702     0.100
          Mantel-Haenszel Chi-Square   1    4.184     0.041
          Fisher's Exact Test (Left)             0.053   (1)
                              (Right)            0.993
                              (2-Tail)           0.086   (2)
          Phi Coefficient                   -0.278
          Contingency Coefficient            0.268
          Cramer's V                        -0.278

          Sample Size = 55
          WARNING:  50% of the cells have expected counts less
                    than 5. Chi-Square may not be a valid test.
```

DETAILS & NOTES

▶ *Fisher's Exact Test* is considered a non-parametric test since it does not rely on any distributional assumptions.

▶ Manual computations for Fisher's exact probabilities can be very tedious using a calculator, especially with larger cell sizes. A statistical program such as SAS is recommended to facilitate the computations.

▶ Fisher's probabilities are not necessarily symmetric. Although some analysts will double the one-tailed p-value to obtain the two-tailed result, this method is usually overly conservative.

To obtain the two-tailed p-value, first compute the probabilities associated with all possible tables having the same row and column totals. The 2-tailed p-value is then found by adding the probability of the observed table with the sum of the probabilities of each table whose probability is less than that of the observed table. To obtain the 2-tailed test for Example 15.1, we first compute the probabilities for each table as follows:

Table		Active	Placebo	Prob.		
1	Resp	0	7			
	Non-Resp	35	13	0.000	+	
2	Resp	1	6			
	Non-Resp	34	14	0.007	+	
3	Resp	2	5			
	Non-Resp	33	15	0.046	+	(Observed)
4	Resp	3	4			
	Non-Resp	32	16	0.156		
5	Resp	4	3			
	Non-Resp	31	17	0.294		
6	Resp	5	2			
	Non-Resp	30	18	0.304		
7	Resp	6	1			
	Non-Resp	29	19	0.160		
8	Resp	7	0			
	Non-Resp	28	20	0.033	+	

1.000

+ = Prob included in 2-tailed p-value

The observed table (# 3) has probability 0.046. Tables 1, 2 and 8 have probabilities less than 0.046 and are included in the p-value for the two-tailed alternative. Thus, the two-tailed p-value is p $= 0.000 + 0.007 + 0.046 + 0.033 = 0.086$.

As noted on the SAS output for Example 15.1, both the one-tailed (1) and two-tailed results (2) for *Fisher's Exact Test* are provided.

▸ *Fisher's Exact Test* can be extended to situations involving more than two treatments. With g treatment groups, we would establish a 2-by-g table of responses by extending the 2-by-2 table exemplified. We may also extend this method to multinomial responses, i.e., responses that can result in one of k possible outcomes (k $>$ 2). With two treatment groups, the 2-by-2 table would be extended to a k-by-2 table, or more generally, to a k-by-g table. An example of a 3-by-6 table is shown in the SAS manual.

CHAPTER 16

McNEMAR's TEST

INTRODUCTION

McNemar's Test is a special case of the *Binomial Test* (Chapter 13) for comparing two proportions using paired samples. *McNemar's Test* is often used in a clinical trials application when binomial outcomes are recorded twice for each patient under different conditions. The conditions may represent different treatments or different measurement times. The goal is to compare response rates under the two sets of conditions. Since measurements come from the same patients, the assumption of independent groups needed for the *Chi-Square Test* and *Fisher's Exact Test* is not met.

Typical examples where *McNemar's Test* might be applicable include testing for a shift in the proportion of abnormal responses from before to after treatment in the same group of patients, or comparing 2 ocular treatments when both are given to each patient, one in each eye.

SYNOPSIS

In general, there are n patients, each observed under two conditions (time points, treatments, etc.) with each condition resulting in a binomial response. Thus, the results can be partitioned into 4 subgroups: the number of patients (A) who respond under both conditions, the number (B) who respond under the first but not the second condition, the number (C) who respond under the second but not the first condition, and the number (D) who fail to respond under either condition, as shown in the 2-by-2 table which follows.

	Conditon 2		
	No. of 'Responders'	No. of 'Non-responders'	Total
Condition 1 — No. of 'Responders'	A	B	A+B
No. of 'Non-responders'	C	D	C+D
Total	A+C	B+D	n = A+B+C+D

The hypothesis of interest is the equality of the response proportions, p_1 and p_2, under conditions 1 and 2, respectively. The test statistic is based on the difference in the discordant cell frequencies (B,C) as shown in the test summary below. This statistic has an approximate chi-square distribution when H_0 is true.

null hypothesis: H_0: $p_1 = p_2$
alt. hypothesis: H_A: $p_1 \neq p_2$

test statistic:

$$\chi^2 = \frac{(B - C)^2}{B + C}$$

decision rule: *reject H_0 if $\chi^2 > \chi^2_1(\alpha)$*

where $\chi^2_1(\alpha)$ is the critical value from the chi-square tables with significance level, α, and 1 degree-of-freedom.

EXAMPLE 16.1 -- "Bilirubin Abnormalities Following Drug Treatment"
Eighty-six patients were treated with an experimental drug for 3-months. Pre- and poststudy clinical laboratory results showed abnormally high total bilirubin values (above the upper limit of the normal range) as indicated in the data table on the next page. Is there evidence of a change in the pre- to posttreatment rates of abnormalities?

Pat. No.	Pre-	Post-	Pat. No.	Pre-	Post-	Pat. No.	Pre-	Post-
1	N	N	31	N	N	61	N	N
2	N	N	32	N	N	62	N	N
3	N	N	33	Y	N	63	N	N
4	N	N	34	N	N	64	N	N
5	N	N	35	N	N	65	N	N
6	N	Y	36	N	N	66	N	N
7	Y	Y	37	N	N	67	N	N
8	N	N	38	N	Y	68	N	N
9	N	N	39	N	Y	69	N	Y
10	N	N	40	N	N	70	N	Y
11	N	N	41	N	N	71	Y	Y
12	Y	N	42	N	Y	72	N	N
13	N	N	43	N	N	73	N	N
14	N	Y	44	Y	N	74	N	Y
15	N	N	45	N	N	75	N	N
16	N	N	46	N	N	76	N	Y
17	N	N	47	Y	Y	77	N	N
18	N	N	48	N	N	78	N	N
19	N	N	49	N	N	79	N	N
20	N	Y	50	N	Y	80	N	N
21	N	N	51	Y	N	81	Y	Y
22	Y	N	52	N	N	82	N	N
23	N	N	53	N	Y	83	N	N
24	N	N	54	N	N	84	N	N
25	Y	N	55	Y	Y	85	N	N
26	N	N	56	N	N	86	N	N
27	N	N	57	N	N			
28	Y	Y	58	N	N			
29	N	Y	59	N	N			
30	N	Y	60	N	N			

N = normal, Y = abnormally high

SOLUTION

Let p_1 and p_2 represent the proportions of patients with abnormally high bilirubin values ('Y') before and after treatment, respectively. The data can be summarized as in the following frequency table:

		Posttreatment		
		'N'	'Y'	Total
Pre-treatment	'N'	60	14	74
	'Y'	6	6	12
	Total	66	20	86

'Y' = T. Bilirubin above upper limit of normal range

The test summary is:

null hypothesis:	H_0: $p_1 = p_2$
alt. hypothesis:	H_A: $p_1 \neq p_2$

test statistic:

$$\chi^2 = \frac{(14 - 6)^2}{14 + 6}$$

$$= \frac{64}{20} = 3.20$$

decision rule: *reject H_0 if $\chi^2 > 3.841$*

conclusion: since 3.20 is not $>$ 3.841, we do not reject H_0, concluding that there is insufficient evidence, at a significance level of 0.05, to conclude that a shift in abnormality rates occurs with treatment.

SAS Analysis of Example 16.1

The actual p-value of 0.074 for the chi-square value of 3.20 above can be found using the SAS expression 1-PROBCHI(3.20,1).

The SAS FREQ procedure using the AGREE option is used to conduct *McNemar's Test* in SAS. The SAS code and output for Example 16.1 are presented on the next page. The chi-square value of 3.20 with a p-value of 0.074 are shown on the output (1).

```
*    SAS Code for Example 16.1 ;

PROC FORMAT;
   VALUE RSLTFMT 0 = 'N'  1 = 'Y';   RUN;

DATA BILI;
INPUT PAT PRE PST @@;
CARDS;
  1 0 0   2 0 0   3 0 0   4 0 0   5 0 0   6 0 1
  7 1 1   8 0 0   9 0 0  10 0 0  11 0 0  12 1 0
 13 0 0  14 0 1  15 0 0  16 0 0  17 0 0  18 0 0
 19 0 0  20 0 1  21 0 0  22 1 0  23 0 0  24 0 0
       (more data lines)...
 78 0 0  79 0 0  80 0 0  81 1 1  82 0 0  83 0 0
 84 0 0  85 0 0  86 0 0
; RUN;

PROC FREQ DATA = BILI; TABLES PRE*PST / AGREE;
FORMAT PRE PST RSLTFMT.;
TITLE1 'McNemar''s Test';
TITLE2 'Example 16.1:  Bilirubin Abnormalities
         Following Drug Treatment';
RUN;
```

```
*   SAS Output for Example 16.1
```

McNemar's Test
Example 16.1: Bilirubin Abnormalities Following Drug Treatment

TABLE OF PRE BY PST

PRE Frequency Percent Row Pct Col Pct	N	Y	Total
N	60 69.77 81.08 90.91	14 16.28 18.92 70.00	74 86.05
Y	6 6.98 50.00 9.09	6 6.98 50.00 30.00	12 13.95
Total	66 76.74	20 23.26	86 100.00

STATISTICS FOR TABLE OF PRE BY PST
McNemar's Test
----

(1)   Statistic = 3.200   DF = 1   Prob = 0.074

Simple Kappa Coefficient

                                        95% Confidence Bounds
        Kappa = 0.243   ASE = 0.121   0.006   0.480

        Sample Size = 86

DETAILS & NOTES

▶ The estimate of p_1 is $(A+B)/n$, and the estimate of p_2 is $(A+C)/n$. The difference in proportions, $p_1 - p_2$ is estimated by $(A+B)/n - (A+C)/n = (B-C)/n$. An approximate 95% confidence interval for p_1-p_2 is given by:

$$\frac{(B - C)}{n} \pm 1.96 \cdot \left(\frac{1}{n}\right) \cdot \sqrt{B + C - \frac{(B - C)^2}{n}} \ .$$

For Example 16.1, the approximate 95% confidence interval for $p_1 - p_2$ is:

$$\frac{(14 - 6)}{86} \pm 1.96 \cdot \left(\frac{1}{86}\right) \cdot \sqrt{14 + 6 - \frac{(14 - 6)^2}{86}}$$

$$= 0.093 \pm 0.100 \quad or \quad [-0.007 \ to \ 0.193].$$

▶ Note that the chi-square test statistic depends only on the discordant cell sizes (B, C), ignoring the concordant cells (A, D). However, the estimates of p_1, p_2 and the size of the confidence interval depend on all cells since they are inversely proportional to the total sample size, n.

▶ Some statisticians insist on the use of a continuity correction in the chi-square test statistic when using *McNemar's Test* as follows:

$$\chi^2 = \frac{(|B - C| - 1)^2}{B + C} \ .$$

This adjustment results in a more conservative test, and the correction factor may be omitted as B+C gets larger. Reanalyzing the data of Example 16.1 with the continuity correction, the test statistic becomes $\chi^2 = 2.45$, which is seen to be smaller and less significant (p=0.118) than the uncorrected value.

▸ A well-known relationship in probability theory is that if a random variable, Z, has a standard normal distribution (i.e., mean 0 and variance 1), then Z^2 has a chi-square distribution with 1 degree-of-freedom. This principle can be used to show the relationship of the *McNemar* chi-square to the *Binomial Test* using the normal approximation as follows.

When the null hypothesis is true, the discordant values, B and C, should be about the same, that is B/(B+C) should be about 1/2. *McNemar's Test* is equivalent to using the *Binomial Test* (Chapter 13) to test H_0: p = 0.5, where p = the fraction of the events which fall in 1 of the 2 discordant cells. Using the setup of Chapter 13 with n = B+C and X = B, the normal approximation to the *Binomial Test* (expressed as a standard normal Z when H_0 is true), is:

$$Z = \frac{(|\hat{p} - 0.5| - \frac{1}{2(B+C)})}{\sqrt{\frac{0.5 \cdot 0.5}{(B+C)}}} = \frac{|B-C|-1}{\sqrt{B+C}}$$

$$since \ \hat{p} = \frac{B}{(B+C)}$$

Therefore,

$$Z^2 = \frac{(|B-C|-1)^2}{(B+C)} = \chi^2 \quad .$$

▸ Since *McNemar's Test* is identical to the *Binomial Test* using a normal approximation, it should be used only when the conditions for which the normal approximation apply (see Chapter 13). Using the notation here, these conditions can be simplified as: $B^2 \geq C(4-B)$ and $C^2 \geq B(4-C)$. Note that these conditions need be checked only if either B or C is less than 4. If the conditions are not satisfied, the binomial tables should be used rather than the normal approximation or the chi-square statistic.

▸ The above application of the *Binomial Test* is an example of the '*Sign Test*' mentioned in Chapter 13. In applying the *Sign Test*, the number of 'increases' (+) are compared with the number of 'decreases' (-), ignoring tied values. In Example 16.1, B represents the number of 'increases', C represents the number of 'decreases', and the concordant values (A and D) represent the ties which are ignored.

▸ The p-value in the SAS output corresponds to a two-tailed hypothesis test. The one-tailed p-value can be found by halving this value.

▸ An extension of *McNemar's Test*, called the *Stuart Maxwell Test*, can be used for a matched layout with 3 response categories. As an example, suppose patients are successively treated with each of 2 treatments given in random order, and the response is the outbreak frequency of a certain condition categorized as 'none', 'occasional' or 'frequent'. The response is trinomial since it can take one of 3 values. The reader is referred to Fleiss [1981] for details of the *Stuart-Maxwell Test*.

CHAPTER 17
The COCHRAN-MANTEL-HAENSZEL TEST

INTRODUCTION

The *Cochran-Mantel-Haenszel Test* is used in clinical trials to compare two binomial proportions based on stratified samples from two independent populations. This test provides a means of combining a number of 2-by-2 tables of the kind discussed in Chapters 14 and 15 when each is from a separate, independent stratum.

The stratification factor may represent patient subgroups such as study centers, gender, age group or disease severity, and acts much like the blocking factor in a *Two-Way ANOVA* (Chapter 6). The *Cochran-Mantel-Haenszel Test* obtains an overall comparison of response rates adjusted for the stratification variable. The adjustment is simply a weighting of the 2-by-2 tables in proportion to the within-strata sample sizes.

The *Cochran-Mantel-Haenszel Test* is often used in the comparison of response rates between two treatment groups in a multi-center study using the study centers as strata.

SYNOPSIS

Assume there are k strata ($k \geq 2$). Within Stratum j, there are N_j patients ($j = 1, 2, ..., k$), randomly allocated to one of two groups. In Group 1, we have n_{1j} patients, X_{1j} of whom are considered 'responders'. Group 2, similarly, has n_{2j} patients with X_{2j} 'responders', as shown in the following layout.

STRATUM		GROUP 1	GROUP 2	TOTAL
1	'Resp.'	X_{11}	X_{21}	$X_{11} + X_{21}$
	'Non-Resp'	$n_{11} - X_{11}$	$n_{21} - X_{21}$	$N_1 - (X_{11} + X_{21})$
	Total	n_{11}	n_{21}	N_1
2	'Resp.'	X_{12}	X_{22}	$X_{12} + X_{22}$
	'Non-Resp'	$n_{12} - X_{12}$	$n_{22} - X_{22}$	$N_2 - (X_{12} + X_{22})$
	Total	n_{12}	n_{22}	N_2
.				
.				
.				
k	'Resp.'	X_{1k}	X_{2k}	$X_{1k} + X_{2k}$
	'Non-Resp'	$n_{1k} - X_{1k}$	$n_{2k} - X_{2k}$	$N_k - (X_{1k} + X_{2k})$
	Total	n_{1k}	n_{2k}	N_k

For Stratum j, compute the quantities:

$$NUM_j = \frac{X_{1j} \cdot n_{2j} - X_{2j} \cdot n_{1j}}{N_j} \qquad and,$$

$$DEN_j = \frac{n_{1j} \cdot n_{2j} \cdot (X_{1j} + X_{2j}) \cdot (N_j - X_{1j} - X_{2j})}{N_j^2 \cdot (N_j - 1)}$$

The *Cochran-Mantel-Haenszel Test* summary is as follows:

null hypothesis: H_0: $p_1 = p_2$

alt. hypothesis: H_A: $p_1 \neq p_2$

test statistic: $\chi^2_{CMH} = \dfrac{\left(\sum\limits_{j=1}^{k} NUM_j\right)^2}{\sum\limits_{j=1}^{k} DEN_j}$

decision rule:

$$reject\ H_0\ if\ \chi^2_{CMH} > \chi^2_1(\alpha)$$

where $\chi^2_1(\alpha)$ is the critical chi-square value with significance level α and 1 degree-of-freedom.

EXAMPLE 17.1 -- *"Dermotel Response in Diabetic Ulcers"*

A multi-center study with 4 centers is testing an experimental treatment, Dermotel, *used to accelerate the healing of dermal foot ulcers in diabetic patients. Sodium hyaluronate was used in a control group. Patients who showed a decrease in ulcer size after 20 weeks of treatment of at least 90% by surface area measurements were considered 'responders'. The numbers of responders in each group are shown below for each study center. Is there an overall difference in response rates between the* Dermotel *and control groups?*

Study Center		*DERMOTEL* Group	CONTROL Group	TOTAL
1	Resp.	26	18	44
	Non-Resp	4	11	15
	Total	30	29	59
2	Resp.	8	7	15
	Non-Resp	3	5	8
	Total	11	12	23
3	Resp.	7	4	11
	Non-Resp	5	6	11
	Total	12	10	22
4	Resp.	11	9	20
	Non-Resp	6	5	11
	Total	17	14	31

SOLUTION

We consider the study centers as separate strata. For Study Center 1, compute:

$$NUM_1 = \frac{X_{11} \cdot n_{21} - X_{21} \cdot n_{11}}{N_1}$$

$$= \frac{26 \cdot 29 - 18 \cdot 30}{59} = 3.6271$$

and,

$$DEN_1 = \frac{n_{11} \cdot n_{12} \cdot (X_{11} + X_{12}) \cdot (N_1 - X_{11} - X_{12})}{N_1^2 \cdot (N_1 - 1)}$$

$$= \frac{30 \cdot 29 \cdot 44 \cdot 15}{59^2 \cdot 58} = 2.8440 \qquad .$$

In a similar manner, we compute these quantities for the other centers with the following results:

STUDY CENTER	NUM_j	DEN_j
1	3.6271	2.8440
2	0.8261	1.3611
3	1.000	1.4286
4	0.0322	1.8162
TOTAL	5.4855	7.4500

The test summary using the *Cochran-Mantel-Haenszel Test* at a significance level of 0.05 is:

null hypothesis: H_0: $p_1 = p_2$
alt. hypothesis: H_A: $p_1 \neq p_2$

test statistic: $$\chi^2_{CMH} = \frac{\left(\sum_{j=1}^{4} NUM_j\right)^2}{\sum_{j=1}^{4} DEN_j}$$

$$= \frac{5.4855^2}{7.4500} = 4.039$$

decision rule: *reject H_0 if χ^2_{CMH} > 3.841*

conclusion: Since 4.039 > 3.841, we reject H_0 at a significance level of α=0.05, and conclude that there is a significant difference in response rates between the *Dermotel* treatment and the control.

SAS Analysis of Example 17.1

The CMH option of the FREQ procedure in SAS can be used to conduct the *Cochran-Mantel-Haenszel Test*, as illustrated on the next 3 pages. The stratification factor (CNTR) must be specified first in the TABLES statement as shown in the SAS code. We use the NOPERCENT and NOROW options to suppress printing of unneeded results (the column percentages will still be printed since the NOCOL option is not specified).

The output shows the 2-by-2 tables for each study center (1). The column percentages are printed under the cell frequencies with the percent for RESP = 'YES' representing the estimated response rate. The *Cochran-Mantel-Haenszel Test* results are shown on the subsequent output page (2), confirming the chi-square statistic of 4.039. The p-value of 0.044 indicates significance when tested at α = 0.05. (The SAS output entitled "Estimates of the Common Relative Risk" is ignored for this example).

The SAS code includes an overall *Chi-Square Test* (Chapter 14), ignoring the stratification factor (Study Center).

```
* SAS Code for Example 17.1 ;

DATA ULCR;
INPUT CNTR $  TRT $  RESP $  FRQ;
CARDS;
1 ACT YES 26
1 CTL YES 18
1 ACT _NO  4
1 CTL _NO 11
2 ACT YES  8
2 CTL YES  7
2 ACT _NO  3
2 CTL _NO  5
3 ACT YES  7
3 CTL YES  4
3 ACT _NO  5
3 CTL _NO  6
4 ACT YES 11
4 CTL YES  9
4 ACT _NO  6
4 CTL _NO  5
;
RUN;

* Analysis using CNTR as stratification factor;
PROC FREQ DATA = ULCR;
  TABLES CNTR*RESP*TRT/CMH NOPERCENT NOROW;
  WEIGHT FRQ;
TITLE1 'The Cochran-Mantel-Haenszel Test';
TITLE2 'Example 17.1:  Response to Dermotel in
        Diabetic Ulcers';
RUN;

* Analysis without stratification
        (ignoring CNTR);
PROC FREQ DATA = ULCR;
  TABLES RESP*TRT/CHISQ NOPERCENT NOROW;
  WEIGHT FRQ;
RUN;
```

```
* SAS Output for Example 17.1


                    The Cochran-Mantel-Haenszel Test
           Example 17.1:  Response to Dermotel in Diabetic Ulcers

           TABLE 1 OF RESP BY TRT CONTROLLING FOR CNTR=1

              RESP        TRT
                                                                    (1)
              Frequency|
              Col Pct  |ACT     |CTL     |  Total
              ---------+--------+--------+
              YES      |     26 |     18 |    44
                       |  86.67 |  62.07 |
              ---------+--------+--------+
              _NO      |      4 |     11 |    15
                       |  13.33 |  37.93 |
              ---------+--------+--------+
              Total          30       29      59


           TABLE 2 OF RESP BY TRT CONTROLLING FOR CNTR=2

              RESP        TRT

              Frequency|
              Col Pct  |ACT     |CTL     |  Total
              ---------+--------+--------+
              YES      |      8 |      7 |    15
                       |  72.73 |  58.33 |
              ---------+--------+--------+
              _NO      |      3 |      5 |     8
                       |  27.27 |  41.67 |
              ---------+--------+--------+
              Total          11       12      23


           TABLE 3 OF RESP BY TRT CONTROLLING FOR CNTR=3

              RESP        TRT

              Frequency|
              Col Pct  |ACT     |CTL     |  Total
              ---------+--------+--------+
              YES      |      7 |      4 |    11
                       |  58.33 |  40.00 |
              ---------+--------+--------+
              _NO      |      5 |      6 |    11
                       |  41.67 |  60.00 |
              ---------+--------+--------+
              Total          12       10      22


           TABLE 4 OF RESP BY TRT CONTROLLING FOR CNTR=4

              RESP        TRT

              Frequency|
              Col Pct  |ACT     |CTL     |  Total
              ---------+--------+--------+
              YES      |     11 |      9 |    20
                       |  64.71 |  64.29 |
              ---------+--------+--------+
              _NO      |      6 |      5 |    11
                       |  35.29 |  35.71 |
              ---------+--------+--------+
              Total          17       14      31
```

```
  * SAS Output for Example 17.1 -- continued


                    The Cochran-Mantel-Haenszel Test
         Example 17.1:  Response to Dermotel in Diabetic Ulcers

                      SUMMARY STATISTICS FOR RESP BY TRT
                          CONTROLLING FOR CNTR


         Cochran-Mantel-Haenszel Statistics (Based on Table Scores)

     Statistic  Alternative Hypothesis    DF    Value    Prob
     -----------------------------------------------------------    (2)
         1        Nonzero Correlation       1    4.039    0.044
         2        Row Mean Scores Differ    1    4.039    0.044
         3        General Association       1    4.039    0.044

            Estimates of the Common Relative Risk (Row1/Row2)
                                                      95%
     Type of Study   Method          Value  Confidence Bounds
     ----------------------------------------------------------
     Case-Control    Mantel-Haenszel   2.147   1.019    4.521
      (Odds Ratio)   Logit             2.123   0.991    4.546

     Cohort          Mantel-Haenszel   1.485   1.010    2.184
      (Col1 Risk)    Logit             1.374   0.917    2.057

     Cohort          Mantel-Haenszel   0.690   0.480    0.991
      (Col2 Risk)    Logit             0.666   0.476    0.930

     The confidence bounds for the M-H estimates are test-based.

          Breslow-Day Test for Homogeneity of the Odds Ratios
     Chi-Square =   1.895          DF =   3          Prob = 0.595

     Total Sample Size = 135



                        TABLE OF RESP BY TRT

         RESP       TRT
         Frequency|
         Col Pct  |ACT     |CTL     |   Total
         ---------+--------+--------+
         YES      |    52  |    38  |    90
                  | 74.29  | 58.46  |
         ---------+--------+--------+
         _NO      |    18  |    27  |    45
                  | 25.71  | 41.54  |
         ---------+--------+--------+
         Total         70       65      135


              STATISTICS FOR TABLE OF RESP BY TRT
     Statistic                     DF    Value    Prob
     ------------------------------------------------------
     Chi-Square                     1    3.798    0.051      (3)
     Likelihood Ratio Chi-Square    1    3.814    0.051
     Continuity Adj. Chi-Square     1    3.119    0.077
     Mantel-Haenszel Chi-Square     1    3.770    0.052
     Fisher's Exact Test (Left)                  0.984
                         (Right)                 0.039
                         (2-Tail)                0.068
     Phi Coefficient                     0.168
     Contingency Coefficient             0.165
     Cramer's V                          0.168
     Sample Size = 135
```

DETAILS & NOTES

▸ A convenient way to summarize the test results by stratum is shown for Example 17.1 in the following table. The response rate for Group i, Stratum j is estimated by $100(X_{ij}/n_{ij})\%$. The overall response rate for Group i is estimated by $100[(X_{i1}+X_{i2}+X_{i3}+X_{i4})/(n_{i1}+n_{i2}+n_{i3}+n_{i4})]\%$.

Study Center	Response Rates				Chi-Square	p-Value
	Active	(n)	Control	(n)		
1	86.7%	(30)	62.1%	(29)	4.706	0.030*
2	72.7%	(11)	58.3%	(12)	0.524	0.469
3	58.3%	(12)	40.0%	(10)	0.733	0.392
4	64.7%	(17)	64.3%	(14)	0.001	0.981
Overall	74.3%	(70)	58.5%	(65)	4.039	0.044*

The chi-square values and p-values can be output for each stratum in the SAS output with PROC FREQ by using the CHISQ option in the TABLES statement.

▸ The SAS output lists 3 statistics in the output, corresponding to *Nonzero Correlation*, *Row Mean Scores Differ*, and *General Association*. For 2-by-2 tables, these are just different ways of expressing the alternative hypothesis, and the test statistic will be same for all three.

▸ By ignoring the strata and combining all the data of Example 17.1 into one simple *Chi-square Test* (Chapter 14), we obtain the following results, as shown in the SAS output (3):

	Active	Control	Total
Resp.	52 (74.3%)	38 (58.5%)	90
Non-Resp.	18	27	45
Total	70	65	135

Chi-Square value = 3.798, p = 0.051.

The test statistic does not quite attain significance at the 0.05 level as with the *Cochran-Mantel-Haenszel Test*. In this example, the within-strata information used by the *Cochran-Mantel-Haenszel Test* is advantageous in revealing greater statistical significance. This may often be the case when there is a large difference in sample sizes among strata.

▶ With some algebraic manipulation,

$$NUM_j = \frac{X_{1j} \cdot n_{2j} - X_{2j} \cdot n_{1j}}{N_j}$$

can be expressed as

$$w_j \cdot (\hat{p}_{1j} - \hat{p}_{2j}) \quad , \qquad where \quad \hat{p}_{ij} = \frac{X_{ij}}{n_{ij}}$$

is the estimate of p_{ij} and w_j is a function of the group sample sizes:

$$w_j = \left(\frac{1}{n_{1j}} + \frac{1}{n_{2j}} \right)^{-1} \quad .$$

Written in this manner, the *Cochran-Mantel-Haenszel* statistic is seen to be based on the within-strata response rate differences combined over all strata, weighted by w_j. Since w_j increases with the n_{ij}'s, it is seen that greater weights are assigned to those strata with larger sample sizes.

▶ The *Cochran-Mantel-Haenszel Test* was originally developed for use with retrospective data in epidemiological applications. The same methodology has been widely applied to prospective clinical trials, such as exemplified here. A number of alternative statistics, similar but with minor variations to the version presented, have also been used.

For example, *Cochran's (Chi-Square) Test* is computed in the same way as the *Cochran-Mantel-Haenszel* statistic with the exception that the denominator of DEN_j is N_j^3 instead of $N_j^2(N_j-1)$. The *Cochran-Mantel-Haenszel Test* is an attempt to improve on *Cochran's Test* by giving the strata with fewer patients less weight in the overall analysis, while leaving strata with large N_j's relatively unaltered. Note that if *Cochran's Test* is used with k = 1, the chi-square value is $(NUM_1)^2 / DEN_1$, which is identical to the *Chi-Square Test* discussed in Chapter 14.

Another variation of the *Cochran-Mantel-Haenszel* statistic is the continuity-corrected value as follows:

$$\chi^2_{CMH} = \frac{\left(\left|\sum_{j=1}^{k} NUM_j\right| - 0.5\right)^2}{\sum_{j=1}^{k} DEN_j}$$

The continuity correction should be used if there are many small cell sizes. However, use of the continuity correction may produce overly conservative results, and it can generally be omitted for reasonable cell sizes.

► An interaction exists if the differences in response rates between groups differ among strata. An example of an interaction is an Active vs. Control response rate comparison of 60% vs. 30% in one stratum and 30% vs. 60% in another stratum. Combining strata may mask this interaction, leading to off-setting responses and no overall differences.

In the presence of an interaction or lack of 'homogeneity' among response differences, each stratum should be analyzed separately, and further analyses might be pursued in an attempt to explain the interaction.

- Combining data across strata into a single 2-by-2 table should only be considered when the individual tables have like proportions. To exemplify the problems that could arise by automatically combining tables without carefully examining each, consider the following results for two strata:

Stratum		GROUP A	GROUP B
1	Responders	10	4
	Non-Responders	38	21
	Total	48	25
	Resp. Rate	21%	16%
2	Responders	20	27
	Non-Responders	10	17
	Total	30	44
	Resp. Rate	67%	61%
Combined	Responders	30	31
	Non-Responders	48	38
	Total	78	69
	Resp. Rate	38%	45%

The response rates for Group A are greater than those of Group B within each stratum. But the overall response rate for Group B is greater for the combined strata. This situation can occur if there is a large difference in response rates among strata and sample sizes are imbalanced between groups in opposite ways among strata.

- The *Cochran-Mantel-Haenszel Test* can be extended to contingency tables larger than the 2-by-2 tables considered here. The general layout is based on k strata of r-by-c contingency tables, where r (number of rows) represents the number of response categories, and c (columns) represents the number of treatment groups. The FREQ procedure of SAS can also be used to analyze results for this more general setup. Caution must be used with larger values of r and c due to interpretation difficulties, smaller cell sizes and the increased potential for interactions.

▸ The *Cochran-Mantel-Haenszel Test* as presented here is a two-tailed test. The p-value from the SAS output can be halved to obtain a one-tailed test.

CHAPTER 18
LOGISTIC REGRESSION

INTRODUCTION

Logistic Regression Analysis is a statistical method for analyzing dichotomous response data while accomodating adjustments for one or more numeric covariates. This method is analogous to *Analysis-of-Covariance* (Chapter 9), which is useful for comparing two or more groups while adjusting for various background factors (covariates). Although both methods include covariate adjustments, ANCOVA analyzes *means* of numeric response measures, while *Logistic Regression* analyzes *proportions* based on binomial responses (e.g., success rates, survival rates or cure rates).

Historically, *Logistic Regression* techniques have been widely used for identifying risk factors associated with disease in epidemiological studies. This method also has popular application in analyzing prospective clinical trials and in identifying potentially important covariates in exploratory analyses of clinical research data.

Examples from clinical research where this procedure might be useful include: (i) comparing survival rates in cancer patients among various treatment groups adjusted for age and duration of disease, (ii) comparing proportions of patients whose dermal ulcers show complete healing between an active and placebo group adjusted for baseline ulcer size, or (iii) comparing the proportion of normalized hypertensive patients between two anti-hypertensive treatment groups adjusted for age, cholesterol level, tobacco use and exercise habits.

SYNOPSIS

We consider response values, Y, that take one of 2 possible values (yes-no, normal-abnormal, present-absent, cured-not cured. died-survived. etc.), with coded values 0 and 1. A response of Y = 1 indicates that the *event* of interest occurs ('event'), and a response of Y=0 indicates that the *event* does not occur ('non-event'). If one or more background factors are suspected to affect the response, we want the analysis to reflect this relationship, and must incorporate the values of the covariates (X) into the analysis.

The methods used to develop *ANCOVA* procedures are not applicable since the responses are not normally distributed. Instead, we apply a transformation of the data using the 'logit function',

$$Y^* = \ln[P/(1-P)],$$

where P is the expected value of Y for a specified set of X-values and 'ln' represents the natural-logarithm function. For now, we assume there is only one covariate, X.

Since Y only takes the values 0 or 1 for a given value of X, the mean of Y equals the probability that Y=1. We denote this probability by P_x, where $0 \le P_x \le 1$. *Logistic Regression* assumes that P_x is related to X in a sigmoidal fashion (Figure 18-1), represented by the equation

$$P_x = \frac{1}{1 + e^{-(\alpha + \beta X)}} \quad .$$

With some algebraic manipulation, this can be re-expressed as

$$\ln\left(\frac{P_x}{1-P_x}\right) = \alpha + \beta X \quad ,$$

the left-hand side of which is the logistic transformation or 'logit' function (Y*). In epidemiology, $P_x/(1-P_x)$ is known as the 'odds', and the logit is sometimes referred to as the 'log-odds'. The log-odds becomes a linear function of the covariate, X, when we assume a sigmoidal relationship between X and P_x, as illustrated in Figure 18-1.

FIGURE 18-1: Logistic Probability Function

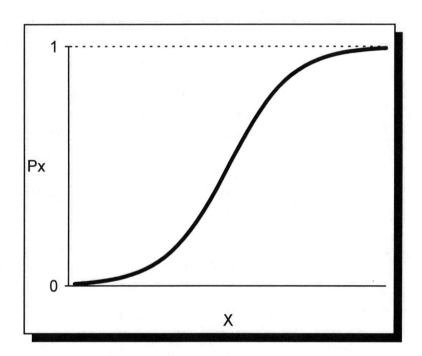

For a fixed value of the covariate, say X = x, we estimate P_x from the data as $\hat{p}_x = y_x/n_x$, where n_x is the number of observations at X = x and y_x is the number of *events* out of the n_x observations. Since y_x is a binomial random variable, $\hat{p}_x$ will be a better estimate when n_x is large.

Suppose Y=12 patients with ulcers secondary to *H. pylori* were cured out of n=20 treated with an antibiotic, broken down as shown below by the ulcer history (X, in years):

X	Y	n	P_x (est)	Logit
1	4	6	0.667	0.693
2	6	10	0.600	0.405
3	2	4	0.500	0.000
TOTAL	12	20	0.600	

We estimate the chance of cure with the antibiotic for patients with a 1-year history ($X = 1$) by $\hat{p}_x = 4/6 = 0.667$. The logit of $\hat{p}_x$ is $\ln(0.667/0.333) = 0.693$.

Estimates of P_x computed from the observed data in this manner can be used to calculate estimates of the model parameters, α and β, which maximize the likelihood of observing the data set collected. The procedure for accomplishing this is known as the 'Maximum-Likelihood Procedure'. Although the mathematical derivations are beyond the scope of this book, this procedure yields a set of simultaneous equations (known as the Maximum-Likelihood equations) which can be solved for a and b, the estimates of α and β. These equations have the form:

$$\sum_{i=1}^{N} Y_i = \sum_{i=1}^{N} \left[1 + e^{-(a+bx_i)}\right]^{-1} \qquad and,$$

$$\sum_{i=1}^{N} X_i \cdot Y_i = \sum_{i=1}^{N} X_i \cdot \left[1 + e^{-(a+bx_i)}\right]^{-1} \quad .$$

Numerical techniques using iterative methods are used to solve these equations, and a computer program (such as SAS) is necessary for all but the smallest of data sets. A simple example illustrating the computational complexities is shown in Appendix E.

In general, the *Logistic Regression* layout has N patients and k covariates, X_1, X_2, ..., X_k, and a typical data set may have the form:

Pat No.	Response	---------- Covariates ----------			
1	y_1	X_{11}	X_{21}	...	X_{k1}
2	y_2	X_{12}	X_{22}	...	X_{k2}
...	...	...	...	...	...
N	y_N	X_{1N}	X_{2N}	...	X_{kN}

The X_i's can be known numeric-valued concomitant factors, such as age, WBC or fasting glucose level. The X_i's can also represent numerically-coded values of ordered categorical data, such as small-medium-large (coded as 0-1-2) or none-mild-moderate-severe (coded as 0-1-2-3). We can also code one of the X_i's as a treatment or group effect (such as 0=placebo, 1=active).

We model P_x as

$$P_x = \frac{1}{1 + e^{-(\alpha + \beta_1 x_1 + \beta_2 x_2 + ... + \beta_k x_k)}}$$

so the logit becomes:

$$\ln\left(\frac{P_x}{1 - P_x}\right) = \alpha + \beta_1 x_1 + \beta_2 x_2 + ... + \beta_k x_k \qquad .$$

The importance of each covariate (x_i) for predicting the *event* probability is measured by the magnitude of the parameter coefficient, β_i. Estimates of these parameters are found by the method of Maximum Likelihood. For large samples, these estimates (b_i) have an approximate normal distribution. If s_b represents the standard error of the estimate, b_i, then b_i/s_b has an approximate standard normal distribution under the null hypothesis that $\beta_i = 0$, and its square has the chi-square distribution with one degree-of-freedom. The test summary for each model parameter, β_i, is based on the 'Wald' chi-square, summarized as follows:

---

null hypothesis: H_0: $\beta_i = 0$

alternative hypothesis: H_A: $\beta_i \neq 0$

test statistic: $\chi^2_w = \left(\dfrac{b_i}{s_b}\right)^2$

decision rule: *reject H_0 if $\chi^2_w > \chi^2_1(\alpha)$*

Example 18.1 illustrates the method for k=2.

EXAMPLE 18.1 -- "Relapse Rate Adjusted for Remission Time in AML"

One-hundred two patients with acute myelogenous leukemia (AML) in remission were enrolled in a study of a new anti-sense oligonucleotide (asODN). Patients were randomly assigned to receive a 10 day infusion of asODN or no treatment ('Control') and were followed for 90 days. Time of remission from diagnosis or prior relapse (X, in months) at study enrollment was considered an important covariate in predicting response. The response data are shown below with Y=1 indicating relapse, death or major intervention such as bone marrow transplant before Day 90. Is there any evidence that administration of asODN is associated with a decreased relapse rate?

----------------- *asODN* Group -----------------

Pat. No.	X	Y	Pat. No.	X	Y	Pat. No.	X	Y
1	3	0	32	9	0	67	12	0
2	3	1	33	6	1	69	12	0
4	3	1	36	6	0	71	12	0
6	6	1	39	6	0	73	9	1
7	15	0	42	6	0	74	6	1
10	6	1	44	3	1	77	12	0
11	6	1	46	18	0	79	6	0
14	6	1	49	9	0	81	15	1
15	15	0	50	12	1	83	9	0
17	15	0	52	6	0	85	3	1
20	12	0	54	9	1	88	9	0
21	18	0	56	9	1	90	9	0
22	6	1	58	3	0	92	9	0
25	15	0	60	9	1	94	9	0
26	6	1	62	12	0	95	9	1
28	15	0	63	12	0	98	12	1
29	12	1	66	3	0	99	3	1
						102	6	1

----------------- Control Group -----------------

Pat. No.	X	Y	Pat. No.	X	Y	Pat. No.	X	Y
3	9	1	38	15	0	72	9	1
5	3	0	40	15	1	75	15	0
8	12	1	41	9	0	76	15	0
9	3	1	43	9	0	78	12	0
12	3	1	45	12	1	80	9	0
13	15	1	47	3	1	82	12	0
16	9	1	48	6	1	84	15	0
18	12	1	51	6	1	86	18	1
19	3	1	53	12	0	87	12	0
23	9	1	55	12	0	89	15	1
24	15	1	57	12	1	91	15	0
27	9	1	59	3	1	93	15	0
30	6	1	61	12	1	96	18	0
31	9	1	64	3	1	97	18	1
34	6	1	65	12	1	100	18	0
35	12	0	68	6	1	101	18	0
37	9	0	70	6	1			

SOLUTION

We define the first factor, X_1, as the Treatment effect:

$$X_1 = \begin{array}{l} 0 \text{ if no treatment (Control Group)} \\ 1 \text{ if treated (\textit{asODN} Group)} \end{array} .$$

The second factor (X_2) is the numeric covariate, prior remission time (X in the data table). Technically, the *Logistic Regression* model incorporates both X_1 and X_2 as 'covariates',

$$P = \frac{1}{1 + e^{-(\alpha + \beta_1 X_1 + \beta_2 X_2)}} .$$

However, since X_1 actually represents a Treatment effect, we will consider the groups separately:

$$P_{x(A)} = \frac{1}{1 + e^{-(\alpha + \beta_1 + \beta_2 X_2)}} \quad \textit{for the Active group,} \quad \textit{and}$$

$$P_{x(C)} = \frac{1}{1 + e^{-(\alpha + \beta_2 X_2)}} \quad \textit{for the Control group} .$$

By constructing a series of 2-by-2 contingency tables from the data (one for each X_2 value), we obtain the following summary table:

X_2 (mos.)	*asODN* Group ($X_1 = 1$)			Control Group ($X_1 = 0$)		
	# of Events	N	Est. P_x	# of Events	N	Est. P_x
3	5	8	0.625	6	7	0.857
6	9	14	0.643	6	6	1.000
9	5	12	0.417	6	10	0.600
12	3	10	0.300	6	12	0.500
15	1	6	0.167	4	10	0.400
18	0	2	0.000	2	5	0.400
TOTAL	23	52	0.442	30	50	0.600

If remission time (X_2) is ignored, overall relapse rates are estimated as 0.442 for the *asODN* group and 0.600 for the Control group. This is not a significant difference using the *Chi-square Test* of Chapter 14 (χ^2 = 2.54, p = 0.111).

A plot of the summary data (Figure 18-2) reveals that the probability of relapse (P_x) appears to depend on the length of prior remission, with higher probabilities of relapse associated with shorter remission times. Using this information in a *Logistic Regression* analysis provides an adjusted treatment group comparison which is found to be significant (p=0.0165), as shown in the SAS analysis which follows.

FIGURE 18-2: Probability of Relapse (Px) vs. Remission Time (X) from Example 18.1

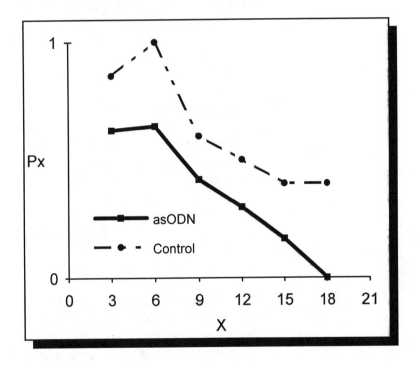

SAS Analysis of Example 18.1

We illustrate the analysis of Example 18.1 using the LOGISTIC procedure of SAS. The 'DESCENDING' option is used in the PROC LOGISTIC statement to let SAS know that the *event* of interest is 'relapse', or Y=1. Otherwise, SAS will model the smaller value of Y (Y=0) as the *event*.

The SAS code for performing the *Logistic Regression* analysis is shown on the next page, followed by the output.

The estimates of the model parameters, α, β_1, and β_2 are seen to be (1) a = 2.614, b_1 = -1.119 and b_2 = -0.200, resulting in estimated logistic regression equations of:

$$\hat{P}_{x(A)} = \frac{1}{1 + e^{-(1.495 - 0.200X)}} \quad \text{for the Active group, \quad and}$$

$$\hat{P}_{x(C)} = \frac{1}{1 + e^{-(2.614 - 0.200X)}} \quad \text{for the Control group },$$

where X = X_2. One question of interest is whether the remission time (X) is an important covariate, tested as follows:

null hypothesis: H_0: $\beta_2 = 0$

alt. hypothesis: H_A: $\beta_2 \neq 0$

test statistic: $\chi^2_w = 12.72$

decision rule: reject H_0 if $\chi^2_w > 3.841$

conclusion: Since 12.72 > 3.841, we reject H_0 indicating a significant covariate, X.

The computer output (2), based on the 'Wald' chi-square statistic, indicates that the time since last remission (X) is a highly significant background factor for predicting the probability of a relapse within 90 days (p=0.0004). This is not taken into account in the unadjusted *Chi-Square Test* (3), which yields relapse rates of 0.442 and 0.600 for the Active and Control groups, respectively (p=0.111).

Comparison of relapse rates between treatment groups (TRT) adjusted for the covariate is tested by the hypothesis

$$H_0: \beta_1 = 0$$

which is seen to be significant (4) with p = 0.0165.

```
* SAS Code for Example 18.1 ;

DATA AML;
INPUT PAT GROUP $   X RELAPSE $ @@;
  IF GROUP   = 'PBO' THEN TRT = 0;
  IF GROUP   = 'ACT' THEN TRT = 1;
  IF RELAPSE = 'YES' THEN  Y  = 1;
  IF RELAPSE = 'NO'  THEN  Y  = 0;
CARDS;
  1 ACT   3 NO     2 ACT   3 YES     4 ACT   3 YES
  6 ACT   6 YES    7 ACT  15 NO     10 ACT   6 YES
 11 ACT   6 YES   14 ACT   6 YES    15 ACT  15 NO
 17 ACT  15 NO    20 ACT  12 NO     21 ACT  18 NO
 22 ACT   6 YES   25 ACT  15 NO     26 ACT   6 YES
 28 ACT  15 NO    29 ACT  12 YES    32 ACT   9 NO
 33 ACT   6 YES   36 ACT   6 NO     39 ACT   6 NO
 42 ACT   6 NO    44 ACT   3 YES    46 ACT  18 NO
 49 ACT   9 NO    50 ACT  12 YES    52 ACT   6 NO
 54 ACT   9 YES   56 ACT   9 YES    58 ACT   3 NO
 60 ACT   9 YES   62 ACT  12 NO     63 ACT  12 NO
 66 ACT   3 NO    67 ACT  12 NO     69 ACT  12 NO
 71 ACT  12 NO    73 ACT   9 YES    74 ACT   6 YES
 77 ACT  12 NO    79 ACT   6 NO     81 ACT  15 YES
 83 ACT   9 NO    85 ACT   3 YES    88 ACT   9 NO
 90 ACT   9 NO    92 ACT   9 NO     94 ACT   9 NO
 95 ACT   9 YES   98 ACT  12 YES    99 ACT   3 YES
102 ACT   6 YES    3 PBO   9 YES     5 PBO   3 NO
  8 PBO  12 YES    9 PBO   3 YES    12 PBO   3 YES
 13 PBO  15 YES   16 PBO   9 YES    18 PBO  12 YES
 19 PBO   3 YES   23 PBO   9 YES    24 PBO  15 YES
 27 PBO   9 YES   30 PBO   6 YES    31 PBO   9 YES
 34 PBO   6 YES   35 PBO  12 NO     37 PBO   9 NO
 38 PBO  15 NO    40 PBO  15 YES    41 PBO   9 NO
 43 PBO   9 NO    45 PBO  12 YES    47 PBO   3 YES
 48 PBO   6 YES   51 PBO   6 YES    53 PBO  12 NO
 55 PBO  12 NO    57 PBO  12 YES    59 PBO   3 YES
 61 PBO  12 YES   64 PBO   3 YES    65 PBO  12 YES
 68 PBO   6 YES   70 PBO   6 YES    72 PBO   9 YES
 75 PBO  15 NO    76 PBO  15 NO     78 PBO  12 NO
 80 PBO   9 NO    82 PBO  12 NO     84 PBO  15 NO
 86 PBO  18 YES   87 PBO  12 NO     89 PBO  15 YES
 91 PBO  15 NO    93 PBO  15 NO     96 PBO  18 NO
 97 PBO  18 YES  100 PBO  18 NO    101 PBO  18 NO
;
RUN;

PROC LOGISTIC DATA = AML DESCENDING;
MODEL Y = TRT X;
TITLE1 'Logistic Regression';
TITLE2 'Example 18.1:  Relapse Rate Adjusted for
        Remission Time in AML';
RUN;

PROC FREQ DATA = AML;
TABLES Y*TRT/EXACT NOROW NOPERCENT NOCUM;
TITLE3 'Chi-Square Test Ignoring the Covariate';
RUN;
```

* SAS Output for Example 18.1

Logistic Regression
Example 18.1: Relapse Rate Adjusted for Remission Time in AML

The LOGISTIC Procedure

Data Set: WORK.AML
Response Variable: Y
Response Levels: 2
Number of Observations: 102
Link Function: Logit

Response Profile

Ordered Value	Y	Count
1	1	53
2	0	49

Criteria for Assessing Model Fit

Criterion	Intercept Only	Intercept and Covariates	Chi-Square for Covariates
AIC	143.245	129.376	.
SC	145.870	137.251	.
-2 LOG L	141.245	123.376	17.869 with 2 DF (p=0.0001)
Score	.	.	16.485 with 2 DF (p=0.0003)

Analysis of Maximum Likelihood Estimates

Variable	DF	Parameter Estimate (1)	Standard Error	Wald Chi-Square	Pr > Chi-Square	Standardized Estimate	Odds Ratio
INTERCPT	1	2.6136	0.7149	13.3672	0.0003	.	13.648
TRT	1	-1.1191	0.4669 (6)	5.7450	0.0165 (4)	-0.30997	0.327 (5)
X	1	-0.1998	0.0560	12.7195	0.0004 (2)	-0.49081	0.819

Chi-Square Test Ignoring the Covariate

TABLE OF Y BY TRT

Y Frequency Col Pct	0	1	Total
0	20 / 40.00	29 / 55.77	49
1	30 / 60.00	23 / 44.23	53
Total	50	52	102

STATISTICS FOR TABLE OF Y BY TRT

Statistic	DF	Value	Prob	
Chi-Square	1	2.539	0.111	(3)
Likelihood Ratio Chi-Square	1	2.551	0.110	
Continuity Adj. Chi-Square	1	1.947	0.163	
Mantel-Haenszel Chi-Square	1	2.514	0.113	
Fisher's Exact Test (Left)			0.081	
(Right)			0.964	
(2-Tail)			0.119	
Phi Coefficient		-0.158		
Contingency Coefficient		0.156		
Cramer's V		-0.158		

Sample Size = 102

We would like to be able to compute covariate-adjusted relapse rates which do not depend on any specific value of the covariate. Such adjusted rates would provide a differential measure of therapeutic effectiveness which is not biased by such baseline differences in the covariate.

The adjusted relapse rates can be found by

$$\bar{P} = \frac{1}{N} \cdot \sum_{i=1}^{N} \hat{P}_{x_i}$$

using the estimated *Logistic Regression* equations for each group. Thus for the Active group (*asODN*), we compute

$$\bar{p}_A = \frac{1}{N} \cdot \sum_{i=1}^{N} \frac{1}{1 + e^{-(1.495 - 0.200X_i)}}$$

and for the Control group,

$$\bar{p}_C = \frac{1}{N} \cdot \sum_{i=1}^{N} \frac{1}{1 + e^{-(2.614 - 0.200X_i)}} \quad .$$

Calculations proceed by first obtaining the estimated P_x for each patient and averaging over all patients. For patients with X=3, we obtain

$$\hat{P}_{3(A)} = \frac{1}{1 + e^{-0.895}} = 0.7100 \quad \textit{for the Active group,}$$

$$\hat{P}_{3(C)} = \frac{1}{1 + e^{-2.014}} = 0.8823 \quad \textit{for the Control group} \quad .$$

Further calculations are shown in the following table.

| | freq. | - Active Group - | | - Control Group - | |
x	(f)	$\hat{p}_{x(A)}$	$f \cdot \hat{p}_{x(A)}$	$\hat{p}_{x(C)}$	$f \cdot \hat{p}_{x(C)}$
3	15	0.7100	10.649	0.8823	13.234
6	20	0.5734	11.469	0.8046	16.091
9	22	0.4247	9.344	0.6933	15.253
12	22	0.2885	6.347	0.5539	12.186
15	16	0.1821	2.914	0.4054	6.487
18	7	0.1090	0.763	0.2725	1.907
	102		41.486		65.158

The final adjusted relapse rate estimates are

$$\bar{P}_A = \frac{41.486}{102} = 0.407 \qquad and,$$

$$\bar{P}_C = \frac{65.158}{102} = 0.639 \qquad .$$

The treatment effect (TRT) in the SAS output (4) is used to compare these adjusted relapse rates using the 'Wald' chi-square (5.745), seen to be significant (p = 0.0165)

In summary, we find the time in remission (X) has a significant bearing on estimates of the chance of a relapse within 90 days. This information has been used to adjust the relapse rates for each group, which are seen to be significantly different, while the unadjusted rates are not, as summarized below:

| | | -- Relapse Rates -- | | |
Analysis	Test	Active	Control	p-Value
Unadjusted	(Chi-Square Test)	0.422	0.600	0.111
Adjusted	(Logistic Regression)	0.407	0.639	0.017 *

* Significant (p < 0.05)

DETAILS & NOTES

▸ *Logistic Regression* is a useful tool for conducting exploratory analyses to identify background factors which may help explain trends observed in treatment comparisons. SAS prints out 2 measures, the Akaike Information Criterion (AIC) and the Schwarz Criterion (SC), whose relative values can be used to assess the 'goodness of fit' of the model. Covariates can be added or removed to obtain the most appropriate model by attempting to minimize the values of these criteria.

▸ In clinical trials, equality of response rates between groups is usually tested by the hypothesis of a zero difference. We can also compare response rates by measuring how close their ratio is to 1. This ratio is called 'relative risk' and is often discussed in epidemiological studies along with the odds ratio.

In Example 18.1, the odds of relapse within 90 days for the Active group is given by

$$O_A = \hat{p}_{x(A)}/(1-\hat{p}_{x(A)}) = e^{(1.495-0.200x)} \ .$$

Similarly, the odds for the Control group is

$$O_C = e^{(2.614-0.200x)}.$$

The odds-ratio is a measure of the odds of relapse in the treated group relative to that of the untreated group. In this example, we compute the odds ratio as

$$\frac{O_A}{O_C} = \frac{e^{(1.495-0.200x)}}{e^{(2.614-0.200x)}} = e^{-1.119} = 0.327 \ ,$$

with the interpretation that the odds of relapse within 90 days is only about one-third (0.327) as great in the Active group compared with the Control group. This measure, which is printed on the SAS output (5), is independent of the covariate, remission time (X). An easy way to compute the odds ratio is by exponentiating the parameter estimate associated with the treatment factor, b_1.

Notice that the unadjusted odds (ignoring remission time) are

$$0.442/0.558 = 0.792 \text{ for the Active group, and}$$

$$0.600/0.400 = 1.500 \text{ for the Control group.}$$

A comparison of these odds results in an odds ratio of $0.792/1.500 = 0.528$, which is considerably larger than the odds ratio (0.327) found using the covariance adjustment.

▸ An approximate 95% confidence interval can be constructed for the odds ratio of the treated group relative to the untreated group by exponentiating the upper and lower confidence limits for β_1, represented by

$$b_1 \pm 1.96 \cdot s(b_1) \ .$$

The standard error of the parameter estimate b_1, $s(b_1)$, can be obtained from the SAS output (6). In Example 18.1, we have $b_1 = -1.119$ and $s(b_1) = 0.4669$, resulting in a 95% confidence interval for β_1 as:

$$-1.119 \pm 1.96 \cdot (0.4669)$$

or,

$$[-2.034 \text{ to } -0.204].$$

An approximate 95% C.I. for O_A/O_C is

$$[e^{-2.034} \text{ to } e^{-0.204}]$$

or,

$$[0.131 \text{ to } 0.815].$$

Confidence intervals for the odds ratios can be obtained by SAS using the RISKLIMITS option of the MODEL statement under PROC LOGISTIC (see SAS manual).

▶ Other transformations, such as the probit (based on the inverse normal distribution) can be used in a manner similar to the logit. The logistic transformation enjoys popular usage because of its application ease and appropriateness as a model for a wide range of natural phenomena. As illustrated in a plot of P vs. its logit function (Figure 18-3), ln(P/(1-P)) is fairly linear in P over a large portion of the range of P (approximately 0.2-0.8). For very large or very small values of P, the logit of P is greatly magnified. This is consistent with a model based on intuition, in which a change in response rates, say, from 45% to 50% may not be as clinically relevant as a change from 5% to 10%.

The logistic transformation also has the advantage of mapping a limited range of observable values (0-1) onto an unlimited range (-∞ to +∞). Thus, the potential problem of obtaining estimates outside the observable range is eliminated.

FIGURE 18-3: Plot of Transformation from P to the Logit(P)

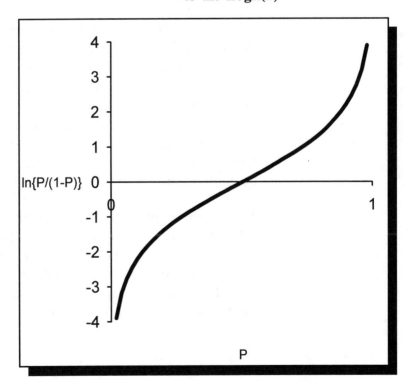

▸ This chapter presents an introduction to *Logistic Regression* using covariates which have either numeric or ordinal values. *Logistic Regression* may also be used with non-ordinal categorical covariates with more than 2 levels by defining dummy variables corrsponding to the levels. For example, suppose geographic region is a covariate of interest, with levels A (North), B (South), C (Midwest) and D (West). One of the levels, say A, is designated as a reference, and 3 dummy variables are created as follows:

$$X_1 = 1 \text{ if from Region B}, \quad X_1 = 0 \text{ otherwise},$$

$$X_2 = 1 \text{ if from Region C}, \quad X_2 = 0 \text{ otherwise},$$

and, $X_3 = 1$ if from Region D, $X_3 = 0$ otherwise.

Using a *Logistic Regression* model with these variables as covariates, the odds-ratios represent the odds of response relative to Region A.

Logistic Regression may also be carried out using the SAS procedure CATMOD. This procedure is recommended for categorical modelling with nominal covariates.

▸ Just as *Analysis-of-Covariance* assumes equal slopes among groups, *Logistic Regression* also assumes that the slope of the logit function is similar among groups. This assumption can be checked by a preliminary plot of the data along with the inclusion of the interaction terms between the appropriate X-variables in the *Logistic Regression* model. Caution must be used in the interpretation of treatment group differences in the presence of interactions.

▸ The maximum-likelihood equations may not always have a solution. In cases with small sample sizes, convergence to a unique solution based on the iterative calculations may not be attainable. As a rule of thumb, the sample size N should be at least 10 times the number of covariates when fitting a *Logistic Regression* model.

CHAPTER 19

The LOG-RANK TEST

INTRODUCTION

The *Log-Rank Test* is a statistical method for comparing distributions of time until the occurrence of an *event* of interest among independent groups. The *event* is often death due to disease, but it may be any binomial outcome, such as cure, response, relapse or failure. The elapsed time from initial treatment or observation until the *event* is the *event* time, often referred to as 'survival time', even when the *event* is not 'death'.

The *Log-Rank Test* provides a method for comparing 'risk-adjusted' *event* rates, useful when patients in a clinical study are subject to varying degrees of opportunity to experience the *event*. Such situations arise frequently in clinical trials due to the finite duration of the study, early termination of the patient or interuption of treatment before the *event* occurs.

Examples where use of the *Log-Rank Test* might be appropriate include comparing survival times in cancer patients who are given a new treatment with those on standard chemotherapy, or comparing times to cure of several doses of a topical antifungal preparation where the patient is treated for 10 weeks or until cured, whichever comes first.

If every patient were followed until the *event* occurrence, the *event* times could be compared between two groups using the *Wilcoxon Rank-Sum Test* (Chapter 11). However, some patients may drop out or complete the study before the *event* occurs. In such cases, the actual time to *event* is unknown since the *event* does not occur while under study observation. The *event* times for these patients are based on the last known time of study observation, and are called 'censored' observations since they represent the lower-bound of the true, unknown *event* times. The *Wilcoxon Rank Sum Test* can be highly biased in the presence of censored data.

SYNOPSIS

The null hypothesis tested by the *Log-Rank Test* is that of equal *event* time distributions among groups. Equality of the distributions of *event* times implies similar *event* rates among groups not only for the clinical trial as a whole, but also for any arbitrary time point during the trial. Rejection of the null hypothesis indicates that the *event* rates differ among groups at one or more time points during the study.

We will examine the case of 2 independent groups, although the same method may be extended to more than 2 groups. A typical data set layout has the following form, where Y represents the time from initial treatment to the *event* occurrence, and a '✓' indicates a censored value.

GROUP 1			GROUP 2		
Pat. No.	*Event* Time		Pat. No.	*Event* Time	
101	Y_{11}		102	Y_{21}	✓
103	Y_{12}	✓	105	Y_{22}	
104	Y_{13}		106	Y_{23}	
.	.	.	.	.	.
.	.	.	.	.	.
.	.	.	.	.	.
N_1	Y_{1N_1}	✓	N_2	Y_{2N_2}	✓

We divide the study into k distinct time periods, t_1, t_2, ..., t_k, where t_j (j=1,2,...k) represents the time point when one or more patients in the combined samples becomes *event-positive*. Let d_{ij} represent the number of patients in Group i (i=1,2) who first experience the *event* at time period t_j, and n_{ij} represent the number of patients in Group i who are at risk at the beginning of time period t_j. "At risk" describes the patients who are 'event-negative' and still in the study. Let $d_j = d_{1j} + d_{2j}$ and $n_j = n_{1j} + n_{2j}$, and, for $j = 1, 2, ..., k$, compute

$$e_{1j} = \frac{n_{1j} \cdot d_j}{n_j} \quad and \quad v_j = \frac{n_{1j} \cdot n_{2j} \cdot d_j \cdot (n_j - d_j)}{n_j^2 \cdot (n_j - 1)} \quad .$$

Finally, we obtain:

$$O_1 = \sum_{j=1}^{k} d_{1j} \quad ,$$

$$E_1 = \sum_{j=1}^{k} e_{1j} \quad , \quad and$$

$$V = \sum_{j=1}^{k} v_j \quad .$$

Denote by Y_i a random variable representing the *event* time for Group i (i=1,2), and let $S_i(t) = \text{Prob}\{Y_i \geq t\}$. The hypothesis test summary for the *Log-Rank Test* is as follows:

null hypothesis: H_0: $S_1(t) = S_2(t)$ (for all times, t)

alt. hypothesis: H_A: $S_1(t) \neq S_2(t)$ (for at least one time, t)

test statistic: $\chi^2 = \frac{(O_1 - E_1)^2}{V}$

decision rule: *reject H_0 if $\chi^2 > \chi^2_1(\alpha)$*

where, $\chi^2_1(\alpha)$ is the critical chi-square value with significance level, α, and 1 degree-of-freedom.

EXAMPLE 19.1 -- "HSV-2 Episodes Following gD2 Vaccine"

Forty-eight patients with genital herpes (HSV-2) were enrolled in a study of a new recombinant herpes vaccine based on the antigen glycoprotein, gD2. Patients were required to have a history of at least 6 HSV-2 episodal outbreaks in the 12 months prior to study enrollment and be in remission at the time of vaccination. Patients were randomly assigned to receive either a single gD2 vaccine injection (n=25) or placebo (n=23), and were followed for 1 year. The data set below shows the time (in weeks) to first recurrence of HSV-2 following immunization for each patient (Y), along with the number of episodes during the 12 month period prior to enrollment (X). Is there evidence that the distributions of the times to recurrence differ between the groups?

------------------------- gD2 Vaccine Group ---------------------

Pat No.	X	Y		Pat No.	X	Y	
1	12	8		26	12	52	✓
3	10	12	✓	28	13	36	
6	7	52	✓	31	8	52	✓
7	10	28		33	10	9	
8	6	44		34	16	11	✓
10	8	14		36	6	52	✓
12	8	3		39	14	15	
14	9	52	✓	40	13	13	
15	11	35		42	13	21	
18	13	6		44	16	24	✓
20	7	12		46	13	52	✓
23	13	7	✓	48	9	28	
24	9	52	✓				

✓ =   censored time   (note: patients with censored times less than 52 weeks were study dropouts)

(Data continued on next page)

| ------------------------------- Placebo Group ------------------------- |||||||
Pat No.	X	Y		Pat No.	X	Y	
2	9	15		27	9	9	✓
4	10	44	✓	29	10	27	
5	12	2	✓	30	17	1	
9	7	8		32	8	12	
11	7	12		35	8	20	
13	7	52	✓	37	8	32	✓
16	7	21		38	8	15	
17	11	19		41	14	5	
19	16	6		43	13	35	
21	16	10		45	9	28	
22	6	15	✓	47	15	6	
25	15	4					

✓ = censored time (note: patients with censored times less than 52 weeks were study dropouts)

SOLUTION

Initially, we analyze the data ignoring the covariate, X. This example is also used in Chapter 20, *The Cox Proportional Hazards Model*, which discusses the comparison of survival distributions using covariate-adjustments.

The first step in manual computation of the *Log-Rank Test* is to construct a table for each *event* time as shown on the next page. At each time period, t_j, the number of patients at risk, n_{ij}, is reduced by the number of *event*-positives (d_{ij}) and censored observations (w_{ij}) from the previous time period, t_{j-1}.

Summary Table for Computing the *Log-Rank Test* for Example 19.1

WEEK	gD2 VACCINE GROUP			PLACEBO GROUP			TOTAL			
t_j	d_{1j}	w_{1j}	n_{1j}	d_{2j}	w_{2j}	n_{2j}	d_j	n_j	e_1	v_1
1	0	0	25	1	0	23	1	48	0.5208	0.2496
2	0	0	25	0	1	22	0	47	0	0
3	1	0	25	0	0	21	1	46	0.5435	0.2481
4	0	0	24	1	0	21	1	45	0.5333	0.2489
5	0	0	24	1	0	20	1	44	0.5455	0.2479
6	1	0	24	2	0	19	3	43	1.6744	0.7046
7	0	1	23	0	0	17	0	40	0	0
8	1	0	22	1	0	17	2	39	1.1282	0.4788
9	1	0	21	0	1	16	1	37	0.5676	0.2454
10	0	0	20	1	0	15	1	35	0.5714	0.2449
11	0	1	20	0	0	14	0	34	0	0
12	1	1	19	2	0	14	3	33	1.7273	0.6870
13	1	0	17	0	0	12	1	29	0.5862	0.2426
14	1	0	16	0	0	12	1	28	0.5714	0.2449
15	1	0	15	2	1	12	3	27	1.6667	0.6838
19	0	0	14	1	0	9	1	23	0.6087	0.2382
20	0	0	14	1	0	8	1	22	0.6364	0.2314
21	1	0	14	1	0	7	2	21	1.3333	0.4222
24	0	1	13	0	0	6	0	19	0	0
27	0	0	12	1	0	6	1	18	0.6667	0.2222
28	2	0	12	1	0	5	3	17	2.1176	0.5450
32	0	0	10	0	1	4	0	14	0	0
35	1	0	10	1	0	3	2	13	1.5385	0.3254
36	1	0	9	0	0	2	1	11	0.8182	0.1488
44	1	0	8	0	1	2	1	10	0.8000	0.1600
52	0	7	7	0	1	1	0	8	0	0
	14 (O_1)			17			31		19.1556 (E_1)	6.8197 (V)

(Highlighted times do not affect the calculations of E_1 and V. These are shown only to account for all censored observations)

Let $S_1(t)$ and $S_2(t)$ represent the cumulative probability distributions of the times from vaccine administration until first HSV-2 recurrence for the gD2 and placebo groups, respectively. The hypothesis test summary is as follows:

null hypothesis: H_0: $S_1(t) = S_2(t)$ (for all times, t)

alt. hypothesis: H_A: $S_1(t) \neq S_2(t)$ (for at least one
time, t)

test statistic: $$\chi^2 = \frac{(O_1 - E_1)^2}{V}$$

$$= \frac{(14 - 19.1556)^2}{6.8197} = 3.8976$$

decision rule: *reject H_0 if $\chi^2 > \chi^2_1(0.05) = 3.841$*

conclusion: Since $3.897 > 3.841$, reject H_0 and conclude that the recurrence times are significantly different between the gD2 and placebo vaccine groups at a 0.05 level of significance.

SAS Analysis of Example 19.1

We use the SAS procedure LIFETEST to apply the *Log-Rank Test* to the data set, as shown in the SAS code and output which follow. The TIME statement following the PROC LIFETEST statement designates the *event* times (WKS) as shown in the data printout (1). Censored times are designated by an indicator variable (CENS). In the example, SAS statements are used to generate the indicator variable, CENS, from the censored times which are input as negative values.

The output shows the *Log-Rank Test* resulting in a chi-square value of 3.8976 (2), confirming our manual calculations. This is a significant result with a p-value of 0.0484 (3). Also shown on the output are the values of $O_1-E_1 = -5.1556$ (4) and $V = 6.89173$ (5).

```
* SAS Code for Example 19.1 ;

  DATA HSV;
  INPUT VAC $ PAT WKS X @@;
    CENS = (WKS < 1);
    WKS  = ABS(WKS);
    IF VAC = 'GD2' THEN TRT = 1;
    IF VAC = 'PBO' THEN TRT = 0;
  CARDS;
GD2   1   8 12   GD2  3 -12 10   GD2  6 -52  7
GD2   7  28 10   GD2  8  44  6   GD2 10  14  8
GD2  12   3  8   GD2 14 -52  9   GD2 15  35 11
GD2  18   6 13   GD2 20  12  7   GD2 23  -7 13
GD2  24 -52  9   GD2 26 -52 12   GD2 28  36 13
GD2  31 -52  8   GD2 33   9 10   GD2 34 -11 16
GD2  36 -52  6   GD2 39  15 14   GD2 40  13 13
GD2  42  21 13   GD2 44 -24 16   GD2 46 -52 13
GD2  48  28  9   PBO  2  15  9   PBO  4 -44 10
PBO   8  -2 12   PBO  9   8  7   PBO 11  12  7
PBO  13 -52  7   PBO 16  21  7   PBO 17  19 11
PBO  19   6 16   PBO 21  10 16   PBO 22 -15  6
PBO  25   4 15   PBO 27  -9  9   PBO 29  27 10
PBO  30   1 17   PBO 32  12  8   PBO 35  20  8
PBO  37 -32  8   PBO 38  15  8   PBO 41   5 14
PBO  43  35 13   PBO 45  28  9   PBO 47   6 15
;
RUN;

PROC SORT DATA = HSV; BY VAC PAT; RUN;
PROC PRINT DATA = HSV;
VAR VAC PAT WKS CENS X;
TITLE1 'The Log-Rank Test';
TITLE2 'Example 19.1: HSV-2 Episodes with gD2
         Vaccine';
RUN;

PROC LIFETEST PLOT=(S) DATA = HSV;
TIME WKS*CENS(1)           ;
STRATA VAC                 ;
RUN;
```

(note: portions of the ouput are omitted)

```
* SAS Output for Example 19.1


                        The Log-Rank Test
        Example 19.1: HSV-2 Episodes with gD2 Vaccine

         OBS    VAC    PAT    WKS    CENS     X

           1    GD2     1      8      0      12
           2    GD2     3     12      1      10
           3    GD2     6     52      1       7
           4    GD2     7     28      0      10
           5    GD2     8     44      0       6
           6    GD2    10     14      0       8
           7    GD2    12      3      0       8
           8    GD2    14     52      1       9
           9    GD2    15     35      0      11
          10    GD2    18      6      0      13
          11    GD2    20     12      0       7
          12    GD2    23      7      1      13
          13    GD2    24     52      1       9
          14    GD2    26     52      1      12
          15    GD2    28     36      0      13
          16    GD2    31     52      1       8
          17    GD2    33      9      0      10
          18    GD2    34     11      1      16
          19    GD2    36     52      1       6
          20    GD2    39     15      0      14
          21    GD2    40     13      0      13
          22    GD2    42     21      0      13
          23    GD2    44     24      1      16       (1)
          24    GD2    46     52      1      13
          25    GD2    48     28      0       9
          26    PBO     2     15      0       9
          27    PBO     4     44      1      10
          28    PBO     8      2      1      12
          29    PBO     9      8      0       7
          30    PBO    11     12      0       7
          31    PBO    13     52      1       7
          32    PBO    16     21      0       7
          33    PBO    17     19      0      11
          34    PBO    19      6      0      16
          35    PBO    21     10      0      16
          36    PBO    22     15      1       6
          37    PBO    25      4      0      15
          38    PBO    27      9      1       9
          39    PBO    29     27      0      10
          40    PBO    30      1      0      17
          41    PBO    32     12      0       8
          42    PBO    35     20      0       8
          43    PBO    37     32      1       8
          44    PBO    38     15      0       8
          45    PBO    41      5      0      14
          46    PBO    43     35      0      13
          47    PBO    45     28      0       9
          48    PBO    47      6      0      15
```

```
            * SAS Output for Example 19.1 -- continued


                         The Log-Rank Test
              Example 19.1: HSV-2 Episodes with gD2 Vaccine
                        The LIFETEST Procedure

               Summary Statistics for Time Variable WKS
                            VAC = GD2
                        Point      95% Confidence Interval
             Quantile   Estimate       [Lower, Upper)

              75%          .           35.0000         .
      (9)     50%       35.0000        15.0000         .
              25%       13.0000         8.0000      28.0000

     (10)    Mean   28.7214        Standard Error   3.2823


                            VAC = PBO
                        Point      95% Confidence Interval
             Quantile   Estimate       [Lower, Upper)

              75%       28.0000        19.0000         .
      (9)     50%       15.0000        10.0000      27.0000
              25%        8.0000         5.0000      15.0000

     (10)    Mean   18.2397        Standard Error   2.5387

        NOTE: The last observation was censored so the estimate of the
        mean is biased.

        Summary of the Number of Censored and Uncensored Values

           VAC       Total    Failed    Censored   %Censored

           GD2         25       14         11       44.0000
           PBO         23       17          6       26.0870

           Total       48       31         17       35.4167


           Testing Homogeneity of Survival Curves over Strata
                        Time Variable WKS

                          Rank Statistics
                 VAC       Log-Rank      Wilcoxon
                             (4)
                 GD2       -5.1556       -160.00
                 PBO        5.1556        160.00

           Covariance Matrix for the Log-Rank Statistics
             VAC              GD2            PBO
                              (5)
             GD2            6.81973       -6.81973
             PBO           -6.81973        6.81973

           Covariance Matrix for the Wilcoxon Statistics
             VAC              GD2            PBO

             GD2            7136.46       -7136.46
             PBO           -7136.46        7136.46

                   Test of Equality over Strata
                                              Pr >
               Test        Chi-Square   DF   Chi-Square

           Log-Rank   (2)    3.8976      1      0.0484   (3)
           Wilcoxon          3.5872      1      0.0582   (6)
           -2Log(LR)         4.2589      1      0.0390   (7)
```

```
                    * SAS Output for Example 19.1 -- continued

                              The Log-Rank Test
                    Example 19.1: HSV-2 Episodes with gD2 Vaccine


                            The LIFETEST Procedure
                          Survival Function Estimates

   SDF |
   1.0 +**--G
       | |  |
       | P--G*-G
       |    | |
       |    PPG--G
   0.9 +      | |                                        (8)
       |      | GG
       |      PP |
       |        G--G
S  0.8 +        | G-G
u      |        P--P   |
r      |           |   GG
v      |           |   |
i  0.7 +           P-P  GG
v      |             |  |
a      |             P-P  G-------G
l      |                  |       |
   0.6 +                  |       G---------G
D      |                  P---P            |
i      |                     |             |
s  0.5 +                     P----P        G--------G
t      |                         |                 |
r      |                         PP                GG
i      |                         PP                |
b  0.4 +                          |                G---------G
u      |                          |                         G
t      |                          P------P
i  0.3 +                                 |
o      |                                 P-P
n      |                                   P-------P
   0.2 +                                           |
F      |                                           P
u  0.1 +
n      |
c      |
t      +-----+-----+-----+-----+-----+-----+-----+-----+-----+-----+
i            0     5    10    15    20    25    30    35    40    45    50
o                                       WKS
n
                          Censored Observations

  Strata
   P +  P       P     P                P          P       P
   G +        G   GG             G              *
      +----+----+----+----+----+----+----+----+----+----+----+--
           0    5   10   15   20   25   30   35   40   45   50
                                   WKS
                        Legend for Strata Symbols
                        G:VAC=GD2   P:VAC=PBO
```

DETAILS & NOTES

▸ The selection of a time point during the clinical study at which to compare *event* rates among groups is not always clearcut. The last double-blind visit is often designated for such use, although drawbacks may exist for this choice. First, the duration of the study itself may be somewhat arbitrary or constrained by safety issues or other considerations unrelated to response. More importantly, the analysis ignores information prior to this evaluation time point which may have an important impact on the results.

If the data of Example 19.1 were analyzed with the *Chi-Square Test* (Chapter 14) for comparing *event* rates at the final visit using a 'last-observation-carried-forward' method, we obtain:

	gD2 Group	Placebo Group	TOTAL
HSV-2 Recurrence	14 (56.0%)	17 (73.9%)	31 (64.6%)
No Recurrence	11	6	17
Total Enrolled	25	23	48

The HSV-2 recurrence rate comparison (56.0% vs. 73.9%) is not significant ($\chi^2 = 1.680$, p = 0.195). This is based on the *Chi-Square Test* (Chapter 14) which ignores the time patients were at risk. By analyzing time to *event* occurrence and accounting for censoring, the *Log-Rank Test* uses *event* rates over the whole trial, rather than relying on a single time point.

▸ For the j-th time period (t_j), we can construct a 2-by-2 contingency table as follows:

	GROUP 1	GROUP 2	TOTAL
'Event Pos.'	d_{1j}	d_{2j}	d_j
'Event Neg.'	$n_{1j} - d_{1j}$	$n_{2j} - d_{2j}$	$n_j - d_j$
Total	n_{1j}	n_{2j}	n_j

The *Log-Rank Test* is simply an application of the *Cochran-Mantel-Haenszel Test* (Chapter 17) using these 2-by-2 tables at each time point as the strata.

▸ Many variations of the *Log-Rank Test* for comparing survival distributions exist. The most common variant has the form:

$$\chi^2 = \frac{(O_1 - E_1)^2}{E_1} + \frac{(O_2 - E_2)^2}{E_2}$$

where O_i and E_i are computed for each group, as in the formulas given previously. This statistic also has an approximate chi-square distribution with 1 degree-of-freedom under H_0.

In Example 19.1, we have $O_1 = 14$, $O_2 = 17$ and $E_1 = 19.1556$. Using the relationship that $O_1 + O_2 = E_1 + E_2$, we obtain $E_2 = 14 + 17 - 19.1556 = 11.8444$, resulting in

$$\chi^2 = \frac{(14 - 19.1556)^2}{19.1556} + \frac{(17 - 11.8444)^2}{11.8444} = 3.632$$

with a p-value of 0.0567. Although computationally easier, this test gives a more conservative result than the version presented.

A continuity correction can also be used by reducing the numerators by 1/2 before squaring. Use of such a correction leads to even further conservatism and may be omitted when sample sizes are moderate or large.

▸ It was previously mentioned that the *Wilcoxon Rank-Sum Test* could be used to analyze the *event* times in the absence of censoring. A *'Generalized Wilcoxon' Test*, sometimes called the *Gehan Test*, based on an approximate chi-square distribution has been developed for use in the presence of censored observations. Manual computations for this procedure can be tedious, and the reader is referred to Dawson-Saunders & Trapp [1990, p. 196] for illustration of a worked example. Results of this test are available on the SAS output. The *Generalized Wilcoxon* chi-square for Example 19.1 is 3.587 with a p-value of 0.0582 (6), which is close to the results of the *Log-Rank Test* for this example, but not significant.

Both the *Log-Rank* and the *Generalized Wilcoxon Tests* are non-parametric tests, and require no assumptions regarding the distribution of *event* times. When the *event* rate is greater early in the trial than toward the end, the *Generalized Wilcoxon Test* is the more appropriate test since it gives greater weight to the earlier differences.

▸ Survival and failure times often follow the exponential distribution. If such a model can be assumed, a more powerful alternative to the *Log-Rank Test* is the *Likelihood Ratio Test*, the results of which are also printed in the SAS output (as '-2Log(LR)'). The output for Example 19.1 shows a likelihood ratio chi-square of 4.259 with a p-value of 0.039 (7).

This parametric test assumes that *event* probabilities are constant over time. That is, the chance that a patient becomes *event*-positive at time t given that he is *event*-negative up to time t does not depend on t. A plot of the negative log of the *event* times distribution showing a linear trend through the origin is consistent with exponential *event* times. The SAS option PLOT=LS can be used to obtain such a plot.

▸ Life tables can be constructed to provide estimates of the *event* time distributions. Estimates commonly used for data sets similar to that of Example 19.1 are known as the Kaplan-Meier estimates. These are the default estimates given by SAS (although they are not included in the printout here).

A plot of the distribution function vs. time provides a good visual description of the distributions. SAS will provide such a plot using the 'PLOT=S' option, as shown in Example 19.1 (8).

▸ Additional summary statistics printed by SAS that may be useful are the estimated median and mean *event* times for each group. The median event times are shown on the output as the 50% quantile, and, if possible to compute, are accompanied by 95% confidence intervals. For Example 19.1, the median times until first recurrence are 35 and 15 weeks, respectively, for the gD2 and placebo vaccine groups (9), while the estimates of the means are 28.7 and 18.2 weeks, respectively (10). The estimates of the means will always be biased unless all patients become *event*-positive by study completion. As noted on the SAS output, these estimates are biased due to censored observations.

▸ The chi-square statistic for the *Log-Rank Test* as presented in this chapter is a two-tailed test. The p-value from the SAS output can be halved to obtain a one-tailed test.

▸ The *Log-Rank Test* is presented here as a means for comparing 2 treatment groups. The same methods can be used with one group to compare 2 strata. For example, a comparison of *event* times between males and females treated with the same test preparation can be made with the *Log-Rank Test*.

▸ The *Log-Rank Test* can easily be extended to more than 2 groups. With g groups or strata, the hypothesis of equal event-time distributions can be tested with

$$\chi^2 = \sum_{i=1}^{g} \frac{(O_i - E_i)^2}{E_i} \quad ,$$

which has an approximate chi-square distribution with g-1 degrees-of-freedom under H_0. It is easy to see that the techniques of the *Log-Rank Test* can be used to compare *event* times among the levels of any categorical factor.

CHAPTER 20
The COX PROPORTIONAL HAZARDS MODEL

INTRODUCTION

Like the *Log-Rank Test* discussed in the previous chapter, the *Cox Proportional Hazards Model* is used to analyze *event* or 'survival' times. This method has become a widely accepted approach in clinical biostatistics for accomplishing this task, since it easily accomodates adjustments for possible effects of covariates on the results.

There are many considerations to make when analyzing survival distributions. Chief among them are the probability distribution of the *event* times, the degree of censoring, and the possible effect of one or more covariates on the analysis. Another important consideration which we will mention here but defer the details to more advanced texts, is that of changing *hazard* functions over time.

Briefly, the *hazard* represents the probability that the *event* of interest occurs at a specified time t given that it has not occurred prior to time t. Some *events* become more likely to occur with the passage of time, such as death due to certain types of cancer. Other types of *events* may become less likely as time goes on. Reinfarction following coronary artery bypass, for example, may have the greatest risk in the weeks immediately following surgery, decreasing with time. Still other types of *events* may be subject to fluctuating risks, both up and down, over time.

The hazard is a function of time, t. If a model for the hazard function can be assumed, then the survival distributions can be specified, and a parametric analysis can be applied, often with greater efficiency than non-parametric methods, such as the *Log-Rank Test*. One of the main advantages of a parametric approach is that, with a known survival distribution, one can easily incorporate covariates into the analysis. Widely used models include the exponential, log-normal, Weibull, gamma and log-logistic distributions. The SAS procedure LIFEREG can be used to fit any of these models with any number of covariates.

The main disadvantage of the parametric approach is that, in many cases, model assumptions may be incorrect and there may not be enough data to adequately test the assumptions, or perhaps the actual hazard function is not well represented by any of those in common usage. In many cases, the results are highly dependent on the appropriate distributional assumptions.

The *Cox Proportional Hazards Model* is a widely used 'semi-parametric' approach which does not require the assumption of any particular hazard function or distribution of survival time data. In this sense, it has the non-parametric features of the *Log-Rank Test*.

However, like regression analysis, this approach models the survival times as a function of the covariates. Various types of functions can be used and different models can also be specified for the distribution of the error variation. In this sense, the *Cox Proportional Hazards Model* is parametric.

In Chapter 19, it was indicated how to test for exponential survival times by checking whether a plot of the log of the survival probabilities is linear through the origin. This test is a direct result of the fact that the exponential distribution is associated with a constant hazard function (independent of time). Most diseases, however, progress in a manner in which the hazard changes over time. It may be more reasonable to assume that the *event* hazard rate changes over time, but that the ratio of *event* hazards between two individuals is constant. This is known as the 'proportional hazards' assumption, which requires that the ratio of hazards between any two fixed sets of covariates not vary with time. If age is a covariate to be used in the analysis, the proportional hazards assumption would require, for example, that the ratio of the hazard for 60-65 year old patients to that for 30-35 year old patients be constant over time.

SYNOPSIS

The *Cox Proportional Hazards Model* is used to test the effect of a specified set of k covariates, X_1, X_2, ..., X_k on the *event* times. The X_i's may be numeric-valued covariates or numerically coded categorical responses which have some natural ordering. They may also be dummy variables representing levels of a nominal categorical factor, as described for *Logistic Regression* (Chapter 18).

The model for the hazard function of the *Cox Proportional Hazards* approach has the form:

$$h(t) = \lambda(t) \cdot e^{(\beta_1 X_1 + \beta_2 X_2 + ... + \beta_k X_k)}$$

where h(t) represents the hazard function, the X_i's represent the covariates, the β_i's represent the parameter coefficients of the X_i's, and $\lambda(t)$ represents an unspecified initial hazard function. As with regression analysis, the magnitudes of the β_i's reflect the importance of the covariates in the model, and inference about these parameters is the focus of our attention.

D. R. Cox, after whom the model is named, developed a method for estimating β_i (i = 1,2,...,k) by b_i based on a 'maximum partial likelihood' approach, which is a modification of the Maximum Likelihood Procedure mentioned in Chapter 18. Solutions generally require numerical techniques using high-speed computers, as manual computations are impractical. The SAS procedure PHREG is recommended for fitting the *Cox Proportional Hazards Model*.

For large samples, these estimates (b_i) have an approximate normal distribution. If s_b represents the standard error of the estimate, b_i, then b_i/s_b has an approximate standard normal distribution under the null hypothesis that $\beta_i = 0$, and its square has the chi-square distribution with one degree-of-freedom. The test summary for each model parameter, β_i, can be summarized as follows:

null hypothesis:	H_0: $\beta_i = 0$
alternative hypothesis:	H_A: $\beta_i \neq 0$
test statistic:	$\chi^2_w = \left(\dfrac{b_i}{s_b} \right)^2$
decision rule:	*reject H_0 if $\chi^2_w > \chi^2_1(\alpha)$*

As an alternative to the *Log-Rank Test*, we may compare *event* time distributions between two groups from a comparative study with the *Cox Proportional Hazards Model*. To do this, we use one X-variable, defined as X=0 for Group A and X=1 for Group B. The hypothesis that the X coefficient parameter, β, equals zero is equivalent to the hypothesis of equal *event* time distributions, as given in Chapter 19.

The strength of the *Cox Proportional Hazards Model*, however, is its ability to incorporate other background factors or covariates. When many covariates are being considered, this method can be used in an exploratory fashion to build a model which includes significant covariates and excludes those which are not important. The SAS manual demonstrates this with an example using stepwise regression.

Example 20.1, which follows, illustrates the *Cox Proportional Hazards* approach with a simple example using one group variable and one numeric covariate.

EXAMPLE 20.1 -- "HSV-2 Episodes with gD2 Vaccine - cont'd."
(See Example 19.1)
We will re-analyze the data of Example 19.1 accounting for history of HSV-2 lesional episodes during the year prior to the study (X). The data are given in Chapter 19. Does the covariate X have any impact on the analysis?

SOLUTION

We use the SAS procedure PHREG to fit the *Cox Proportional Hazards Model* using the following SAS statements:

```
*   SAS Code for Example 20.1 ;

PROC PHREG DATA = HSV;
MODEL WKS*CENS(1) = TRT X/ TIES = EXACT;
TITLE1 'Cox Proportional Hazards Model';
TITLE2 'Example 20.1: HSV-2 Episodes with gD2
             Vaccine - cont''d.' ;
RUN;
```

Since the X-variables to be included in the model must have numeric values, we first convert the group field, VAC, to a numeric field. This is done with the new variable, TRT, which takes the value 1 for the gD2 vaccine group and 0 for placebo (see SAS code in Example 19.1).

With PHREG, the MODEL statement is used with the time variable and censoring indicator on the left side and the covariates on the right side of the equal sign. We specify the vaccine group factor, TRT $(=X_1)$, and the HSV-2 lesion frequency during the prior year, X $(=X_2)$, as the two covariates. The TIES statement is used in the event of more than one observation with tied *event* times. This is discussed further in DETAILS & NOTES.

The SAS output is shown on the next page. The estimate of the parameter associated with the covariate, X, is 0.176 (1) which is significant (p = 0.0073) (2) based on the Wald chi-square (χ^2_w). This means that prior lesional frequency is an important consideration when analyzing the *event* times. The test for the group effect (TRT) is also significant (3) (p = 0.0160), indicating a difference in the distributions of *event* times between vaccine groups after adjusting for the covariate, X.

```
     *    SAS Output for Example 20.1


                   Cox Proportional Hazards Model
             Example 20.1: HSV-2 Episodes with gD2 Vaccine - cont'd.

                        The PHREG Procedure

          Data Set: WORK.HSV
          Dependent Variable: WKS
          Censoring Variable: CENS
          Censoring Value(s): 1
          Ties Handling: EXACT


                          Summary of the Number of
                          Event and Censored Values

                                                      Percent
                     Total      Event    Censored    Censored
                      48         31         17        35.42


                  Testing Global Null Hypothesis: BETA=0

                      Without    With
           Criterion  Covariates Covariates      Model Chi-Square

(4)        -2 LOG L   183.628    172.792    10.836 with 2 DF (p=0.0044)
           Score          .          .      11.016 with 2 DF (p=0.0041)
           Wald           .          .      10.724 with 2 DF (p=0.0047)


              Analysis of Maximum Likelihood Estimates
                      Parameter   Standard   Wald      Pr >      Risk
           Variable DF Estimate    Error   Chi-Square Chi-Square Ratio
                                                        (3)
           TRT    1  -0.905790   0.37600   5.80342    0.0160    0.404
           X      1   0.176273   0.06574   7.18967    0.0073    1.193
                         (1)                            (2)      (5)
```

The *Log-Rank Test* using the same data set (ignoring the covariate, X) resulted in a significant finding with a p-value close to 0.05 (Example 19.1). The *Cox Proportional Hazards Model* resulted in even greater significance (p = 0.016) after adjusting for the important covariate, X.

DETAILS & NOTES

▶ The SAS PHREG procedure prints out the results of a global test which determines whether any of the covariates included in the model are significant after adjusting for all the other covariates. As shown in the output for Example 20.1 (4), three different methods are used: "-2Log L", "Score" and "Wald". Each of these is a goodness-of-fit test with an approximate chi-square distribution with 2 degrees-of-freedom under the global null hypothesis of 'no covariate effects'. With the significant results of $p < 0.005$ for all 3 methods in the example, we conclude that fluctuations in *event* times are associated with either vaccine group (TRT) or prior lesional frequency (X), or both. Non-significance would suggest that the *event* times are not affected by the set of covariates used in the model.

▸ A positive parameter estimate indicates an increasing hazard with increasing values of the covariate. A negative value indicates that the hazard decreases with increasing values of the covariate. In Example 20.1, the negative parameter estimate for TRT (-0.906) indicates that the hazard decreases with active treatment (TRT = 1) compared with placebo (TRT = 0). The hazard increases with larger prior lesional frequencies (X), as seen by the positive parameter estimate for X (0.176).

▸ The model for the hazard function of the *Cox Proportional Hazards* with only one covariate (k = 1) is:

$$h(t) = \lambda(t) \cdot e^{\beta X}$$

For two patients with different values of X, say X_u and X_v, the ratio of hazards at time *t* is

$$\frac{h_u(t)}{h_v(t)} = \frac{\lambda(t) \cdot e^{\beta X_u}}{\lambda(t) \cdot e^{\beta X_v}} = e^{\beta(X_u - X_v)}$$

which is constant with respect to time, *t*. This is the proportional hazards assumption.

If X is a dummy variable with $X_u = 1$ (say, active group) and $X_v = 0$ (say, placebo group), $X_u - X_v = 1$ so that e^{β} represents the ratio of the hazard associated with active treatment to that of placebo. This is the hazard ratio estimated by the 'risk ratio' in the SAS printout, as shown for Example 20.1 (5).

The risk ratio for TRT is $e^{-0.906} = 0.404$ which can be interpreted to mean that the hazard at any time t for the active group is only 40.4% of the placebo group's hazard. The 'risk ratio' for X is 1.193. Since X is a numeric variable (rather than a numerically-coded categorical variable), this means that we could expect a 19.3% increase in the hazard of an HSV-2 recurrence for each additional prior lesion experienced.

▸ The natural log of the hazard function given above is

$$\ln h(t) = \lambda(t) + \beta X.$$

If the event times have an exponential distribution, $\lambda(t)$ is a constant, independent of t, say α, and the model becomes

$$\ln h(t) = \alpha + \beta X$$

which means the hazard is a simple linear function of the covariate, X, on the log-scale.

▸ Some covariates may change over time. For example, diet, exercise or smoking habits may be thought to be important covariates, but may change during the course of a study. The SAS PHREG procedure can easily accomodate such 'time-dependent' covariates.

▸ The proportional hazards assumption can be checked using a time-dependent covariate, as illustrated in the SAS manual. A visual aid in determining conformance with this assumption is a plot of the log(-log(S(t))) versus time, where S(t) is the estimated survival distribution. The graphs of these functions for each group should be parallel under the proportional hazards assumption. Lack of parallelism suggests deviations from the proportional hazards assumption.

Even if the proportional hazards assumption does not appear to hold for a certain covariate, the *Cox Proportional Hazards Model* may still be used by performing the analysis within each of a series of subintervals of the range of the covariate's values, then combining the results. In SAS, this is done using the STRATA statement in PROC PHREG.

▸ An adjustment may be necessary when ties occur in event times. SAS has 4 different adjustment options for handling ties: "Breslow", "Efron", "Exact" and "Discrete". The Breslow method is the default, although this may not be the best option to choose. With small data sets or a small number of ties, the Exact option is usually preferrable. Because of computational resources, this option is not efficient for larger data sets. The Efron option provides a good approximation and is computationally faster when large amounts of data are being anlayzed.

APPENDIX A.1
PROBABILITIES of the STANDARD NORMAL DISTRIBUTION

z	P	z	P	z	P	z	P	z	P	z	P	z	P	z	P	z	P	z	P
0.00	0.5000																		
0.01	0.4960	0.31	0.3783	0.61	0.2709	0.91	0.1814	1.21	0.1131	1.51	0.0655	1.81	0.0351	2.11	0.0174	2.41	0.0080	2.71	0.0034
0.02	0.4920	0.32	0.3745	0.62	0.2676	0.92	0.1788	1.22	0.1112	1.52	0.0643	1.82	0.0344	2.12	0.0170	2.42	0.0078	2.72	0.0033
0.03	0.4880	0.33	0.3707	0.63	0.2643	0.93	0.1762	1.23	0.1093	1.53	0.0630	1.83	0.0336	2.13	0.0166	2.43	0.0075	2.73	0.0032
0.04	0.4840	0.34	0.3669	0.64	0.2611	0.94	0.1736	1.24	0.1075	1.54	0.0618	1.84	0.0329	2.14	0.0162	2.44	0.0073	2.74	0.0031
0.05	0.4801	0.35	0.3632	0.65	0.2578	0.95	0.1711	1.25	0.1056	1.55	0.0606	1.85	0.0322	2.15	0.0158	2.45	0.0071	2.75	0.0030
0.06	0.4761	0.36	0.3594	0.66	0.2546	0.96	0.1685	1.26	0.1038	1.56	0.0594	1.86	0.0314	2.16	0.0154	2.46	0.0069	2.76	0.0029
0.07	0.4721	0.37	0.3557	0.67	0.2514	0.97	0.1660	1.27	0.1020	1.57	0.0582	1.87	0.0307	2.17	0.0150	2.47	0.0068	2.77	0.0028
0.08	0.4681	0.38	0.3520	0.68	0.2483	0.98	0.1635	1.28	0.1003	1.58	0.0571	1.88	0.0301	2.18	0.0146	2.48	0.0066	2.78	0.0027
0.09	0.4641	0.39	0.3483	0.69	0.2451	0.99	0.1611	1.29	0.0985	1.59	0.0559	1.89	0.0294	2.19	0.0143	2.49	0.0064	2.79	0.0026
0.10	0.4602	0.40	0.3446	0.70	0.2420	1.00	0.1587	1.30	0.0968	1.60	0.0548	1.90	0.0287	2.20	0.0139	2.50	0.0062	2.80	0.0026
0.11	0.4562	0.41	0.3409	0.71	0.2389	1.01	0.1562	1.31	0.0951	1.61	0.0537	1.91	0.0281	2.21	0.0136	2.51	0.0060	2.81	0.0025
0.12	0.4522	0.42	0.3372	0.72	0.2358	1.02	0.1539	1.32	0.0934	1.62	0.0526	1.92	0.0274	2.22	0.0132	2.52	0.0059	2.82	0.0024
0.13	0.4483	0.43	0.3336	0.73	0.2327	1.03	0.1515	1.33	0.0918	1.63	0.0516	1.93	0.0268	2.23	0.0129	2.53	0.0057	2.83	0.0023
0.14	0.4443	0.44	0.3300	0.74	0.2296	1.04	0.1492	1.34	0.0901	1.64	0.0505	1.94	0.0262	2.24	0.0125	2.54	0.0055	2.84	0.0023
0.15	0.4404	0.45	0.3264	0.75	0.2266	1.05	0.1469	1.35	0.0885	1.65	0.0495	1.95	0.0256	2.25	0.0122	2.55	0.0054	2.85	0.0022
0.16	0.4364	0.46	0.3228	0.76	0.2236	1.06	0.1446	1.36	0.0869	1.66	0.0485	1.96	0.0250	2.26	0.0119	2.56	0.0052	2.86	0.0021
0.17	0.4325	0.47	0.3192	0.77	0.2206	1.07	0.1423	1.37	0.0853	1.67	0.0475	1.97	0.0244	2.27	0.0116	2.57	0.0051	2.87	0.0021
0.18	0.4286	0.48	0.3156	0.78	0.2177	1.08	0.1401	1.38	0.0838	1.68	0.0465	1.98	0.0239	2.28	0.0113	2.58	0.0049	2.88	0.0020
0.19	0.4247	0.49	0.3121	0.79	0.2148	1.09	0.1379	1.39	0.0823	1.69	0.0455	1.99	0.0233	2.29	0.0110	2.59	0.0048	2.89	0.0019
0.20	0.4207	0.50	0.3085	0.80	0.2119	1.10	0.1357	1.40	0.0808	1.70	0.0446	2.00	0.0228	2.30	0.0107	2.60	0.0047	2.90	0.0019
0.21	0.4168	0.51	0.3050	0.81	0.2090	1.11	0.1335	1.41	0.0793	1.71	0.0436	2.01	0.0222	2.31	0.0104	2.61	0.0045	2.91	0.0018
0.22	0.4129	0.52	0.3015	0.82	0.2061	1.12	0.1314	1.42	0.0778	1.72	0.0427	2.02	0.0217	2.32	0.0102	2.62	0.0044	2.92	0.0018
0.23	0.4090	0.53	0.2981	0.83	0.2033	1.13	0.1292	1.43	0.0764	1.73	0.0418	2.03	0.0212	2.33	0.0099	2.63	0.0043	2.93	0.0017
0.24	0.4052	0.54	0.2946	0.84	0.2005	1.14	0.1271	1.44	0.0749	1.74	0.0409	2.04	0.0207	2.34	0.0096	2.64	0.0041	2.94	0.0016
0.25	0.4013	0.55	0.2912	0.85	0.1977	1.15	0.1251	1.45	0.0735	1.75	0.0401	2.05	0.0202	2.35	0.0094	2.65	0.0040	2.95	0.0016
0.26	0.3974	0.56	0.2877	0.86	0.1949	1.16	0.1230	1.46	0.0721	1.76	0.0392	2.06	0.0197	2.36	0.0091	2.66	0.0039	2.96	0.0015
0.27	0.3936	0.57	0.2843	0.87	0.1922	1.17	0.1210	1.47	0.0708	1.77	0.0384	2.07	0.0192	2.37	0.0089	2.67	0.0038	2.97	0.0015
0.28	0.3897	0.58	0.2810	0.88	0.1894	1.18	0.1190	1.48	0.0694	1.78	0.0375	2.08	0.0188	2.38	0.0087	2.68	0.0037	2.98	0.0014
0.29	0.3859	0.59	0.2776	0.89	0.1867	1.19	0.1170	1.49	0.0681	1.79	0.0367	2.09	0.0183	2.39	0.0084	2.69	0.0036	2.99	0.0014
0.30	0.3821	0.60	0.2743	0.90	0.1841	1.20	0.1151	1.50	0.0668	1.80	0.0359	2.10	0.0179	2.40	0.0082	2.70	0.0035	3.00	0.0013

APPENDIX A.2
CRITICAL VALUES of the t-DISTRIBUTION

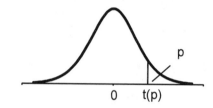

d.f.	t(0.100)	t(0.050)	t(0.025)	t(0.010)	t(0.005)
1	3.078	6.314	12.706	31.821	63.656
2	1.886	2.920	4.303	6.965	9.925
3	1.638	2.353	3.182	4.541	5.841
4	1.533	2.132	2.776	3.747	4.604
5	1.476	2.015	2.571	3.365	4.032
6	1.440	1.943	2.447	3.143	3.707
7	1.415	1.895	2.365	2.998	3.499
8	1.397	1.860	2.306	2.896	3.355
9	1.383	1.833	2.262	2.821	3.250
10	1.372	1.812	2.228	2.764	3.169
11	1.363	1.796	2.201	2.718	3.106
12	1.356	1.782	2.179	2.681	3.055
13	1.350	1.771	2.160	2.650	3.012
14	1.345	1.761	2.145	2.624	2.977
15	1.341	1.753	2.131	2.602	2.947
16	1.337	1.746	2.120	2.583	2.921
17	1.333	1.740	2.110	2.567	2.898
18	1.330	1.734	2.101	2.552	2.878
19	1.328	1.729	2.093	2.539	2.861
20	1.325	1.725	2.086	2.528	2.845
21	1.323	1.721	2.080	2.518	2.831
22	1.321	1.717	2.074	2.508	2.819
23	1.319	1.714	2.069	2.500	2.807
24	1.318	1.711	2.064	2.492	2.797
25	1.316	1.708	2.060	2.485	2.787
26	1.315	1.706	2.056	2.479	2.779
27	1.314	1.703	2.052	2.473	2.771
28	1.313	1.701	2.048	2.467	2.763
29	1.311	1.699	2.045	2.462	2.756
30	1.310	1.697	2.042	2.457	2.750
31	1.309	1.696	2.040	2.453	2.744
32	1.309	1.694	2.037	2.449	2.738
33	1.308	1.692	2.035	2.445	2.733
34	1.307	1.691	2.032	2.441	2.728
35	1.306	1.690	2.030	2.438	2.724

COMMON DISTRIBUTIONS USED IN STATISTICAL INFERENCE

▸ NOTATION

$X \sim N(\mu, \sigma^2)$

means that the random variable, X, is normally distributed with mean, μ and variance, σ^2.

$X \sim \chi^2_{\upsilon}$

means that the random variable, X, has the chi-square distribution with υ degrees-of-freedom (d.f.).

$X \sim F^{\upsilon 1}_{\upsilon 2}$

means that the random variable, X, has the F-distribution with υ_1 upper and υ_2 lower d.f.

$X \sim t_{\upsilon}$

means that the random variable, X, has the Student-t distribution with υ d.f.

▸ PROPERTIES

1. If $X \sim N(\mu, \sigma^2)$ and $Z = (X-\mu)/\sigma$

then $Z \sim N(0, 1)$.

Z is called a 'standard normal' random variable.

2. If $X_1 \sim N(\mu_1, \sigma^2_1)$ and $X_2 \sim N(\mu_2, \sigma^2_2)$, X_1 and X_2 are independent, and $Y = X_1 + X_2$,

then $Y \sim N(\mu_1 + \mu_2, \sigma^2_1 + \sigma^2_2)$.

More generally, for any constants, a_1, a_2, ..., a_k, if $X_i \sim N(\mu_i, \sigma^2_i)$ independently for $i = 1, 2, ..., k$, and $Y = a_1X_1 + a_2X_2 + ... + a_kX_k$, then

$$Y \sim N\left(\sum_{i=1}^{k} a_i\mu_i \, , \, \sum_{i=1}^{k} a_i^2\sigma_i^2\right)$$

3. If $Z \sim N(0, 1)$

then $Z^2 \sim \chi^2_1$.

4. If $Z_i \sim N(0, 1)$ independently for $i = 1, 2, ..., n$, and $Y = Z^2_1 + Z^2_2 + ... + Z^2_n$,

then $Y \sim \chi^2_n$.

5. If $X \sim \chi^2_m$ and $Y \sim \chi^2_n$ independently, and $U = X + Y$,

then $U \sim \chi^2_{m+n}$

6. If $Z \sim N(0, 1)$ and $Y \sim \chi^2_\upsilon$ independently, and $t = Z/(Y/\upsilon)^{1/2}$,

then $T \sim t_\upsilon$

7. If $X \sim \chi^2_m$ and $Y \sim \chi^2_n$, independently, and $F = (n/m) (X/Y)$,

then $F \sim F^m_n$

▸ RESULTS

Let $X_i \sim N(\mu, \sigma^2)$ independently for $i = 1, 2, \ldots, n$, and let

$$\bar{X} = \frac{\sum_{i=1}^{n} X_i}{n}$$

represent the sample mean. Then,

Property 2 $\Rightarrow$ $\quad \bar{X} \sim N(\mu, \sigma^2/n)$ $\hfill (i)$

Property 1 $\Rightarrow$ $\quad Z = \frac{\sqrt{n}(\bar{X} - \mu)}{\sigma} \sim N(0, 1)$ $\hfill (ii)$

Property 3 $\Rightarrow$ $\quad Z^2 = \frac{n(\bar{X} - \mu)^2}{\sigma^2} \sim \chi^2_1$ $\hfill (iii)$.

Also,

Property 1 $\Rightarrow$ $\quad \frac{X_i - \mu}{\sigma} \sim N(0, 1)$ $\hfill (iv)$

$\qquad\qquad$ *and*

Property 4 $\Rightarrow$ $\quad \sum_{i=1}^{n} \frac{(X_i - \mu)^2}{\sigma^2} \sim \chi^2_n$ $\hfill (v)$.

It can be shown that

$$\sum (X_i - \mu)^2 = \sum (X_i - \bar{X})^2 + n(\bar{X} - \mu)^2$$

and that the summations on the right hand side are independent, so that,

$$\frac{(n-1)s^2}{\sigma^2} = \frac{\sum (X_i - \mu)^2}{\sigma^2} - \frac{n(\bar{X} - \mu)^2}{\sigma^2}$$

where s^2 is the sample variance given by

$$s^2 = \frac{\sum (X_i - \bar{X})^2}{n-1} \quad .$$

Property 5 and Results (iii), (v)

$$\Rightarrow \qquad \frac{(n-1) \cdot s^2}{\sigma^2} \quad \sim \quad \chi^2_{n-1} \qquad\qquad (vi)$$

Furthermore, Property 6 and Results (ii), (vi)

$$\Rightarrow \quad t = \frac{\left(\dfrac{(\bar{X} - \mu)}{\sigma/\sqrt{n}} \right)}{\left(\dfrac{s}{\sigma} \right)} = \frac{(\bar{X} - \mu)}{s/\sqrt{n}} \sim t_{n-1} \qquad (vii)$$

and Property 7 and Results (iii), (vi)

$$\Rightarrow \qquad F = t^2 \quad \sim \quad F^1_{n-1} \qquad\qquad (viii)$$

With applications to *ANOVA*, let MS_1 and MS_2 represent two independent, unbiased estimates of the error variance, σ^2 based on υ_1 and υ_2 d.f., respectively. Then,

$$\frac{\upsilon_1 MS_1}{\sigma^2} \sim \chi^2_{\upsilon_1} \quad and \quad \frac{\upsilon_2 MS_2}{\sigma^2} \sim \chi^2_{\upsilon_2} \qquad (ix)$$

which, together with Property 7

$$\Rightarrow \qquad \frac{MS_1}{MS_2} \quad \sim \quad F^{\upsilon_1}_{\upsilon_2} \qquad\qquad (x)$$

FIGURE B-1: Distributional 'Shapes'

The
NORMAL
Distribution

The
CHI-SQUARE
Distribution

The
F
Distribution

The
STUDENT-t
Distribution

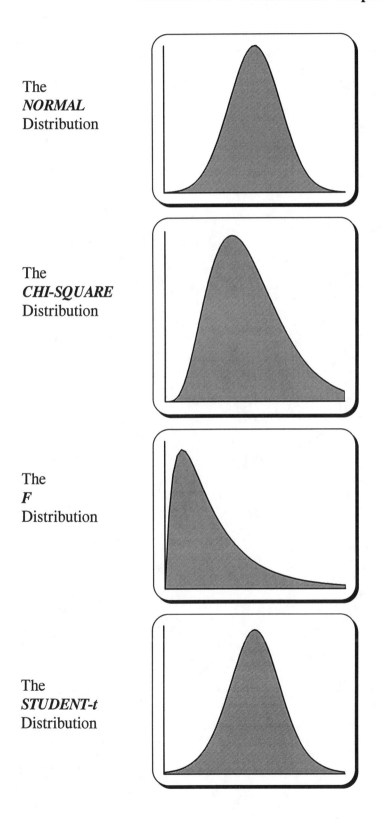

APPENDIX C
BASIC ANOVA CONCEPTS

C.1. WITHIN- vs. BETWEEN-GROUP VARIATION

Suppose 12 recent college graduates are assigned to 3 groups: 4 to an exercise group (I), 4 to a drug treatment group (II), and 4 to a control group (III). The age, pulse rates, diastolic blood pressure and triglyceride measurements are taken after 8 weeks in the study, with the following results.

	--- GROUP ---		
1. AGE (years)	I	II	III
The age measurements are the same for all 12 subjects. Clearly, there is no variation among the group means, and therefore no difference in groups with respect to age.	22	22	22
	22	22	22
	22	22	22
	22	22	22

2. PULSE RATES (beats/min.)	I	II	III
The pulse rate measurements are the same for all 4 subjects within each group, but vary across groups. Observation of these data without further analysis would likely lead to the conclusion of a difference in mean pulse rates among the three groups.	64	59	70
	64	59	70
	64	59	70
	64	59	70

3. Diastolic BP (mm Hg)	I	II	III
Diastolic blood pressure measurements show a variation both within- and among-groups.	74	81	89
Within-group measurements vary by no more than 2 mm Hg, while the variation	76	80	89
among the group means is as much as 14 mm. Because the among-group variation is	75	79	88
large compared with the within-group variation, we would likely believe that there is a difference among groups in mean diastolic blood pressure.	75	80	90

4. Triglycerides (mg/dl)	I	II	III
The triglyceride measurements have considerable variation both within- and	85	72	141
among-groups. Since the variation within groups no longer allows our intuition to	101	130	78
distinguish among groups, it is not clear	68	91	91
whether a group effect exists.	121	99	121

For the triglyceride results, there may be no real difference that can be attributed to the groups, but we need an analytic method to determine this. ANOVA methods are used for exactly this purpose: to analyze the variability among groups relative to the variability within groups to determine if differences among groups are meaningful or significant.

ANOVA methods seek to identify sources of variation for each measurement, and decompose the total variability into components associated with each source. The total variability can generally be described as the sum of squared deviations of each measurement from the overall mean. This is comprised of a sum of squares due to suspected sources of variation, often called the 'model sum-of-squares', and a sum of squares (SS) due to error or 'SSE'.

The error variability includes such things as measurement error, normal variation due to repeated sampling and variation among 'like' experimental units from other unknown factors. Such sources may be difficult to control even in a well-designed study. The sources that can be identified and controlled are included in the model SS:

$$SS(\text{Total}) = SS(\text{Model}) + SS(\text{Error}) .$$

ANOVA is conducted using F-tests which are constructed from the ratio of between-group to within-group variance estimates. Assumptions usually entail independent samples from normally distributed populations with equal variances.

In the example given above, the 3 groups (I, II, III) represent levels of a factor we call 'GROUP'. A 'significant GROUP effect' indicates that there are significant differences in mean responses among the levels of the factor GROUP.

The *One-Way ANOVA* has *one* main effect or grouping factor with 2 or more levels. In analyzing clinical trials, the main effect will often be a treatment effect. The levels of the factor 'TREATMENT' might be, for example, 'low dose', 'middle dose', 'high dose', and 'placebo'. The *Two-Way ANOVA* has *two* main effects, usually a grouping or treatment factor and a blocking factor (such as gender, study center, diagnosis group, etc.).

Statistical interactions among main effects can also be analyzed when two or more factors are used. An interaction occurs when differences among the levels of one factor change at different levels of another factor. A *Two-Way ANOVA* can have only one two-way interaction. A *Three-Way ANOVA* has *three* main effects, say A, B and C, 3 two-way interactions (A-by-B, A-by-C and B-by-C) and one three-way interaction (A-by-B-by-C). Multi-way ANOVA setups can have any number of factors each at any number of levels. The *Two-Way ANOVA*, discussed in Chapter 6, is one of the most commonly used analyses for multi-center clinical studies, with Treatment or Dose Group and Study Center as the 2 main effects.

Other types of commonly used ANOVA's include the *Repeated-Measures ANOVA* (Chapter 7), nested or random-effects ANOVA and ANOVA of mixed models. *Analysis-of-Covariance* (Chapter 9) is a special type of ANOVA which includes adjustments of treatment effects for a numeric covariate.

In most types of ANOVA used in clinical trials, the primary question the researcher wants to answer is whether there are any differences among the group population means based on the sample data. The null hypothesis to be tested is 'there is no Group effect', or equivalently, 'the mean responses are the same for all groups'. The alternative hypothesis is that 'the Group effect is important', or equivalently, 'the Group means differ for at least one pair of groups'.

The *One-Way ANOVA*, whose setup is exemplified above, involves a straightforward comparison of the between-group variation to the within-group variation. ANOVA's involving blocking factors or covariates seek to refine treatment comparisons by factoring out extraneous variation due to <u>known</u> sources.

C.2. NOISE REDUCTION BY BLOCKING

The more extraneous variability or 'background noise' we can account for, the more precise our Group comparisons become. Accounting for known blocking factors is one means of reducing such noise.

Suppose we collect body weight data (in pounds) on 31 patients randomized to two groups, as shown on the next page. We wish to determine whether the groups, representing Treatment A or Treatment B, have different mean weights. Initially, we use the *One-Way ANOVA* methods shown in Chapter 5.

Mean weights are computed to be 148.1 and 162.5 for Treatment Groups A and B, respectively. *One-Way ANOVA* (with k = 2 groups) produces an F-test statistic of 1.23 with 1 upper and 29 lower d.f.'s, as shown in the ANOVA summary table. This results in a p-value of 0.277, leading to a conclusion of no significant difference in mean weights between the groups.

ANOVA

Source	d.f	SS	MS	F
TREATMENT	1	1612.8	1612.8	F = 1.23
Error	29	38154.9	1315.7	
Total	30	39767.7		

F = 1.23 is not significant (p=0.277)

Treatment Group A		Treatment Group B	
Pat. No.	Weight	Pat. No.	Weight
10	110	11	121
12	101	13	116
14	124	15	144
17	120	16	125
18	111	19	115
21	117	20	118
22	120	23	127
24	131	30	205
31	185	33	193
35	181	34	196
37	173	36	189
40	190	38	180
42	181	39	193
44	202	41	210
45	175	43	189
		46	179

Now suppose we know that patients with patient-numbers less than 30 are all females and those with patient-numbers of 30 or above are all males. It is clear from scanning the data that the males weigh more than the females. Since the error variance, σ^2, is a within-group (patient-to-patient) variability, the MSE of 1315.7 overestimates σ^2 since it includes a component due to variation between genders. The inflated estimate using this MSE leads to an F-value for Treatment Group differences which is smaller and less significant than if a more precise estimate of σ^2 were obtained. Removing the Gender variation from the MSE might result in a more precise comparsion of the groups.

Once we identify 'Gender' as a source of variation, we can include that factor in the ANOVA by computing a sum-of-squares, mean-square and an F-value for this factor similar to the methods used for the Group effect in a *One-Way ANOVA* (Chapter 5). In this *Two-Way ANOVA* we can test whether 'Gender' is a significant factor, as well as removing its variation from the MSE to get a more precise test for the 'Treatment' effect.

As seen in the ANOVA table which follows, 'Gender' is not only significant, but the estimate of error variance, MSE = 93.9, is substantially reduced from that of the *One-Way ANOVA* (MSE = 1315.7). This leads to greater precision in testing for the 'Treatment Group' effect, which is now seen to be significant.

ANOVA

Source	d.f	SS	MS	F
TREATMENT	1	480.1	480.1	F_t = 5.1 *
GENDER	1	35526.6	35526.6	F_b = 378.5 **
Error	28	2628.3	93.9	
Total	30	39767.7		

* Significant (p = 0.032)   ** Signficant (p < 0.001)

The general setup of a two-way layout with g levels of a 'treatment' factor 'GROUP' and b levels of a 'blocking' factor, 'BLOCK' is shown below. From each GROUP-by-BLOCK combination or 'cell', we independently sample a number of observations, letting y_{ijk} represent the k-th data value from Group i and Block j. The number of data values within Cell i-j is represented by n_{ij}.

GROUP	BLOCK			
	1	2	...	b
1	n_{11}	n_{12}	...	n_{1b}
2	n_{21}	n_{22}	...	n_{2b}
...	...	...	...	...
g	n_{g1}	n_{g2}	...	n_{gb}

In the weight example above, we have g = 2, b = 2, and n_{ij} as follows:

TREATMENT (GROUP)	GENDER (BLOCK)	
	Females	Males
A	$n_{11} = 8$	$n_{12} = 7$
B	$n_{21} = 7$	$n_{22} = 9$

If each cell in the two-way layout has the same number of observations (n_{ij} = n for all i,j), we have a 'balanced' design. Computing formulas for balanced designs are straightforward, and similar to those given for the one-way layout (Chapter 5). With imbalance, there are a number of different ways to compute the sums-of-squares. In SAS, four types of sums-of-squares computations are available, called Type I, Type II, Type III and Type IV. The differences among these types are discussed in Appendix D. The Type III sums-of-squares from the SAS GLM procedure is predominantly used in analyzing clinical trials ANOVA.

We note in the previous 'weight' example, a p-value for 'Gender' of < 0.001, meaning that there is a highly significant difference in mean weights between the males and the females. Furthermore, the p-value of 0.0317 for 'Treatment' now tells us that a significant (< 0.05) difference in mean weights *does* exist between the two treatment groups, A and B. This difference was masked by the large variability when we ignored the 'Gender' factor.

The ANOVA results given do not include the interaction between Treatment Group and Gender as a source of variation. A statistical interaction between two effects suggests that differences in response means among the levels of one effect are not consistent across the levels of the other effect. A significant Treatment-by-Gender interaction in the 'weight' example would indicate that the difference in mean weight between Treatment A and Treatment B depends on whether we're talking about males or females.

Different response patterns indicating interactions and no interactions are shown in Chapter 6. Cell means from the weight example would depict a pattern as shown below, suggestive of no interaction. The ANOVA summary with interaction confirms this as shown in the ANOVA summary which follows.

ANOVA

Source	d.f	SS	MS	F
TREATMENT	1	476.8	476.8	$F_t = 4.9 *$
GENDER	1	35475.8	35475.8	$F_b = 365.3 **$
TREATMENT x GENDER	1	6.5	6.5	$F_{tg} = 0.07$
Error	28	2621.8	97.1	
Total		30	39767.7	

* Significant ($p = 0.035$)   ** Signficant ($p < 0.001$)

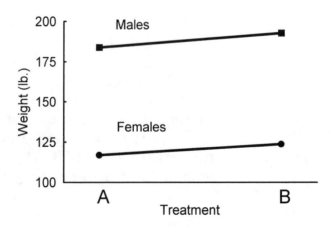

C.3. 'LEAST-SQUARES MEANS'

In the development of a new recumbent exercise bicycle, the designers needed to estimate the average height of potential users. One-hundred members of a local health club chain were sampled, and the mean height was computed as:

$$\overline{X} = \frac{\sum_{i=1}^{100} x_i}{100}$$

where x_i represents the height of the i-th member. Is this a good estimate? Suppose it is known that the clubs selected have mostly male members, and that 90 of the 100 selected were male. The sample mean above can be represented as:

$$\overline{X} = \frac{(90 \cdot \overline{X}_m) + (10 \cdot \overline{X}_f)}{100} = 0.9 \cdot \overline{X}_m + 0.1 \cdot \overline{X}_f$$

where $\overline{X}_m$ *and* $\overline{X}_f$

represent the mean heights of the males and females, respectively. This estimate is a good one if the population is composed of approximately 90% males, i.e., if 90% of the potential users of the new exercise equipment are male. However, if the sample taken is not in proportion to the true population composition, this simple average may be a poor estimate.

Suppose it is known that users of the recumbent cycle are, in general, equally distributed between males and females. Under such an assumption, the mean computed above would tend to overestimate the population mean since it is highly weighted by the males, who are known to be taller than females in the general population.

A mean height for males of 70 inches and a mean height for females of 62 inches would produce an overall mean height estimate of 69.2 inches using the weighted approach above. A better estimate might be $(70 + 62)/2 = 66$ inches, or in general,

$$\overline{X} = \frac{(\overline{X}_m + \overline{X}_f)}{2} = 0.5 \cdot \overline{X}_m + 0.5 \cdot \overline{X}_f$$

This estimate is called a "Least-Squares" mean or 'LS-mean'. This is the estimate computed by SAS when using the 'Type III' sum-of-squares.

In clinical trials, we often use LS-means for estimating treatment effects when blocking by study center. A typical trial may involve a larger number of patients from one study center than from another. The LS-mean of the treatment effect would be equivalent to a combined average over centers *as if the same number of patients were studied within each center*.

If the sample sizes from each center are proportional to the population sizes, the usual arithmetic mean would be appropriate. Often, however, the population sizes are considered 'infinite', and the LS-mean is used to give equal weighting to the effect sizes from each center. Estimates based on the LS-mean can differ markedly from that of the usual arithmetic mean if either the cell means or cell sample sizes within any dose group differ substantially between centers. In such situations, the analyst must examine the assumptions of population sizes and sample representation to decide which estimate is more appropriate.

In Example 6.2 (Chapter 6), the means and LS-means of the number of items correctly remembered for the 3 dose groups in the memory study are shown as follows.

CENTER		------------ DOSE GROUP -------------		
		Placebo	30 mg	60 mg
Dr. Abel	Mean	5.67	8.38	10.11
	N	12	8	9
Dr. Best	Mean	6.82	6.40	12.11
	N	11	10	9
	Mean	6.22	7.28	11.11
	LS-Mean	6.24	7.39	11.11

Notice that the two estimates are very close to each other. This may not be the case if, for example, there are 25 patients in one center and only 5 in another. When such a degree of imbalance occurs in the sampling, it is important to consider the use of LS-means in the estimation of treatment effects.

APPENDIX D
SAS TYPES I, II, III and IV
METHODS for an IMBALANCED
TWO-WAY LAYOUT

D.1 SAS SS-TYPES

This section uses the randomized block design to illustrate the differences among the various ANOVA types of sums-of-squares (SS) computed by SAS: Type I, Type II, Type III and Type IV.

Consider the unbalanced two-way layout with 2 treatment groups (A and B) and 3 study centers (1, 2 and 3). Let μ_{ij} and n_{ij} represent the mean and sample size, respectively, for Treatment i, Center j. For this example, 8 patients receive Treatment A and 6 receive Treatment B distributed among centers as shown below.

| | ----------- Treatment ------------- | |
Center	A	B
1	μ_{11} $n_{11} = 2$	μ_{21} $n_{21} = 1$
2	μ_{12} $n_{12} = 2$	μ_{22} $n_{22} = 3$
3	μ_{13} $n_{13} = 4$	μ_{23} $n_{23} = 2$
	μ_A $n_A = 8$	μ_B $n_B = 6$

Denote each treatment mean as a linear combination of the cell means for that treatment:

$$\mu_A = a_1\mu_{11} + a_2\mu_{12} + a_3\mu_{13}$$
$$\mu_B = b_1\mu_{21} + b_2\mu_{22} + b_3\mu_{23} \ .$$

Our goal is to test the hypothesis of equality of treatment means: H_0: $\mu_A = \mu_B$. The method used to make this test depends on how we define the 'treatment means' in terms of the cell means. We consider the following 3 cases.

Case (i): Let $a_j = n_{1j}/n_A$, $b_j = n_{2j}/n_B$ (j = 1,2,3)

The hypothesis of equal treatment means becomes:

H_0: $(2/8)\mu_{11}+(2/8)\mu_{12}+(4/8)\mu_{13} =$
$$(1/6)\mu_{21}+(3/6)\mu_{22}+(2/6)\mu_{23} \ .$$

The treatment means are the weighted averages of the cell means for that treatment, weighted by the cell sample sizes. This is the hypothesis tested by the SAS Type I sum-of-squares for Treatment, providing the 'Treatment' factor is specified first in the MODEL statement.

Case (ii): Let $a_j = b_j = u_j/U$ (j = 1,2,3)
where, $u_1 = n_{11}\,n_{21}\,(n_{12}+n_{22})\,(n_{13}+n_{23})$,
$u_2 = n_{12}\,n_{22}\,(n_{11}+n_{21})\,(n_{13}+n_{23})$,
$u_3 = n_{13}\,n_{23}\,(n_{11}+n_{21})\,(n_{12}+n_{22})$,
and, $U = u_1 + u_2 + u_3$

The hypothesis of equal treatment means becomes:

H_0: $(5/24)\mu_{11}+(9/24)\mu_{12}+(10/24)\mu_{13} =$
$$(5/24)\mu_{21}+(9/24)\mu_{22}+(9/24)\mu_{23} \ .$$

The treatment means are the weighted average of the cell means, weighted by a complex function of the cell sample sizes. This is the hypothesis tested by the SAS Type II sum-of-squares for Treatment.

> Case (iii): Let $a_1 = a_2 = a_3 = b_1 = b_2 = b_3 (= 1/3)$

The hypothesis of equal treatment means becomes:

$$H_0: \quad (1/3)\mu_{11} + (1/3)\mu_{12} + (1/3)\mu_{13} =$$
$$(1/3)\mu_{21} + (1/3)\mu_{22} + (1/3)\mu_{23} \, ,$$

which does not depend on the sample sizes. This is the hypothesis tested by the SAS Type III and Type IV sums-of-squares for Treatment.

NOTE: *The SAS Type III and Type IV methods are identical in a two-way layout with no empty cells. If $n_{ij} = 0$ for at least one cell, the Type III and IV sum-of-squares for Treatment will differ if there are more than 2 levels of the factor Treatment. In the case of empty cells, it is recommended that the Type IV tests be used (see Section D.3, "Empty Cell Case", later in this appendix).*

D.2 HOW TO DETERMINE THE SAS HYPOTHESES

We can express the mean response for cell i-j in terms of model parameters as follows:

$$\mu_{ij} = \mu + \alpha_i + \beta_j + \gamma_{ij}$$

where μ represents an overall mean, α_i represents the average additive effect of Treatment i, β_j is the average additive effect of Center j, and γ_{ij} is the average additive effect of the Treatment-i-by-Center-j combination (interaction).   SAS uses vectors of the parameter coefficients and matrices to compute sums-of-squares, and it is also convenient to express hypotheses in terms of matrix algebra. With 2 treatment groups, the hypotheses tested by SAS are of the form

$$H_0: \underline{a}'\underline{\beta} = 0 \ ,$$

where $\underline{\beta}$ is the vector of parameters and $\underline{a}$ is a vector of parameter coefficients. In our example with 2 treatments and 3 centers, the parameter vector is

$$\underline{\beta}' = [\mu \ \ \alpha_1 \ \ \alpha_2 \ \ \beta_1 \ \ \beta_2 \ \ \beta_3 \ \ \gamma_{11} \ \ \gamma_{12} \ \ \gamma_{13} \ \ \gamma_{21} \ \ \gamma_{22} \ \ \gamma_{23}]$$

We can use the SAS statements,

```
PROC GLM; CLASSES TRT CENTER;
MODEL Y = TRT CENTER TRT*CENTER / E1 E2 E3 E4;
```

to generate the ANOVA and print out the form of the parameter coefficient vectors for each of the 4 types of sums-of-squares. It is shown below how these vectors can be used to convert the hypothesis from a parametric one ($\underline{a}'\underline{\beta}=0$) to one based on the cell means.

Type I Hypotheses

The output of the vector of parameter coefficients ($\underline{a}$) for the Type I estimable functions for Treatment is shown from the SAS output as follows:

Type I Estimable Functions for: TRT		
Effect		Coefficients
INTERCEPT		0
TRT	A	L2
	B	-L2
CNTR	1	0.0833*L2
	2	-0.25*L2
	3	0.1667*L2
TRT*CNTR	A 1	0.25*L2
	A 2	0.25*L2
	A 3	0.5*L2
	B 1	-0.1667*L2
	B 2	-0.5*L2
	B 3	-0.3333*L2

The L2 refers to any constant free to be chosen by the analyst. Setting L2 = 12, the hypothesis becomes:

$$\underline{a}'\,\underline{\beta} = 0\cdot\mu \quad +$$

$$12\alpha_1 - 12\alpha_2 \;+$$

$$1\beta_1 - 3\beta_2 + 2\beta_3 \;+$$

$$3\cdot\gamma_{11} + 3\cdot\gamma_{12} + 6\cdot\gamma_{13} -$$

$$2\cdot\gamma_{21} - 6\cdot\gamma_{22} - 4\cdot\gamma_{23}$$

$$= 0 \qquad .$$

Algebraic manipulation of this equation yields

$$(3\mu + 3\alpha_1 + 3\beta_1 + 3\gamma_{11}) \;+$$

$$(3\mu + 3\alpha_1 + 3\beta_2 + 3\gamma_{12}) \;+$$

$$(6\mu + 6\alpha_1 + 6\beta_3 + 6\gamma_{13}) \;=$$

$$(2\mu + 2\alpha_2 + 2\beta_1 + 2\gamma_{21}) \;+$$

$$(6\mu + 6\alpha_2 + 6\beta_2 + 6\gamma_{22}) \;+$$

$$(4\mu + 4\alpha_2 + 4\beta_3 + 4\gamma_{23})$$

which can be expressed in terms of the cell means as:,

$$3\mu_{11} + 3\mu_{12} + 6\mu_{13} = 2\mu_{21} + 6\mu_{22} + 4\mu_{23}$$

or,

$$(1/8)(2\mu_{11} + 2\mu_{12} + 4\mu_{13}) = (1/6)(\mu_{21} + 3\mu_{22} + 2\mu_{23}).$$

This is the SAS Type I hypothesis.

The form of the Type I hypothesis for Treatment depends on the order in which the factors are listed in the MODEL statement. If Treatment is listed before Center, the Type I hypothesis is as given above. If Center is listed before Treatment, the Type I hypothesis for Treatment is the same as the Type II hypothesis for Treatment. Types II, III and IV do not depend on the order of the factors as listed in the MODEL statement.

Type II Hypotheses

The output of the vector of parameter coefficients for the Type II estimable functions for Treatment is shown as follows:

```
Type II Estimable Functions for: TRT

Effect              Coefficients

INTERCEPT           0

TRT         A       L2
            B       -L2

CNTR        1       0
            2       0
            3       0

TRT*CNTR    A 1     0.2083*L2
            A 2     0.375*L2
            A 3     0.4167*L2
            B 1     -0.2083*L2
            B 2     -0.375*L2
            B 3     -0.4167*L2
```

By substituting 24 for L2, the hypothesis becomes

$$\underline{a}' \, \beta = 0 \cdot \mu \; +$$

$$24\alpha_1 - 24\alpha_2 \; +$$

$$0\beta_1 + 0\beta_2 + 0\beta_3 \; +$$

$$5 \cdot \gamma_{11} + 9 \cdot \gamma_{12} + 10 \cdot \gamma_{13} -$$

$$5 \cdot \gamma_{21} - 9 \cdot \gamma_{22} - 10 \cdot \gamma_{23}$$

$$= 0 \quad .$$

Algebraic manipulation of this equation results in

$$(5\mu + 5\alpha_1 + 5\beta_1 + 5\gamma_{11}) +$$

$$(9\mu + 9\alpha_1 + 9\beta_2 + 9\gamma_{12}) +$$

$$(10\mu + 10\alpha_1 + 10\beta_3 + 10\gamma_{13}) =$$

$$(5\mu + 5\alpha_2 + 5\beta_1 + 5\gamma_{21}) +$$

$$(9\mu + 9\alpha_2 + 9\beta_2 + 9\gamma_{22}) +$$

$$(10\mu + 10\alpha_2 + 10\beta_3 + 10\gamma_{23})$$

which is expressed in terms of the cell means as the SAS Type II hypothesis:

$$(1/24)(5\mu_{11} + 9\mu_{12} + 10\mu_{13}) =$$
$$(1/24)(5\mu_{21} + 9\mu_{22} + 10\mu_{23}) \ .$$

Type III Hypotheses

The form of the Type III hypotheses for Treatment is a vector of parameter coefficients which appears as follows in the SAS output.

```
Type III Estimable Functions for: TRT

Effect              Coefficients

INTERCEPT           0

TRT          A      L2
             B      -L2

CNTR         1      0
             2      0
             3      0

TRT*CNTR   A 1      0.3333*L2
           A 2      0.3333*L2
           A 3      0.3333*L2
           B 1      -0.3333*L2
           B 2      -0.3333*L2
           B 3      -0.3333*L2
```

By substituting 3 for L2, the hypothesis becomes:

$$\underline{a}' \beta = 0 \cdot \mu \quad +$$

$$3\alpha_1 - 3\alpha_2 \; +$$

$$0\beta_1 - 0\beta_2 + 0\beta_3 \; +$$

$$1 \cdot \gamma_{11} + 1 \cdot \gamma_{12} + 1 \cdot \gamma_{13} -$$

$$1 \cdot \gamma_{21} - 1 \cdot \gamma_{22} - 1 \cdot \gamma_{23}$$

$$= 0 \quad .$$

Algebraic manipulation of this equation yields

$$(\mu + \alpha_1 + \beta_1 + \gamma_{11}) \; +$$

$$(\mu + \alpha_1 + \beta_2 + \gamma_{12}) \; +$$

$$(\mu + \alpha_1 + \beta_3 + \gamma_{13}) \; =$$

$$(\mu + \alpha_2 + \beta_1 + \gamma_{21}) \; +$$

$$(\mu + \alpha_2 + \beta_2 + \gamma_{22}) \; +$$

$$(\mu + \alpha_2 + \beta_3 + \gamma_{23})$$

which can be re-expressed in terms of the cell means as the SAS Type III hypothesis:

$$(1/3)(\mu_{11} + \mu_{12} + \mu_{13}) = (1/3)(\mu_{21} + \mu_{22} + \mu_{23}) \; .$$

Type IV Hypotheses

As previously mentioned the Type IV hypotheses for Treatment are identical to the Type III hypotheses when there are no empty cells. The empty cell case is discussed in Section D.3.

D.3 EMPTY CELL CASE:

The SAS Type III and Type IV sums-of-squares for Treatment are identical when each cell in the 2-way layout has at least one observation. In the event of an empty cell ($n_{ij} = 0$ for some i-j combination), these two methods will be the same if there are 2 treatment groups, but differ if there are more than 2 treatment groups (see Section D.4). By printing out the form of the Type IV parameter coefficient vector for Treatment in the presence of one empty cell, it is seen that the treatment means are unweighted averages of the cell means excluding the block containing the empty cell.

For example, in the 2x3 example (Section D.1), suppose that the i=2, j=2 cell has no observations ($n_{22} = 0$). The SAS Type IV sum-of-squares for Treatment tests the cell means hypothesis, H_0: $(\mu_{11} + \mu_{13}) = (\mu_{21} + \mu_{23})$. Note that Center 2 does not enter into the hypothesis at all because of its incomplete data.

In cases with many empty cells, the *Two-Way ANOVA* can result in testing hypotheses which exclude many of the cell means. Such an analysis may not be desirable due to the differences in the hypotheses actually tested versus those planned in the design phase of the study.

One method of circumventing these difficulties is to remove the Treatment-by-Center interaction effect as a source of variation if it can be assumed that no interaction exists, or if preliminary tests suggests that such an assumption is credible. The SAS Type I, II, III and IV tests for the interaction effect are the same regardless of the empty cell pattern. This test for interaction, while not including all cells, can provide an indication of whether an interaction is present. If this test is not significant, the analysis might be rerun using just the main effects, Treatment and Center. With no interaction in the MODEL statement, the SAS Types II, III and IV sums-of-squares are identical, and each tests the hypothesis of equality of treatment means when the treatment means are represented by an unweighted average of the cell means for that treatment.

Sometimes, creative ways can be found to combine blocks to eliminate empty cells while retaining the advantages of blocking and ease of interpretation. As an example, suppose a study using 10 study centers is conducted using 2 treatment groups, targeting 5 patients per cell. At the end of the study, perhaps a number of empty cells exist due to patient attrition or protocol violations leading to patient exclusion. It might be possible to combine centers by specialty, region or some other common factor. By combining centers from the same geographic regions, the analyst could ignore Center, and instead use Geographic Region (e.g., North, South, West, Midwest) as a new blocking factor. This technique can help eliminate the empty cell problem by combining like blocks.

If a preliminary test for interaction is significant, one might proceed immediately to treatment comparsions *within* each level of the blocking factor (e.g., Center or Geographic Region) using a *Two-Sample t-Test* (Chapter 4) or *One-Way ANOVA* (Chapter 5). This can often be helpful in revealing subgroups of study centers (or regions) with similar response patterns within each subgroup. In general, caution must be used in the analysis and interpretation of results when empty cells are present.

D.4 THE CASE OF MORE THAN 2 TREATMENTS

The examples discussed above apply to the often-used case of 2 treatment groups. When there are g (g > 2) treatment groups, the hypothesis of 'no Treatment effect' is tested by SAS using simultaneous statements of the form:

$$H_0: \quad \underline{a}_2'\underline{\beta} = \underline{a}_3'\underline{\beta} = \ldots = \underline{a}_g'\underline{\beta} = 0 \ .$$

By requesting the form for the parameter coefficient vectors using the E1, E2, E3 or E4 options of the SAS GLM MODEL statement, values denoted by L2, L3, ..., Lg appear on the SAS output. The analyst is free to select g-1 sets of values for L2 through Lg to obtain the actual coefficients which determine the simultaneous statements comprising the hypothesis. One set of selections for the (L2,L3,...,Lg) values is {(1,0,...,0), (0,1,...,0), ..., (0,0,...,1)}.

Suppose, for example, g = 3, in a layout as follows:

Center	----------------------- Treatment -----------------------		
	A	B	C
1	μ_{11} $n_{11} = 3$	μ_{21} $n_{21} = 5$	μ_{31} $n_{31} = 4$
2	μ_{12} $n_{12} = 1$	μ_{22} $n_{22} = 2$	μ_{32} $n_{32} = 3$
3	μ_{13} $n_{13} = 3$	μ_{23} $n_{23} = 4$	μ_{33} $n_{33} = 2$
4	μ_{14} $n_{14} = 4$	μ_{24} $n_{24} = 1$	μ_{34} $n_{34} = 2$
5	μ_{15} $n_{15} = 3$	μ_{25} $n_{25} = 3$	μ_{35} $n_{35} = 2$
	μ_A $n_A = 14$	μ_B $n_B = 15$	μ_C $n_C = 13$

The parameter coefficient vectors for the Type III hypotheses for Treatment generated by SAS are of the form:

```
Type III Estimable Functions for: TRT
Effect          Coefficients

INTERCEPT       0

TRT      A      L2
         B      L3
         C      -L2-L3

CNTR     1      0
         2      0
         3      0
         4      0
         5      0

TRT*CNTR A 1    0.2*L2
         A 2    0.2*L2
         A 3    0.2*L2
         A 4    0.2*L2
         A 5    0.2*L2
         B 1    0.2*L3
         B 2    0.2*L3
         B 3    0.2*L3
         B 4    0.2*L3
         B 5    0.2*L3
         C 1    -0.2*L2-0.2*L3
         C 2    -0.2*L2-0.2*L3
         C 3    -0.2*L2-0.2*L3
         C 4    -0.2*L2-0.2*L3
         C 5    -0.2*L2-0.2*L3
```

Following the procedure shown in the previous examples, this printout can be used to state the hypotheses in terms of cell means. Using the selection set of $\{(1,0), (0,1)\}$ for the (L2,L3) values results in the vectors $\underline{a}_2$ and $\underline{a}_3$ as follows:

H_0: $\underline{a}_2'\underline{\beta} = 0 \Rightarrow$
H_0: $(1/5)\mu_{11}+(1/5)\mu_{12}+(1/5)\mu_{13}+ (1/5)\mu_{14} + (1/5)\mu_{15} =$
$\qquad (1/5)\mu_{31} + (1/5)\mu_{32} + (1/5)\mu_{33} + (1/5)\mu_{34} + (1/5)\mu_{35}$

H_0: $\underline{a}_3'\underline{\beta} = 0 \Rightarrow$
H_0: $(1/5)\mu_{21}+(1/5)\mu_{22}+(1/5)\mu_{23}+ (1/5)\mu_{24} + (1/5)\mu_{25} =$
$\qquad (1/5)\mu_{31} + (1/5)\mu_{32} + (1/5)\mu_{33} + (1/5)\mu_{34} + (1/5)\mu_{35}$

Taken together, the hypothesis tested by the Type III sum-of-squares for Treatment is the equality of treatment means, H_0: $\mu_A = \mu_B = \mu_C$, when the treatment means are an unweighted average of the cell means for that treatment.

For this case with no empty cells, the Type IV hypothesis for Treatment is the same as the Type III. However, suppose a number of empty cells exist, say cells 1-1, 2-4 and 3-5 (i.e., $n_{11} = n_{24} = n_{35} = 0$), as shown below.

	Treatment		
Center	A	B	C
1	0	5	4
2	1	2	3
3	3	4	2
4	4	0	2
5	3	3	0

The SAS Type IV sum-of-squares simultaneously tests the equality of pairs of treatment means when the treatment means are an unweighted average of the cell means for that treatment excluding any cell in a block with one or more empty cells. The hypothesis is framed in terms of statements about the cell means as:

$$H_0: \quad \mu_{12} + \mu_{13} + \mu_{14} = \mu_{32} + \mu_{33} + \mu_{34}, \quad \text{and}$$
$$\mu_{21} + \mu_{22} + \mu_{23} = \mu_{31} + \mu_{32} + \mu_{33}.$$

The Type III hypothesis for the same configuration defines a treatment mean in terms of its cell means plus extraneous effects from other treatments, and is very difficult to interpret. Therefore, the Type IV results appear to be more useful in the empty-cell case with more than 2 treatment groups. As before, if the interaction is omitted as a source of variation from the ANOVA, the Types II, III and IV results are the same, each testing for pure treatment effects free of block effects and are not a function of the cell sizes.

D.5 SUMMARY

Knowledge of the sampling plan and reasons for design imbalance will help the analyst determine the most appropriate SAS SS-type to use when performing analysis-of-variance. The first step in the analysis is to request a printout from SAS of the form of the estimable functions using the GLM Model statement option 'E1 E2 E3 E4'. It is then possible to specify the hypotheses tested by each SS-type. Selection of the most appropriate type can then be made by most closely matching the hypothesis actually tested with the intended hypothesis. The Type III sum-of-squares, which ignores the cell sample sizes, is often used in the analysis of clinical study data under the assumption of 'infinite' or very large population sizes within each Block level.

The Type I tests weight the cell means in proportion to the amount of information they contribute, i.e., the cell sample sizes. The Type II tests also weight the amount of information contributed to the treatment means, but do so by block and cell rather than just individual cells. The Type II tests for Treatment also have the appealing characteristic that they will always be free of block effects, regardless of the degree of imbalance. This can be seen in the example shown (page D.6) where the coefficients of the block effects (β_1, β_2, β_3) are zero. The same is true of the Type III methods, which, in addition, are simple to interpret and do not depend on the sample sizes in each cell. As mentioned in Chapter 5, the Type III tests are generally the choice of clinical data analysts and should be used when the LS-means are used for estimation (LS-means are discussed in Appendix C.3). However, Type I or II methods would be preferrable if it is known that the sample sizes are proportional to the population sizes. In each analysis, the assumptions should be reviewed before automatically selecting one of the SAS Types of sum-of-squares.

APPENDIX E
COMPUTATIONAL PROCEDURES
FOR LOGISTIC REGRESSION

▸ INTRODUCTION

Estimation of model parameters in *Logistic Regression* (Chapter 18) uses the method of Maximum Likelihood. This is a technique from probability theory which is widely used in the derivation of statistical tests. As its name implies, Maximum Likelihood is a method which provides estimates of the parameters which maximize the likelihood of observing the data set actually collected.

The Maximum Likelihood method establishes a set of equations involving the estimates of the model parameters. These equations are then solved simultaneously to obtain the 'Maximum Likelihood estimates'. When they are linear or 'well-behaved' equations, a closed solution can usually be obtained. However, in *Logistic Regression*, the Maximum Likelihood equations are complex functions which do not produce a closed solution for the parameter estimates. Even the simplest of *Logistic Regression* setups require the use of computers and a method known as "iteratively reweighted least-squares" to obtain solutions to the Maximum Likelihood equations.

This section illustrates the complexities involved for a simple *Logistic Regression* problem, exemplifying why manual solutions are impractical.

► ILLUSTRATION

We use as an example a case involving 2 treatment groups, one numeric covariate and 7 observations, 3 in one group and 4 in the other. Let X_1 represent the Group effect, with Groups 1 and 2 coded as $X_1 = 0$ and 1, respectively. Suppose X_2 is a numeric covariate taking values 0-3, resulting in the following data layout:

Group 1 ($X_1 = 0$)		Group 2 ($X_1 = 1$)	
X_2	Y	X_2	Y
0	1	0	1
1	1	1	0
2	0	1	0
		3	1

The *Logistic Regression* model is

$$P = \frac{1}{1 + e^{-(\alpha + \beta X_1 + \gamma X_2)}} \quad ,$$

which is estimated by

$$\hat{P} = \frac{1}{1 + e^{-(a + bX_1 + cX_2)}} \quad .$$

The goal is to determine a, b and c, the Maximum Likelihood estimates (MLE) of the parameters α, β and γ. This is done by simultaneously solving the MLE equations given by:

1.) $\quad \sum Y = \sum \hat{P}$

2.) $\quad \sum X_1 \cdot Y = \sum X_1 \cdot \hat{P}$

3.) $\quad \sum X_2 \cdot Y = \sum X_2 \cdot \hat{P}$

The estimates of P are shown below:

Group 1 ($X_1 = 0$)			Group 2 ($X_1 = 1$)		
X_2	Y	$\hat{p}$	X_2	Y	$\hat{p}$
0	1	$[1+e^{-a}]^{-1}$	0	1	$[1+e^{-(a+b)}]^{-1}$
1	1	$[1+e^{-(a+c)}]^{-1}$	1	0	$[1+e^{-(a+b+c)}]^{-1}$
2	0	$[1+e^{-(a+2c)}]^{-1}$	1	0	$[1+e^{-(a+b+c)}]^{-1}$
			3	1	$[1+e^{-(a+b+3c)}]^{-1}$

Substituting the $\hat{p}$ estimates into the MLE equations yields:

$$1.) \Rightarrow 4 = \frac{1}{[1+e^{-a}]} + \frac{1}{[1+e^{-(a+c)}]} + \frac{1}{[1+e^{-(a+2c)}]} +$$

$$\frac{1}{[1+e^{-(a+b)}]} + \frac{2}{[1+e^{-(a+b+c)}]} + \frac{1}{[1+e^{-(a+b+3c)}]}$$

$$2.) \Rightarrow 2 = \frac{1}{[1+e^{-(a+b)}]} + \frac{2}{[1+e^{-(a+b+c)}]} + \frac{1}{[1+e^{-(a+b+3c)}]}$$

$$3.) \Rightarrow 4 = \frac{1}{[1+e^{-(a+c)}]} + \frac{2}{[1+e^{-(a+2c)}]} + \frac{2}{[1+e^{-(a+b+c)}]} +$$

$$\frac{3}{[1+e^{-(a+b+3c)}]}$$

Solving these equations simultaneously for a, b and c is performed using iterative numerical techniques. The computer program starts with a 'guessed' solution, then iteratively adjusts the guessed values until they converge on a solution. Convergence for the above equations results in a = 1.0155, b = -0.6281 and c = -0.3116, resulting in the fitted model:

$$\hat{P} = \frac{1}{1 + e^{-(1.0155 - 0.6281X_1 - 0.3116X_2)}}$$

The estimated probabilities for each group are as follows:

Group 1 ($X_1 = 0$)			Group 2 ($X_1 = 1$)		
X_2	Y	$\hat{p}$	X_2	Y	$\hat{p}$
0	1	0.7341	0	1	0.5957
1	1	0.6691	1	0	0.5189
2	0	0.5968	1	0	0.5189
			3	1	0.3665

▸ SUMMARY

Even for the simple layout given, manual computations to produce this solution would be overwhelming. This example illustrates the impracticality of manual computations for *Logistic Regression* analysis.

REFERENCES
and Additional Reading

Allison PD, Survival Analysis Using the SAS System: A Practical Guide, SAS Institue, Inc, Cary NC (1995)

Altman DG, Practical Statistics for Medical Research, Chapman & Hall, New York (1991)

Anderson S, A Auquier, WW Hauck, D Oakes, W Vandaele and HI Weisberg, Statistical Methods for Comparative Studies, John Wiley & Sons, New York (1980)

Armitage P and G Berry, Statistical Methods in Medical Research, second edition, Blackwell Scientific Publications, Palo Alto CA (1987)

Bancroft TA, Topics in Intermediate Statistical Methods, Volume One, The Iowa University Press, Ames IOWA (1968)

Cochran WG and GM Cox, Experimental Designs, second edition, John Wiley & Sons, New York (1957)

Conover WJ and RL Iman, "*Rank Transformations as a Bridge Between Parametric and Nonparametric Statistics*", The American Statistician, Vol 35 #3 (Aug 1981), pp 124-129

Cox DR and D Oakes, Analysis of Survival Data, Chapman & Hall, New York (1984)

D'Agostino RB, J Massaro, H Kwan and H Cabral, "*Strategies for Dealing with Multiple Treatment Comparsions in Confirmatory Clinical Trials*", Drug Information Journal, Vol 27 (1993), pp 625-641

Dawson-Saunders B and RG Trapp, Basic and Clinical Biostatistics, Appleton & Lange, San Mateo (1990)

Fleiss JL, Statistical Methods for Rates and Proportions, second edition, John Wiley & Sons (1981)

Gillings D and Gary Koch, "*The Application of the Principle of Intention-to-Treat to the Analysis of Clinical Trials*", Drug Information Journal, Vol 25 (1991), pp 411-424

Hand DJ, CC Taylor, Multivariate Analysis of Variance and Repeated-Measures, Chapman Hall, New York (1987)

Hollander M and DA Wolfe, Nonparametric Statistical Methods, John Wiley & Sons, New York (1973)

Hosmer DW and S Lemeshow, Applied Logistic Regression, John Wiley & Sons, New York (1989)

Kalbfleisch JD and RL Prentice, The Statistical Analysis of Failure Time Data, John Wiley & Sons, New York (1980)

Lachin JM, "*Introduction to Sample Size Determination and Power Analysis for Clinical Trials*", Controlled Clinical Trials, Vol 2 (1981), pp 93-113

Lee J, "*Covariance Adjustment of Rates Based on the Multiple Logistic Regression Model*", Journal of Chronic Diseases, Vol 34 (1981), pp 415-426

Mendenhall W, Introduction to Probability and Statistics, fourth edition, Duxbury Press, North Scituate MA (1975)

Munro BH and EB Page, Statistical Methods for Health Care Research, second edition, JB Lippincott Co, Philadelphia (1993)

O'Brien PC and TR Fleming, "*A Multiple Testing Procedure for Clinical Trials*", Biometrics, Vol 35 (1979), pp 549-556

Pocock SJ, "*Interim Analyses for Randomized Clinical Trials: The Group Sequential Approach*", Biometrics, Vol 38 (1982), pp 153-162

Tibshirani R, "*A Plain Man's Guide to the Proportional Hazards Model*", Clinical and Investigative Medicine, Vol 5 (1982) pp 63-68

SAS/STAT® User's Guide, Version 6, fourth edition, Volumes 1 & 2, SAS Institue, Inc., Cary NC (1989)

SAS/STAT® Software: Changes and Enhancements Through Release 6.11, SAS Institute, Inc., Cary NC (1996)

Winer BJ, Statistical Principles in Experimental Designs, second edition McGraw-Hill, New York (1971)

Call your local SAS® office to order these other books and tapes available through the Books by Users℠ program:

An Array of Challenges — Test Your SAS® Skills
by **Robert Virgile**..................................Order No. A55625

Applied Multivariate Statistics with SAS® Software
by **Ravindra Khattree**
and **Dayanand N. Naik**........................Order No. A55234

Applied Statistics and the SAS® Programming Language, Fourth Edition
by **Ronald P. Cody**
and **Jeffrey K. Smith**...........................Order No. A55984

Beyond the Obvious with SAS® Screen Control Language
by **Don Stanley** ....Order No. A55073

The Cartoon Guide to Statistics
by **Larry Gonick**
and **Woollcott Smith**...........................Order No. A55153

Categorical Data Analysis Using the SAS® System
by **Maura E. Stokes, Charles E. Davis,**
and **Gary G. Koch** ....Order No. A55320

Concepts and Case Studies in Data Management
by **William S. Calvert**
and **J. Meimei Ma**................................Order No. A55220

Essential Client/Server Survival Guide, Second Edition
by **Robert Orfali, Dan Harkey,**
and **Jeri Edwards**................................Order No. A56285

Extending SAS® Survival Analysis Techniques for Medical Research
by **Alan Cantor**....................................Order No. A55504

Survival Analysis Using the SAS® System: A Practical Guide
by **Paul D. Allison**...............................Order No. A55233

The How-To Book for SAS/GRAPH® Software
by **Thomas Miron** ....Order No. A55203

In the Know ... SAS® Tips and Techniques From Around the Globe
by **Phil Mason** ....Order No. A55513

Learning SAS® in the Computer Lab
by **Rebecca J. Elliott** ....Order No. A55273

The Little SAS® Book: A Primer
by **Lora D. Delwiche**
and **Susan J. Slaughter**.......................Order No. A55200

Mastering the SAS® System, Second Edition
by **Jay A. Jaffe** ....Order No. A55123

Painless Windows 3.1: A Beginner's Handbook for SAS® Users
by **Jodie Gilmore** ....Order No. A55505

Professional SAS® Programmer's Pocket Reference
by **Rick Aster** ....Order No. A56198

Professional SAS® Programming Secrets, Second Edition
by **Rick Aster**
and **Rhena Seidman** ....Order No. A56279

Professional SAS® User Interfaces
by **Rick Aster** ....Order No. A56197

Quick Results with SAS/GRAPH® Software
by **Arthur L. Carpenter**
and **Charles E. Shipp** ....Order No. A55127

Quick Start to Data Analysis with SAS®
by **Frank C. Dilorio**
and **Kenneth A. Hardy** ....Order No. A55550

Reporting from the Field: SAS® Software Experts Present Real-World Report-Writing Applications ....Order No. A55135

SAS® Applications Programming: A Gentle Introduction
by **Frank C. Dilorio** ....Order No. A55193

SAS® Foundations: From Installation to Operation
by **Rick Aster** ....Order No. A55093

SAS® Programming by Example
by **Ronald P. Cody**
and **Ray Pass** ....Order No. A55126

SAS® Programming for Researchers and Social Scientists
by **Paul E. Spector** ....Order No. A56199

SAS® Software Roadmaps: Your Guide to Discovering the SAS® System
by **Laurie Burch**
and **SherriJoyce King** ....Order No. A56195

SAS® Software Solutions
by **Thomas Miron**................................Order No. A56196